Instructor Resources

Symmetry, Shape, and Space
An Introduction to Mathematics Through Geometry

L. Christine Kinsey
Canisius College

Teresa E. Moore
Ithaca College

Key College Publishing

www.keycollege.com

L. Christine Kinsey
Department of Mathematics
Canisius College
Buffalo, NY 14208, USA
kinsey@canisius.edu

Teresa E. Moore
Department of Mathematics and
Computer Science
Ithaca College
Ithaca, NY 14850, USA
moore@ithaca.edu

Cover illustration: René Magritte, "The Blank Signature." Collection of Mr. and Mrs. Paul Mellon, © 2001 Board of Trustees, National Gallery of Art, Washington, DC. Reproduced with permission.

Key College Publishing was founded in 1999 as a division of Key Curriculum Press in cooperation with Springer-Verlag New York, Inc. It publishes innovative curriculum materials for undergraduate courses in mathematics, statistics, and mathematics and statistics education. For more information, visit us at www.keycollege.com.

Key College Publishing
1150 65th Street
Emeryville, CA 94608
www.keycollege.com
(510) 595-7000

Published by Key College Publishing, an imprint of Key Curriculum Press.

Project Editor: Susan Minarcin
Production Editor: Angela Chen
Manager, Editorial Production: Deborah Cogan
Production Director: Diana Jean Parks
Printer/Binder: DeHart's Printing Services

Executive Editor: Richard Bonacci
General Manager: Mike Simpson
Publisher: Steven Rasmussen

Printed in the United States of America

9 8 7 6 5 4 3 2 1 04 03 02

ISBN 1-930190-74-3

Dedicated to

Lisa Marie,
Steve,
Chance,
and
Buster

Contents

Introduction

This book combines the functions of a solutions manual and an instructor's guide for the text <u>Symmetry, Shape, and Space</u>. The text was written so that many of the chapters are independent and in each chapter the instructor might choose not to cover all of the sections. We have decided to interleave the Helpful Hints to the instructor with the solutions so that all material related to a particular section or a particular exercise is contained in that section. Thus, you will only need to read through those sections pertaining to the parts of the text you have chosen for your course. This introduction has four sections: adjusting student attitudes and expectations, designing a course using the text, how to use this instructor's manual, and information on the templates contained at the end of this book.

Adjusting Student Attitudes and Expectations

Our intent, not always perfectly realized, was to develop materials for use in a course that implemented a guided discovery model of learning. We have the students work in groups of no more than three or four students and keep the lecture portion of the course to a minimum, usually 10 or 15 minutes a week introducing a new section and explaining basic concepts and terminology, with occasional five-minute time-outs to explain a point of general confusion.

We usually start the semester with a campus-specific group-bonding exercise. For example, here is the one the first-named author uses at Canisius College:

> ▷ **Exercise 1.** Measure the height of Churchill Tower (the really, really ugly round building that looks like a battery in front of Old Main on Main Street). Measure the circumference around the base and also around the second story where the building juts out. Do this in your group. You can use any method you like, but try to be as accurate as possible and don't duplicate a method some other group is using (check with me on this). After doing the computations as a group, write up your results individually, explaining carefully your method and computations. Your write-up should consist of several paragraphs, outlining how you chose your method, any difficulties in carrying your plan out, and details of any possibilities for error.

> ▷ **Exercise 2.** Measure how long St. Peter Canisius's legs are (the statue in the middle of the quadrangle between Old Main and the chapel). Explain why artists should take math.

This activity has several advantages in its use at the beginning of the semester: The freshman have to explore campus a bit, the groups learn to brainstorm and exchange ideas on how to attack the problem, and it convinces them from the outset that this is not going to be a traditional math class. It should be noted that one of St. Peter Canisius's legs is six inches longer than the other.

The second-named author, at Ithaca College, also spends the first day convincing students that the course will be nontraditional. After introducing herself, she asks for a pair of volunteers and tells the rest of the students to move the chairs back. The activity that follows allows each student to get to know at least one person in the class and allows us to introduce problem-solving steps on the first day. It takes two five-foot-long pieces of string for a pair of students. Tie one end of a string to the first person's wrist and the other end to her other wrist. The knots should be snug and the loops should not slip off her hands. Repeat the process for the second student but before tying the string to his second wrist, link it through the first student's string. Some students will remember doing this at a party or other event in their past, but few remember the solution and none relate it to mathematics. The instructions are simple: get yourselves apart without altering the string. You can't cut it, break it, untie it or in any other way remove it from your wrists. As the first pair of students begins to twist and turn, break the rest of the class into pairs and get them all working. If there are an odd number of students, make one group with a triple link and assure them their situation is no worse than that of the others. Persistence is the first lesson. Just because you can't solve a problem in three minutes doesn't mean you should quit. The students also begin to learn that we won't be giving out answers. The first hint we give (after about 10 minutes) is that only one person has to move. (If there is someone in a wheelchair or with a broken leg, we give this hint almost immediately.) This is enough to get some students to rethink their approach. The second lesson is that persistence is not always enough. Go back and rethink your approach. It simply might not work. Ask them if two linked circles can be separated. When we agree that the answer is no, tell the students there is some way that they are different from circles and some students begin to focus on the wrist connections. Some students will solve the puzzle on their own, but usually we end up telling people to think about a model. If they could take the string off one wrist, the second string would slide between the hand and the first string. Even without removing the first string, tell them to put the second string between the first string and the hand. Once a pair gets separated, tell them to reattach themselves to make sure they understand the solution. The first few successful pairs are told not to help others, but getting everyone free before the end of class usually is a group effort. They look at a problem, try a solution, rethink their approach, look for information that they missed the first time, model the situation, and review their solution to insure they understand it. And most of them have fun doing it.

The second exercise used at Ithaca is to measure the height of the West Tower before they come to class the second day. Most will pair with their string partner or someone they know from outside class. Other campus-specific activities we have used that involve brainstorming, learning about campus, and getting outside are: estimating the surface area of the pond, measuring the height of the tree in the Centennial Garden, figuring out the number of blades of grass in a small region near Job Hall, and finding the number of bricks on the back of Muller Faculty Center. Whatever the activity, we find the students work better if they get connected to several colleagues in the first week.

You will, of course, have to find your own method of classroom instruction, but we include a few more notes on what we do. As stated previously, we have students working in groups of three or four and keep the lecture portion of the course to a brief introduction of each section. The remainder of our time is spent roaming from group to group and fielding questions. In general, we do not answer questions but offer suggestions of what a group could consider next. (Our students learn not to ask if something is right. We will tell them to explain their reasoning to the other people in their group and see if everyone else is convinced.) We now expect to find comments on end-of-the-semester student statements saying, "Everything I learned in this class, I had to teach myself." We also see, "She would never tell me if I had the right answer," or "How can she take off points for a wrong answer if she never told us how to do the problem?" The students consider all of these to be bad things, but the first two tell me we're doing our jobs right. The third means they haven't accepted that they should be able to thoroughly justify their work to themselves and their group and that they need to understand what they are doing rather than answering by rote.

If you have students working together, you always need to watch group interaction. Some groups work well while others let one person carry the load. We let them choose their partners for the first two sections but put them into groups for the third. By the fourth or fifth week, most students have found a comfortable working situation. Then, we only intervene if socializing takes priority over learning. Note that if you answer the same question for three different groups, it is usually worth calling everyone together and clearing up the point.

We have used undergraduate teaching assistants with success. Ideally these would be chosen from excellent students from previous semesters of the course, or one can use math education majors or mathematics majors with an interest in teaching. Such assistants (with this manual) help one handle larger classes or underprepared students who may need more reassurance and support.

Designing a Course Using <u>Symmetry, Shape, and Space</u>

We wrote <u>Symmetry, Shape, and Space</u> to provide as much flexibility as possible. The text contains about three times as much material as is possible to cover in a single semester as an introductory level mathematics course for nonscience or education majors. The first chapter of the text, The Basics, covers fundamental notions that will be used throughout the text and should always be included, though these sections can be somewhat abbreviated. This is explained in more detail in that section of this manual. The other chapters are somewhat independent and offer many variations to choose from. You may choose to do an entire chapter or to cover only the first section of a chapter and then pass on to another topic. The way in which each section depends on other sections in the chapter or from previous chapters is given at the start of each chapter and is summarized in the table below (except dependency on the first chapter is assumed). At the start of each chapter of this instructor's guide is a general description of the chapter and each section. The star notation used there gives some indication of the level of difficulty of each section, ranging from ★ (accessible to all students with minimal background) to ★★★ (more difficult content and requiring more sophisticated thinking on the part of the student). Use the stars, the general descriptions, and dependencies and references to design a course for your particular group of students.

Dependence of Sections

Section	Dependency	Section	Dependency	Section	Dependency
1.2	1.1	5.4	5.3	10.1	None
2.1	None	5.5	5.3, 5.4	10.2	None
2.2	None	6.1	None	11.1	None
3.1	None	6.2	6.1	11.2	None
3.2	3.1	7.1	None	11.3	None
3.3	3.1, 3.2	7.2	7.1	11.4	11.1, 11.3
3.4	None	7.3	7.1, 7.2	11.5	11.1, 11.3, 11.4
3.5	None	7.4	7.1, 7.2, 7.3	12.1	None
4.1	None	7.5	7.1, 7.2	12.2	12.1
4.2	4.1	7.6	4.1, 7.1, 7.2, 7.3	12.3	12.1, 12.2
4.3	3.2, 4.1	8.1	7.1, 7.2, 7.3, 7.6	13.1	None
5.1	None	8.2	7.1, 7.2, 8.1	13.2	None
5.2	None	9.1	None	13.3	13.2
5.3	None	9.2	None	13.4	13.2, 13.3

Chapters 2 through 5 deal with geometrical ideas in two dimensions. The sixth chapter introduces the idea of higher dimensions by trying to get students to use their imaginations—first, to understand how a planar being (such as in Abbott's <u>Flatland</u>) would comprehend three dimensions; then, to explore the fourth dimension for themselves. Chapters 7 and 8 are devoted to the study of polyhedra in three dimensions. Chapter 9, 10, and 11 are independent of the other chapters and of each other. Chapters 12 and 13 introduce the fields of graph theory and topology. We usually choose to cover the first chapter, several sections from the planar group (Chapters 2–5), then use either Chapter 6 or either section of Chapter 10 as a transition to some of the material on polyhedra in Chapters 7 and 8, and then a selection of the later sections so that students gain a variety of experiences in different dimensions. However, an interesting course could just as easily be designed using only the planar sections of the text,

The number of sections you can cover in a semester depends on your students, your attitude, and your goals. We have found that most sections take about a week. If your students respond well to deadlines, planning 10 to 12 sections for a term is reasonable. We have found that we can usually cover about 10 sections of the text in a 15-week semester when there is a mixture of students that includes a number with weak backgrounds. With a homogeneous group of reasonably well-prepared students, it would be possible to cover 12 sections, allowing time for the introductory activity and review classes before the midterm and final exams. If you have students who are not afraid to work outside of class, you can cover even more. However, if you allow students extra time when they are confused (or not trying very hard) or if you plan to have students work on out-of-class projects and give presentations during the last two weeks, your students may only complete eight or nine sections. Note that topics in the book which you do not cover in class can lead to some very nice student presentations.

In deciding what sections to cover in your course, your main guide should be to choose sections that you are interested in and think your students will be excited by. We have tried to make the chapters largely independent while still related by a common theme of geometry.

How to Use This Instructor's Manual

Each chapter of this manual begins with an overview of the chapter and each of its sections, explaining how the sections relate to each other. The stars give a rough idea of level of difficulty. The list of dependencies gives sections that ought to be covered before trying the section, while the list of references gives sections that are related but not essential for an understanding of the material in the section.

For each section, we have tried to provide detailed solutions, including explanations of how one gets the answer. Interleaved with the solutions are indented and italicized Helpful Hints. These comments are the product of our experiences in the classroom. We have tried to make suggestions about where students may have difficulties, ways to guide the students without completely giving away the answers, practical advice on building models and manipulatives, and anything else we could think of. Exercises that can be omitted without loss of continuity are noted, if one is pressed for time.

The Templates

In the appendix at the end of this manual are templates to photocopy for use with the text. At the beginning of the appendix, you will find a list of these, grouped by the section where they can be used. Some of these (such as the polygon templates) will be used in several sections. Some of the exercises from the text that require student drawings are reproduced at a more useful size in these templates. Refer to each relevant section for the use of the templates and whether they should be enlarged or not and photocopied onto cardstock or regular paper. These will also be made available on the Key College Web site for the text.

Chapter 1. The Basics

★ **1.1. Measurement**
   Dependencies: None

- Length
- Pythagorean Theorem
- Perimeter
- Area
- Angles

★ **1.2. Polygons**
   Dependencies: Chapter 1.1

- Polygons
- Tangrams
- Vertex and interior angles
- Regular tilings

This chapter and its two sections give very basic facts and terminology about geometry that will be needed in the rest of the book. Most, if not all, of this should be familiar to the student from high school. Some of the exercises can be omitted (these are detailed as they appear herein) if you choose to cut these preliminaries to the minimum.

The first section begins with some activities on measuring length. Next follows the statement of the Pythagorean Theorem, with two different proofs and some applications. Basic definitions and formulae are given for perimeter and area with exercises to apply these. The measurement of angles is reviewed both in terms of degree measure and in terms of slope. Angles are also described in terms of the concept of pitch, related to the idea of slope and in common use in the building trades. This section ends with a short description of how to measure the angle between two curves. The bare minimum required is familiarity with the Pythagorean Theorem (Exercises 6 and 7) and computing perimeter and area (Exercises 9, 10, and 14).

The second section reviews polygons. It begins with the traditional terminology for describing various triangles and the congruence theorems for triangles. Terminology for different quadrilaterals is given. Students usually enjoy the exercises on tangrams. Nomenclature for polygons with various numbers of sides is explained. Students are asked to derive the formula for the sum of the angles of an n-sided polygon as well as the formula for one vertex angle of a regular n-sided polygon. Exercises 5 and 6 lead to the essential formulae of Exercises 7 and 8, and Exercises 9–13 provide practice applying these formulae. The results of Exercise 14 are used at several places in the text.

1.1. Measurement

The answers to Exercises 1–4 will vary with each person. These exercises are designed to get the students moving around and talking to each other. We usually also have them measure something big on campus, such as a large building. The first-named author also makes them measure the legs of a statue on campus, of St. Peter Canisius, since one of his legs is a good six inches than the other (artists should study more math). If the instructor uses a group-learning model, as we do, these exercises are excellent for team-building; however they can be considered as optional.

▷ **Exercise 1.**   This exercise is person-specific.

▷ **Exercise 2.**   This exercise is person-specific.

▷ **Exercise 3.**   This exercise is person-specific.

▷ **Exercise 4.**   This exercise is person-specific.

Exercises 5–8 test whether the student understands the proof and application of the Pythagorean Theorem. Exercise 5 is optional, and some students may need help setting this problem up.

▷ **Exercise 5.**   In this case, $y = a = b$ and $z = 0$, so the arrangement is as shown below:

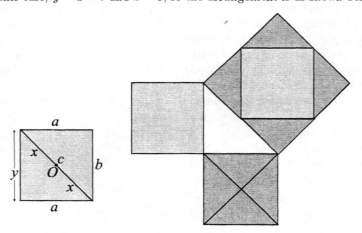

▷ **Exercise 6.**   A triangle with sides of lengths 3, 4, and 5 is a right triangle, by the converse to the Pythagorean Theorem, and the right angle lies opposite the side of length 5, between the 3 and 4 sides.

▷ **Exercise 7.**   If a right triangle has shorter sides of lengths 5 and 12, the hypotenuse is $\sqrt{5^2 + 12^2} = \sqrt{169} = 13$ units long.

▷ **Exercise 8.** There are infinitely many Pythagorean triples, such as 7-24-25, 8-15-17, 12-35-37, 9-40-41, 16-63-65, as well as 6-8-10 (twice 3-4-5), 12-16-20, etc. More advanced students can be led to realize that triples can be generated using the formulae $a = m^2 - n^2$, $b = 2mn$, $c = m^2 + n^2$ for any positive integers m and n.

Exercises 9 and 10 apply the formulae for perimeters. Most students should get these without undue effort. You may need to explain that the dotted lines in (d), (e), and (f) indicate circular bits.

▷ **Exercise 9.** (a) $P = 3\pi$. Note that this only includes the arc forming the half-circle.   (b) $r = 4$

▷ **Exercise 10.** (a) 26   (b) 12   (c) $6\pi \approx 18.85$ (d) $30 + 5\pi \approx 45.71$ (e) $30 + 3\pi \approx 39.42$
(f) $14 + \frac{5\pi}{2} \approx 21.85$ (g) 36

In Exercises 11–13, students are asked to derive area formulae, using the explanation of the area of a parallelogram as a model. One must insist that they make an effort to explain why their formula makes sense, rather than merely recalling the formula from previous courses. These exercises can be omitted if the students already know the formulae and you would prefer to save the time to devote to other material. Exercise 14 is a straightforward application of the area formulae. Again, the dotted lines in (g), (h), (i), and (j) are radii or diameters for parts of circles.

▷ **Exercise 11.** Placing two copies of the triangle together forms a parallelogram with base b and height h, so $A = \frac{1}{2}bh$.

▷ **Exercise 12.** $A = 8$

▷ **Exercise 13.** Two copies of the trapezoid can be put together to form a parallelogram with base $b_1 + b_2$ and height h, so $A = \frac{1}{2}(b_1 + b_2)h$.

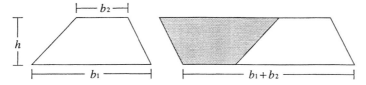

Alternatively, divide the trapezoid into two triangles, one with base b_1 and height h, and the other with base b_2 and height h, so $A = \frac{1}{2}b_1h + \frac{1}{2}b_2h = \frac{1}{2}(b_1 + b_2)h$.

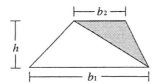

▷ **Exercise 14.** (a) 30   (b) 24   (c) 6   (d) 30   (e) 25   (f) 6   (g) $9\pi \approx 28.27$
     (h) $100 + 12.5\pi \approx 139.27$ (i) $86 + 4.5\pi \approx 100.14$ (j) $11 + 6.25\pi \approx 30.63$ (k) 44   (l) 34

> *Exercises 15–17 involve various ways of looking at angles as used in various professions and applications of the Pythagorean Theorem and area. For students who are already comfortable with measuring angles both in degrees and as slope and if time presses, these can also be omitted.*

▷ **Exercise 15.**   45°

▷ **Exercise 16.** The peak is 25 feet from the attic floor. The rafters must be $1 + 25\sqrt{2} \approx 36.36$ feet. The area of the roof (including both sides) is $2 \cdot 75 \cdot (1 + 25\sqrt{2}) \approx 5453.3$ square feet.

▷ **Exercise 17.** The peak is $8\frac{1}{3}$ feet from the attic floor. The rafters must be $1 + \sqrt{25^2 + 8.33^2} \approx 27.35$ feet. The area of the roof is $2 \cdot 75 \cdot (1 + \sqrt{25^2 + 8.33^2}) \approx 4102.85$ square feet.

▷ **Exercise 18.** One such stair uses 15 steps with a riser of six inches. Another would be 18 steps of five inches. The tread depth, as long as it is greater than 11 inches, is immaterial.

> *We have found a surprising number of noncompliant handicapped ramps, especially at older campuses. Searching for these and measuring them is excellent for making students aware of the difficulties faced by those in wheelchairs or on crutches.*

▷ **Exercise 19.** This is site-specific.

1.2. Polygons

Students, especially elementary education majors, enjoy the tangram problems. Doing these develops visualization abilities, but Exercises 1–3 may be omitted. Loyd's invented history for the puzzle is still reported as true in many books, and some students will find this amusing. Exercise 2 can be done in two ways: either by applying the area formula from Section 1.1 or by showing how each piece relates to others of known area. Encourage the students to involve others — fellow students, friends, small siblings — in finding the solutions for Exercise 3. Remember that these solutions are not unique.

▷ **Exercise 1.** The sizes of the tangram pieces are figured out by using the way they fit together and the Pythagorean Theorem: the square (some students persist in calling it a diamond) is 1 on each side; the smallest triangles are 1 on the shorter sides and $\sqrt{2}$ along the hypotenuse; the parallelogram is 1 on the shorter sides and $\sqrt{2}$ on the longer sides; the middle-sized triangle is $\sqrt{2}$ on the shorter sides and 2 on the hypotenuse; the big triangles are 2 on the shorter sides and $2\sqrt{2}$ on the hypotenuse.

▷ **Exercise 2.** The square has area 1. The smallest triangles have area $\frac{1}{2}$. Note that two of the smallest triangles can be put together to make a square. The parallelogram has area 1. Note that two of the smallest triangles can be put together to make the parallelogram. The middle-sized triangle has area 1. Note that two of the smallest triangles can be put together to make this triangle. The big triangles have area 2. Note that two of the middle-sized triangles can be put together to make this triangle.

Exercise 3 allows the student to play with the tangram puzzle and to gain familiarity with putting the pieces together correctly. Some students who think that they have no mathematical ability but have strong visual ability will excel in this exercise, which gives a great boost to their confidence before proceeding through the rest of the course. Ask the students to make sure their solutions are clear by either color coding the pieces or labeling them, since it is difficult to distinguish the different sizes of triangles in a rough sketch. Notice that (b), (d), (e), and (i) each have a square constructed of the five smaller pieces (these may look different at first, but they are really rotations and reflections of each other). The two large triangles are added to form the different puzzle shapes. The solution of (a) can be changed to (l) by moving a single small triangle, and vice versa. Puzzle (g) can also be changed to a new solution to (f) by moving a single small triangle and rotating by 45°. Puzzle (h) can be changed to (k) by moving three pieces (a large triangle, the square, and a small triangle).

5

▷ **Exercise 3.** Many of these have more than one solution, but here is one for each:

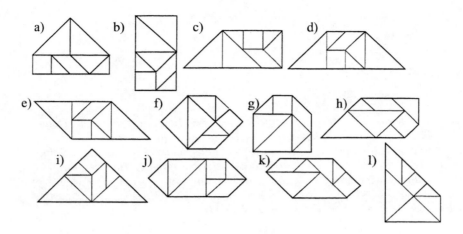

For Exercises 4–7, students need to show an understanding of the proof given that any convex quadrilateral has angle sum 360° and to be able to generalize the basic idea of dividing any polygon up into triangles, as shown below. The technique of reducing a general problem to a number of simpler (triangular) problems is common throughout the course and throughout mathematics, but the proof of Exercise 4 can be omitted.

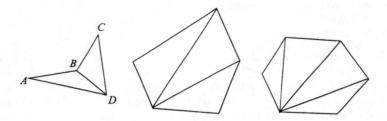

▷ **Exercise 4.** Divide the quadrilateral into two triangles as shown below, and label so that $\angle B = \angle 1 + \angle 2$ and $\angle D = \angle 3 + \angle 4$. Then

$$
\begin{aligned}
\angle A + \angle B + \angle C + \angle D &= \angle A + (\angle 1 + \angle 2) + \angle C + (\angle 3 + \angle 4) \\
&= (\angle A + \angle 1 + \angle 3) + (\angle 2 + \angle C + \angle 4) \\
&= 180° + 180° \\
&= 360°
\end{aligned}
$$

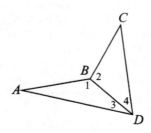

▷ **Exercise 5.** The sum of the vertex angles of an arbitrary pentagon is 540°.

6

▷ **Exercise 6.** The sum of the vertex angles of an arbitrary hexagon is 720°.

The solutions to Exercises 7 and 8 will be used repeatedly throughout the text, so make sure that the students get these correct and encourage them to record the answer somewhere convenient. These exercises ask the student to move to a more abstract level of thinking: generalizing their thinking and the results of Exercises 4–6 to the case of a general n-sided polygon and giving the answer as an equation in n rather than a single number. If students have difficulty making this leap, ask about the angle sum for a heptagon and octagon. Ask how many triangles an n-sided polygon will be divided into.

▷ **Exercise 7.** The sum of the vertex angles of an arbitrary n-sided polygon is $(n-2)180°$.

▷ **Exercise 8.** Each of the vertex angles of a regular n-sided polygon will measure $\frac{(n-2)180°}{n}$.

Exercises 9 and 11–13 are straightforward applications of the formulae found. In Exercise 10, the students must realize that the regular hexagon can be divided up into six equilateral triangles.

▷ **Exercise 9.** This regular polygon will have 24 sides.

▷ **Exercise 10.** Each side of the hexagon has length 1.

▷ **Exercise 11.** For a regular pentagon, an interior angle measures 72° and a vertex angle measures 108°.

▷ **Exercise 12.** For a regular octagon, an interior angle measures 45° and a vertex angle measures 135°.

▷ **Exercise 13.** For a regular dodecagon, an interior angle measures 30°, and a vertex angle measures 150°.

While Chapter 4 is devoted entirely to studying tilings, the three regular tilings recur in several places in this book.

▷ **Exercise 14.** The three ways of tiling the plane using a single regular tile are with equilateral triangles, squares, and regular hexagons.

Chapter 2. Grids

★ **2.1. Billiards**
   Dependencies: None
   - Billiards on various-sized tables using an angle of 45°
   - Billiards using other angles
   - Analyzing billiard trajectories

★ ★ **2.2. Celtic Knots**
   Dependencies: None
   - Rules for drawing plain celtic knots
   - Drawing knots with obstructing bars
   - Alternating knots

In this chapter we make use of grids to generate drawings, first, to represent the path or trajectory of a billiard ball and, second, to analyze and create celtic knotwork. The intention is to develop skill with following instructions carefully, to reinforce the concept of slope of a line and the idea of scaling, and to analyze the patterns created.

In Chapter 2.1, the investigation begins with a quite artificial model of a billiard game in which tables vary in size (a real billiard table is always twice as long as it is wide) and balls are always shot at an angle of 45°. This situation is quite amenable to mathematical analysis: students generate simple rules predicting which pocket the ball will end up in and how many times it will bounce off the walls. This analysis begins with tables with integer dimensions and is then generalized to rational dimensions. Trajectories with rational slope are then introduced and analyzed. The idea of unfolding trajectories is developed, allowing the student to compute the length of the trajectory. This also leads to the application of some of the ideas of the section to real-life billiard problems. If the instructor wishes, this section could be curtailed either after Exercise 13 or after Exercise 16, to omit the subsections on angles other than 45° or on unfolding trajectories.

While Chapter 2.2 is formally independent of the previous section, experience in dealing with grids and developing the rules for the billiard trajectories will help in investigating similar but somewhat less transparent rules for celtic knots. Knot patterns are generated using various grids and restrictions. Finally, an algorithm for drawing an alternating knot is given. The section could be curtailed after Exercise 16 to omit the subsection on why it is always possible to alternate overpasses and underpasses.

2.1. Billiards

Each student will need a supply of graph paper (4 or 5 squares to the inch) for this section, or you can copy Template 1 of the Appendix.

▷ **Exercise 1.**

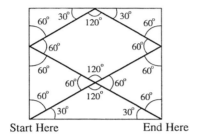

Start Here   End Here

The purpose of Exercise 2 is to generate enough examples to draw some inferences for the exercises that follow. As such, make sure that the students do these carefully. Some students immediately understand the application of the up one–over one rule. Others will try to guess where the ball will bounce and sketch the lines with a ruler. Occasionally this will lead to lines that do not fit the grid precisely enough to generate the correct pattern. A surprising number of students have trouble deciding what to do after hitting the first wall. If you have them working in groups, they tend to help each other through both of these potential problems. If not, either use an overhead projector to demonstrate how to trace the trajectory of a billiard ball using a grid and a 45° angle and an integer-dimensioned table (such as (f) or (g) of Exercise 2), or plan to spend a lot of time showing students where they went wrong and dealing with their frustration when they need to redraw several tables.

▷ **Exercise 2.**

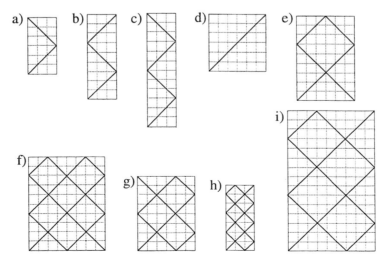

9

▷ **Exercise 3.** Answers are not unique. Any multiple of the original dimensions will also satisfy the question. (a) 2 by 1 (b) 3 by 1 (c) 4 by 1 (d) 1 by 1 (e) 3 by 2 (f) 5 by 4 (g) 4 by 3 (h) 14 by 6 (i) 5 by 3

Suggest that the students organize their data: listing in separate columns the dimensions of those tables from the text and Exercise 2 where the ball landed in each corner, and further, how many hits each makes, for use in answering Exercises 4 and 6. When they get to Exercise 7, information on the type of symmetry can be added to the table. Note that our dimensions are always given as height by width. If you have students drawing a 2 by 1 table as ▢▢ , their rules will be different but may be correct as long as they are consistent. You may point out, however, that although the choice between height by width and width by height is arbitrary and does not matter as long as they are consistent, the instructor's life is easier if everyone uses the same conventions.

Billiards

Dimensions	Reduced Dimensions	Corner	Hits	Symmetry
10 by 5	2 by 1	upper left	3	horizontal reflection
6 by 3	2 by 1	upper left	3	horizontal reflection
9 by 3	3 by 1	upper right	4	rotation
12 by 3	4 by 1	upper left	5	horizontal reflection
6 by 6	1 by 1	upper right	2	rotation
9 by 6	3 by 2	lower right	5	vertical reflection
10 by 8	5 by 4	lower right	9	vertical reflection
8 by 6	4 by 3	upper left	7	horizontal reflection
7 by 3	7 by 3	upper right	10	rotation
15 by 9	5 by 3	upper right	8	rotation

Be prepared to suggest additional table sizes to try in Exercises 4, 5, and 8. You may also need to reinforce the idea of "necessary and sufficient." For example, my students have written rules like "if one of the dimensions is 3, then the ball ends up in the upper right corner" because they are looking at tables with dimensions 1 by 3, 3 by 9, and 3 by 7. Only when I ask about the 3 by 6 table do they think to add the words "in reduced terms." If I then ask about the 3 by 4 table, they add that the other dimension cannot be even. At this point, they have a statement such as "if one dimension is 3 and the other is odd, then the ball ends up in the upper right corner." This statement is sufficient to guarantee the conclusion. To address the idea of necessity, I would have them try a 5 by 7 table, or any other table with reduced dimensions both odd. Note that using tables with one of the dimensions equal to 1 always seems to confuse students and leads them to express their rules in a form such as "if the dimensions are odd and not equal to 1, then . . . ." Students may also need some prompting to recall terms such as greatest common factor, least common multiple, and relatively prime, and then may confuse these terms even if they have the right idea. This is an opportunity to point out that mathematics depends on the precise and careful usage of terminology.

▷ **Exercise 4.** (a) The ball will end up in the upper right corner if the reduced dimensions (divide both dimensions by the greatest common factor) are of the form "odd by odd."
(b) The ball will end up in the upper left corner if the reduced dimensions are of the form "even by odd."
(c) The ball will end up in the lower right corner if the reduced dimensions are of the form "odd by even."

If a student needs an additional hint for Exercise 5, refer to the series of drawings at the bottom of page 22 in the text.

▷ **Exercise 5.** The ball will go through every square if the dimensions are relatively prime.

▷ **Exercise 6.** The number of hits that the ball will make equals the sum of the reduced dimensions.

Most students quickly figure out the answers to Exercises 7 and 8, but may have trouble explaining their answer. Try to get them to see that the trajectory forces the symmetry (or equivalently, that the symmetry forces the trajectory).

▷ **Exercise 7.** (a) horizontal reflection   (b) rotation   (c) horizontal reflection   (d) rotation
(e) vertical reflection   (f) vertical reflection   (g) horizontal reflection   (h) rotation
(i) rotation

▷ **Exercise 8.** (a) The trajectory will have rotational symmetry if the reduced dimensions are of the form "odd by odd."
(b) The trajectory will have a horizontal reflection if the reduced dimensions are of the form "even by odd."
(c) The trajectory will have a vertical reflection if the reduced dimensions are of the form "odd by even."
(d) If a trajectory has a horizontal reflection, then the end point must be the horizontal reflection of the starting point, and so must end at the upper left corner. Similarly, a vertical reflection forces the ball to end at the lower right corner, and a rotation by 180° forces the ball to end at the upper right corner.

In Exercises 9–12, we make the transition from tables with integral dimensions to those with rational dimensions. The important idea is that any rational table can be scaled to an equivalent table with integral dimensions. Many students will scale their drawing without prompting. Others will try to squash the drawing into $1\frac{1}{3}$ squares, which is usually too small for accuracy. Working in groups often lets them fix these problems without the assistance of the instructor. I make them tell me how many squares represent one unit if they scale the drawing. For example, in the second drawing of Exercise 10, one unit is three squares long.

▷ **Exercise 9.** Note that the pattern is the same as a 10 by 5 table.

▷ **Exercise 10.** Note that the pattern is the same as a 7 by 6 table.

 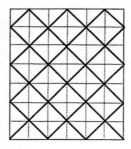

▷ **Exercise 11.** Note that the pattern is the same as an 8 by 9 table.

 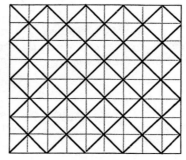

▷ **Exercise 12.** To deal with tables with fractional dimensions, scale the table up by the least common multiple of the denominators to eliminate the fractions.

At this point, it has been shown under the current assumptions that the ball will always end in a corner on a table with integer or rational dimensions. It sometimes takes a surprising amount of time for students to remember that there are other types of numbers. When asked about other types of numbers, many suggest repeating decimals, so be prepared to convince them that repeating decimals are rational. With enough prompting, someone in the group will come up with π or $\sqrt{2}$. However, note that the trajectory on a $\sqrt{2}$ by $2\sqrt{2}$ table will be the same as on a 1 by 2 table.

▷ **Exercise 13.** Any finite or repeating decimal can be written in fractional form and reduced to a table with integer sides as in Exercise 12. The ball has an unending trajectory on any table whose sides bear an irrational proportion to each other, such as a $\sqrt{2}$ by 1 table.

Just as scaling can be used to reduce a 45° billiard problem on a table with rational dimensions, in Exercises 14–16 we learn to use scaling to convert billiard trajectories with rational slope to 45° trajectories, which we have already analyzed. Again, some students will have trouble getting the patterns right. With a slope of 1 when the ball hits a side wall, students can turn their drawing 90° and continue to go up one–over one. That doesn't work with other slopes, since rotating the paper switches up/down with left/right. For example, this maneuver would change a slope of ±2 to a slope of $\pm\frac{1}{2}$.

12

▷ **Exercise 14.**

a) 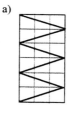 b)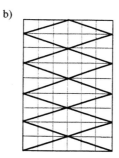

▷ **Exercise 15.**

a) 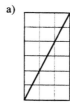 b)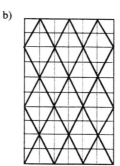

▷ **Exercise 16.** The Exercise 14 problems are the same as a 6 by 1 table and a 9 by 2 table, or any equivalent table where both dimensions are multiplied by the same number. The Exercise 15 problems are the same as a 3 by 3 (or 1 by 1) table and a 5 by 6 table.

> *The idea of unfolding trajectories gives a visual explanation of the rule for number of hits, found in Exercise 6, allows us to compute the length of the trajectory easily, and will be used in applying our very theoretical development of billiards to real problems. The examples of Exercise 17 and 18 provide data for the rule to be devised in Exercise 19.*

Unfolded Trajectories

Dimensions	Unfolded Table
6 by 4	12 by 12
6 by 3	6 by 6
9 by 3	9 by 9
4 by 8	8 by 8
4 by 3	12 by 12
10 by 4	20 by 20

13

▷ **Exercise 17.**

a) b) c) d) e)

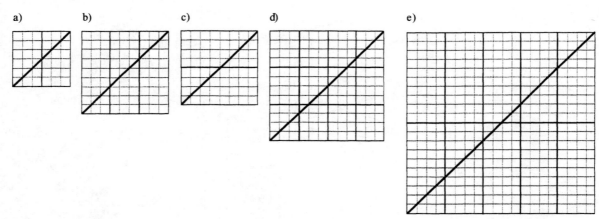

▷ **Exercise 18.** (a) $6\sqrt{2}$ (b) $9\sqrt{2}$ (c) $8\sqrt{2}$ (d) $12\sqrt{2}$ (e) $20\sqrt{2}$

▷ **Exercise 19.** Each dimension of the square unfolded table is the least common multiple of the dimensions of the original table. Note also that the number of repeats of the table lined up in one direction is the reduced dimension of the other direction. For example, a 6 by 3 table reduces to 2 by 1, so we need two copies of the original 6 by 3 table across and one copy up as shown in the solution of Exercise 17(a). A 4 by 3 table does not reduce, so we need four copies of the table across and three copies up, as shown in the solution of Exercise 17(d).

▷ **Exercise 20.**

a) b)

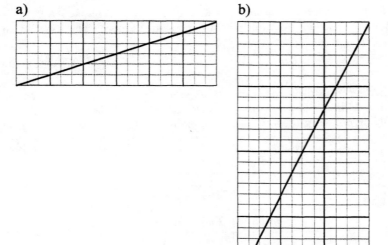

In Exercises 21 and 22, the idea of unfolding trajectories is applied to planning shots for real billiard problems. Emphasize that the trajectory is unfolded by reflecting the table across one of its edges, and that the position of any balls will also be reflected.

14

▷ **Exercise 21.**

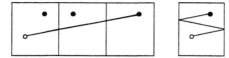

▷ **Exercise 22.** Below are pictured the shots where the cue ball hits first the west wall, then the east, followed by east-west, north-south, south-north, west-north, west-south, south-east, and north-east. Unfolding trajectories will show why east-south, east-north, north-west, and south-west are impossible.

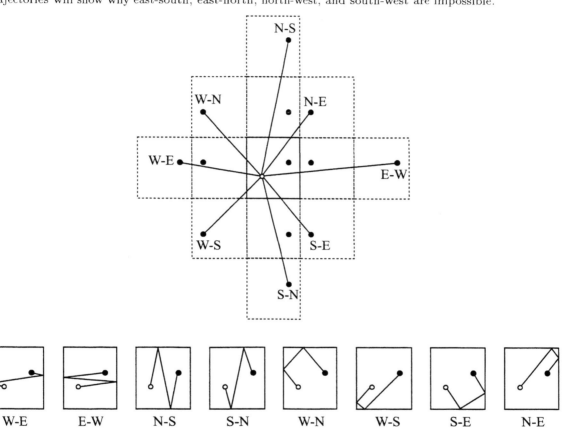

15

2.2. Celtic Knots

Since the illustrations in the text are in black and white, emphasize that ideally the dots of the grid would be drawn with two colors in alternation, always beginning with a colored dot in the upper left corner. A template with a grid of dots is contained in the Appendix (Template 2). The dimensions of a knot are given as height by width, where these dimensions are measured as length, not number of dots. That is, make sure your students are counting squares instead of dots. For example, a 1 × 1 knot will have 4 dots in the four corners of a square. Exercises 1–7 are designed for the student to gain familiarity with applying the rules and to generate some examples from which conclusions can be drawn in Exercises 8 and 9. It is fairly common for students eventually to start skipping the step of putting in all the diagonals and later erasing for the underpasses. Instead, they will draw lines with gaps at every other dot. If you have students trying this approach, make sure they don't count the outside edges and corners as crossing points.

▷ **Exercise 1.**

▷ **Exercise 2.**

▷ **Exercise 3.**

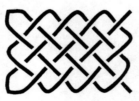

▷ **Exercise 4.**

▷ **Exercise 5.**

▷ **Exercise 6.**

▷ **Exercise 7.**

Encourage the students to organize their findings from the previous exercises and the examples in a list or table. As in Section 2.1, be prepared to suggest carefully chosen sizes for other knots they can draw to direct their thinking on Exercises 8, 9, and 11. These suggestions will, of course, depend on their preliminary hypotheses. If students switch the convention of writing the dimensions as width × height, their answer for Exercise 9 will be reversed.

▷ **Exercise 8.** A celtic knot will have loose ends if one of the dimensions is odd. Only when both dimensions are even are there blue dots in each of the four corners where the knot can turn around.

Celtic Knots

Reference	Dimensions	Closed	Loose Ends
Text	6×4	yes	
Text	6×5	no	lower left and lower right
Text	7×3	no	lower left and upper right
Exercise 1	10×5	no	lower left and lower right
Exercise 2	9×3	no	lower left and upper right
Exercise 3	9×6	no	upper right and lower right
Exercise 4	6×6	yes	
Exercise 5	8×6	yes	
Exercise 6	12×4	yes	
Exercise 7	12×8	yes	

▷ **Exercise 9.** If the dimensions of the knot are even by even, the knot will have no loose ends. If the dimensions of the knot are even by odd, the knot will have loose ends at the lower left and the lower right. If the dimensions of the knot are odd by even, the knot will have ends at the upper right and lower right. If the dimensions of the knot are odd by odd, the knot will have ends at the upper right and the lower left.

▷ **Exercise 10.** There must be an equal number of overpasses and underpasses, since each crossing forms both an overpass and an underpass.

If students get stuck on Exercise 11, I tell my students that a factor of 2 has been "used up" in ensuring that the knot is closed. Suggest that they divide all dimensions of closed knots by 2 and then try again to figure out the number of strands. A second approach has them counting black dots only in each direction. A 6 × 4 knot will have a grid with 3 × 2 black dots, and so with this method there is no need to divide by 2 to find the desired pattern.

▷ **Exercise 11.** The number of strands for a closed knot (which will have both dimensions even) is one-half of the greatest common factor of the dimensions.

Closed Celtic Knots

Dimensions	GCF	Strands
6 × 4	2	1
6 × 6	6	3
8 × 6	2	1
12 × 4	4	2
12 × 8	4	2

Note that in the case of a knot with loose ends, at least one of the dimensions will be odd, so one-half of the greatest common factor of the dimensions must be a fraction. In this case, add $\frac{1}{2}$ to get the next integer (or equivalently, round up). This can be assigned as a further exercise following Exercise 11.

Celtic Knots with Loose Ends

Dimensions	GCF	Strands
6 × 5	1	1
7 × 3	1	1
10 × 5	5	3
9 × 3	3	2
9 × 6	3	2

Exercises 12–16 provide practice in drawing celtic knots with obstructions.

18

▷ Exercise 12.

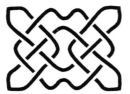

▷ Exercise 13.

▷ Exercise 14.

▷ Exercise 15.

▷ Exercise 16.

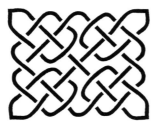

You may want to tell the students that there are 20 possible arrangements that they need to find for Exercise 17. You can provide further hints by telling them to note that there is only one arrangement in which the five circles form five components, one where there are four components, three with three components, six with two components, and nine with one component.

▷ **Exercise 17.**

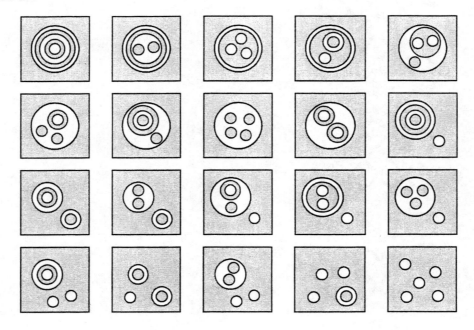

▷ **Exercise 18.**

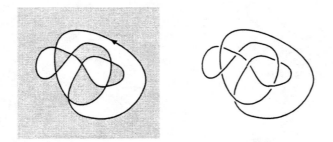

Chapter 3. Constructions

★ ★ ★ 3.1. Ruler and Compass Constructions
Dependencies: None

- Basic ruler and compass constructions
- Constructibility of lengths, angles, and polygons
- Gauss's Theorem

★ ★ ★ 3.2. The Pentagon and the Golden Ratio
Dependencies: Chapter 3.1

- The golden triangle and the golden ratio
- Construction of the pentagon by ruler and compass
- The golden ratio in art and architecture

★ ★ ★ 3.3. Theoretical Origami
Dependencies: Chapter 3.1, 3.2

- Basic origami constructions
- Construction of polygons using origami
- Trisection of an angle by origami

★ 3.4. Knots and Stars
Dependencies: None
References: Chapter 2.1 (star polygons can be considered as billiards on a circle using angles of the form $180°(\frac{n-2k}{n})$), 3.1, 3.2, 3.3 (regarding constructions of polygons)

- Polygonal knots
- Star polygons

★ ★ 3.5. Linkages
Dependencies: None

- Variable-based triangle linkage
- The pantograph and parallelogram linkages
- Peaucellier's linkage

This chapter and its five sections investigate questions and means of construction of two-dimensional geometric figures, especially polygons. The first section covers very traditional material, most of which should be familiar from high school. This is not one of the more popular sections with the students, so it helps to mention the connections that will be made in Sections 3.2 and 3.3. On the other hand, students do genuinely like the introduction to origami in Section 3.3 which depends on this section. We usually supplement the exercises on origami with instructions for birds and flowers and such to help maintain their interest. See the reference texts for ideas and instructions. Euclid's ruler and compass postulates (Postulates 1–3) are stated, and then six basic constructions (all of which occur as propositions in Euclid) are given. Proving that these give the desired result requires a knowledge of euclidean geometry. They are then applied to answer questions about what lengths and angles are constructible with ruler and compass. It is shown how to construct any rational length and square roots of integers. It is stated (but not proved) that these (and combinations of these using sums, differences, products, and quotients) are the only constructible lengths.

21

Similarly, it is stated that it is impossible to trisect an arbitrary angle with ruler and compass. Gauss's Theorem on the constructibility of regular polygons is stated, again without proof, though students will be able to construct n-sided polygons with $n = 3 \cdot 2^k$ and $n = 5 \cdot 2^k$.

The second section is devoted to the construction of the pentagon and investigation of the golden ratio. After developing the definition of the golden ratio and its relationship to the pentagon, the algebraic properties of the golden ratio are investigated. We show how to construct a line segment of length equal to the golden ratio, and this is used to construct a regular pentagon. Finally, some of the myths surrounding the golden ratio are discussed.

Section 3.3 extends the idea of constructibility to paper folding, or origami. Origami postulates are given, and we show that each of the ruler and compass constructions of Sections 3.1 and 3.2 can be duplicated by these means. It thus follows that anything that is constructible with ruler and compass is also constructible by origami. Exercises are given in which the students construct an equilateral triangle, a square, a hexagon, and an octagon. Finally, a last origami postulate is introduced that allows the trisection of any acute angle.

Section 3.4 has proved to be extremely popular. It is independent of the other sections of this chapter and relates star polygons and polygonal knots (torus knots constructed with strips of paper tape). Star polygons embody modular arithmetic, and these arithmetic properties are studied without any mention of the algebraic structure underlying them. A formula for the vertex angle of a star polygon is derived.

The last section of this chapter, on simple mechanical linkages, is also independent of the others. Properties of parallelograms and similar triangles are exploited to build linkages with various rational scaling factors.

3.1. Ruler and Compass Constructions

Most students should recall the basic constructions (Exercises 1-4 at least) from their high school geometry course with only a little prompting from the instructor. The Geometer's Sketchpad® or Cabri® can be used instead of the traditional tools, if either is available. Emphasize that each construction is built by steps from the basic constructions. Reinforce the idea that they are not allowed to measure lengths or angles, since the straightedge has no markings and the protractor has not yet been invented.

▷ **Exercise 1.** Construct a perpendicular bisector following directions in the text.

▷ **Exercise 2.** Erect a perpendicular following directions in the text.

▷ **Exercise 3.** (1) Draw a circle centered at C and intersecting the line AB at two points, D and E.
(2) Draw circles of equal radii (with this radius greater than half of DE) centered at D and E, which meet each other at F below the line AB.
(3) The line CF, meeting AB at G, is perpendicular to AB.

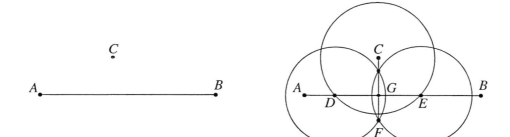

▷ **Exercise 4.** (1) Draw a circle centered at B and intersecting $\angle ABC$ at points D and E.
(2) Draw circles of equal radii (chosen to be greater than DE) centered at D and E, intersecting at point F. (There will be two points of intersection. Choose either for F.)
(3) The line BF will bisect $\angle ABC$.

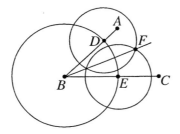

▷ **Exercise 5.**   Given line AB and point C, draw a line from C to an arbitrary point D on AB. Construct $\angle ECD$ to be equal to $\angle BDC$, using R&C Construction 5.

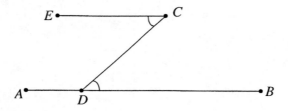

▷ **Exercise 6.**   Extend the line, and setting your compass at a radius equal to the line segment AB shown, proceed as follows, and the line segment AD will be 3 units long.

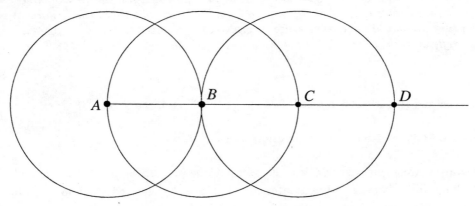

Insist that students perform the constructions of Exercise 7 and 8 by straightedge and compass (or using The Geometer's Sketchpad®). Entirely too many of them will want to use the markings on the ruler to space the points or a protractor to draw the parallel lines.

▷ **Exercise 7.**

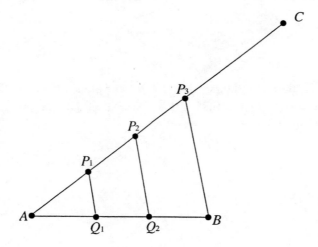

▷ **Exercise 8.**   Divide the 2-inch line segment into three pieces using R&C Construction 6. The second mark will be $\frac{4}{3}$.

▷ **Exercise 9.**

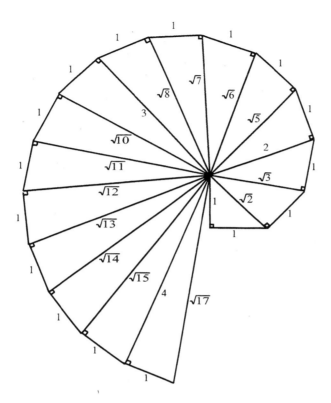

▷ **Exercise 10.**

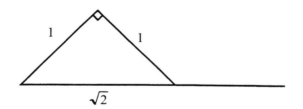

Many students will recall the construction of Exercise 11 from high school. For those that do not, a hint may be given by asking them what they know about the sides of an equilateral triangle. The proportions of the sides of a 30°-60°-90° triangle as in Exercise 12 will recur occasionally in the text.

▷ **Exercise 11.** Given the base AB, draw circles centered at A and B, both with radius AB. They will intersect at point C, and $\triangle ABC$ is equilateral.

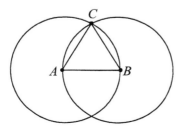

25

▷ **Exercise 12.** Each of the three angles measures 60°. If each side measures 1 inch, then consider the 30°-60°-90° formed by dropping a perpendicular from the top vertex (or, equivalently, bisecting the top vertex angle). This triangle has base of length $\frac{1}{2}$ and hypotenuse 1, so using the Pythagorean Theorem we find that the altitude or height of the triangle is $\frac{\sqrt{3}}{2}$.

There are, of course, other ways of constructing a square, though the one given below is the simplest. It also has the advantage of leading to the idea of constructing an n-sided polygon by spacing n points equally around a circle, which will help in Exercises 14 and 15.

▷ **Exercise 13.** The easiest way to construct a square with ruler and compass is to draw two perpendicular lines, AB and CD. Draw a circle centered where these lines intersect. The four points where the lines AB and CD intersect the circle are the four corners of a square.

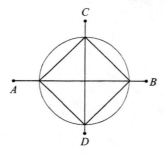

▷ **Exercise 14.** Draw a circle. Keeping your compass set on the radius of the circle, mark off six equally spaced points around the circle, for the six vertices of the hexagon.

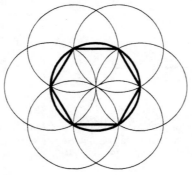

▷ **Exercise 15.** Bisect the right angles forming the diagonals of a square (see the Exercise 13 illustration):

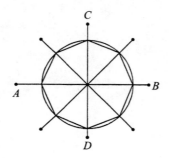

For Exercise 16, one can use a variant of Eratosthenes's sieve: list the numbers from 1 to 100 and then circle those which are of the form $3 \cdot 2^n$, then repeat for numbers of the form $5 \cdot 2^n$, and then $17 \cdot 2^n$, and then go on to circle the numbers of the form $3 \cdot 5 \cdot 2^n$, $3 \cdot 17 \cdot 2^n$, and $5 \cdot 17 \cdot 2^n$. Some students are initially appalled at this exercise and don't know where to start, but after figuring out a method of approach (and many students will come up with a variation of Eratosthenes's sieve by themselves), they find this problem easy.

▷ **Exercise 16.** Regular polygons with 3, 4, 5, 6, 8, 10, 12, 15, 16, 17, 20, 24, 30, 32, 34, 40, 48, 51, 60, 64, 68, 80, 85, and 96 sides are constructible with ruler and compass.

3.2. The Pentagon and the Golden Ratio

This section assumes the previous one and continues the discussion of ruler and compass constructions involving the pentagon and the golden ratio. While many students find the algebraic simplifications in this section either difficult or tedious, they like examining the theory about the beauty of the ratio and its existence in art and architecture. The first two exercises find crucial properties of a regular pentagon, and the text following uses these to compute the golden ratio ϕ.

▷ **Exercise 1.** Since $\triangle EAD$ is isosceles, $\angle EAD = \angle EDA$. We know that $\angle AED = 108°$ and $\angle AED + \angle EAD + \angle EDA = 180°$, so $\angle EAD = \angle EDA = 36°$. Similarly, $\angle BAC = \angle BCA = 36°$. Since $\angle EAD + \angle DAC + \angle BAC = 108°$, $\angle DAC = 36°$. Since $\angle EDA + \angle ADC = 108°$, $\angle ADC = 72°$, and similarly $\angle ACD = 72°$.

▷ **Exercise 2.** We know that $\angle DAC = 36°$ and $\angle ADC = \angle ACD = 72°$. Since DF bisects $\angle ADC$, $\angle ADF = \angle CDF = 36°$. Since $\angle DAF + \angle ADF + \angle AFD = 180°$, $\angle AFD = 108°$, and so $\angle DFC = 72°$.

Emphasize that the solutions to Exercises 3 and 4 should be simplified to involve only constants and ϕ. Some students will have difficulty expressing their answers to Exercise 3(e) and 4(f) formally, even if they see the pattern. One can either accept a clear verbal explanation, or take advantage of this opportunity to help them gain familiarity with the mathematical conventions of notation. When they ask why anyone would want to do this, ask them which computation is easier: multiplying a number by an integer and adding or raising the number to a high power.

▷ **Exercise 3.** (a) $\phi^4 = 3\phi + 2$
(b) $\phi^5 = 5\phi + 3$
(c) $\phi^6 = 8\phi + 5$
(d) $\phi^7 = 13\phi + 8$
(e) Add the last two terms to get the next: $\phi^n = \phi^{n-1} + \phi^{n-2}$. Alternatively, one can introduce the Fibonacci numbers: let $s_0 = 1, s_1 = 1$, and $s_n = s_{n-1} + s_{n-2}$. Then $\phi^n = s_{n-1}\phi + s_{n-2}$.

▷ **Exercise 4.** (a) $\phi^{-3} = 2\phi - 3$
(b) $\phi^{-4} = -3\phi + 5$
(c) $\phi^{-5} = 5\phi - 8$
(d) $\phi^{-6} = -8\phi + 13$
(e) $\phi^{-7} = 13\phi - 21$
(f) Subtract the last term from the next to the last to get the next: $\phi^{-n} = \phi^{-(n-2)} - \phi^{-(n-1)}$. Alternatively, using the Fibonacci numbers as suggested in the solution to Exercise 3, $\phi^{-n} = (-1)^{n-1}(s_{n-1}\phi - s_n)$.

▷ **Exercise 5.** (a) $\frac{CG}{GF} = \frac{CF}{GF} = \phi$
(b) $\frac{FG}{GH} = \frac{FH}{GH} = \phi$

▷ **Exercise 6.** Since $AB = BD = DE = EA = 1$ and F is the midpoint of AB, $FB = \frac{1}{2}$. Use the Pythagorean Theorem for the right triangle FBD and get $FC^2 = FD^2 = 1^2 + (\frac{1}{2})^2 = \frac{5}{4}$. Thus, $FC = FD = \frac{\sqrt{5}}{2}$, and $AC = AF + FC = \frac{1}{2} + \frac{\sqrt{5}}{2} = \frac{1+\sqrt{5}}{2} = \phi$.

Note that the constructions of Exercises 7 and 8 should be built on top of the previous construction of the golden ratio as in R & C Construction 7 in the text. There are other (more efficient) ways of constructing a regular pentagon, but we have decided to present this one because it is the one in Euclid and because of the central role played by the golden ratio in the development.

▷ **Exercise 7.** Perform R&C Construction 7, and then set your compass to the length of AC to find point G so that $AG = AC = BG$.

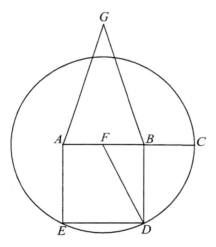

▷ **Exercise 8.** After constructing a golden triangle AGB as in Exercise 7, set your compass on length AB and mark points H and I so that $AH = GH = AB$ and $BI = GI = AB$.

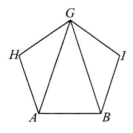

Refer students puzzled by Exercise 9 back to their results in Exercises 3 and 4.

▷ **Exercise 9.** (a) $\dfrac{HI}{IG} = \dfrac{\phi-1}{1-(\phi-1)} = \dfrac{\phi-1}{2-\phi} = \dfrac{\frac{1}{\phi}}{\frac{1}{\phi^2}} = \phi$

(b) $\dfrac{DH}{HJ} = \dfrac{2-\phi}{(\phi-1)-(2-\phi)} = \dfrac{2-\phi}{2\phi-3} = \dfrac{\frac{1}{\phi^2}}{\frac{1}{\phi^3}} = \phi$

29

This is a good opportunity to tell students of the prevalence of myth in mathematics and science as well as other disciplines. The article by Markowsky is particularly good. However, note that the golden ratio was consciously utilized by many later artists and architects, such as Mondrian and Le Corbusier.

▷ **Exercise 10.** There is, of course, no one correct answer. The fifth rectangle in the top row is a golden rectangle.

▷ **Exercise 11.** Collect data from at least a dozen people on preference in rectangles.

▷ **Exercise 12.** Find the ratio of height : height to navel.

▷ **Exercise 13.** Collect data from at least a dozen people on ratio of height : height to navel.

Collect the data for Exercises 11 and 13 from the whole class and analyze it. Discuss the margin of error and whether the data supports the hypothesis that the ideal rectangle is golden. For the data of Exercise 13, one can also sort it by sex and closeness to ideal beauty (though this can be somewhat delicate to make public judgments on). One can further discuss the ways in which ideal beauty is dictated by one's culture.

3.3. Theoretical Origami

This section builds on the previous two and is a pleasing extension of material and techniques to which the students have been exposed in high school. The first five exercises provide the framework and allow students to start getting some idea of origami methods.

▷ **Exercise 1.** Folding between two points forms a straight line.

▷ **Exercise 2.** The fold forms the perpendicular bisector of the line segment connecting the two points. The fold line is shown as dashed:

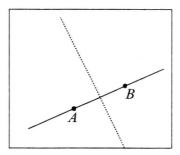

There are two cases to consider for Origami Postulate 4: the case where the lines intersect (Exercise 3) and the case where the lines happen to be parallel (Exercise 4). We do not explain how to fold parallel lines until later, so for this exercise we must assume that the parallel lines required were constructed by other means, either with ruler and compass or by simpler modern means, such as using the two parallel sides of a ruler (guaranteed by the manufacturer to be parallel).

▷ **Exercise 3.** The fold bisects the angle formed by the two lines. The fold line is shown as dashed:

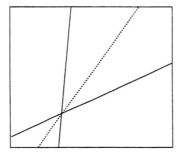

▷ **Exercise 4.** The fold is parallel to the two lines and lies halfway between them. The fold line is shown as dashed:

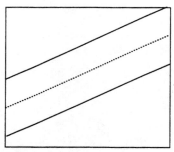

While the results of Origami Postulates 1–4 are easy for the students to accept, the use of Origami Postulate 5 is less transparent. Note that the dashed fold line through B in the picture below is the perpendicular bisector of the gray line from A to a point on the solid line.

▷ **Exercise 5.** The fold line is shown as dashed for the two cases:

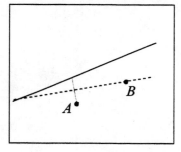 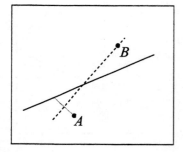

Exercises 6–10 involve formalizing the basic origami constructions, in parallel with the ruler and compass constructions of Chapter 3.1. Emphasize the use of the origami postulates, even though these are different from the ruler and compass postulates. Since the same basic constructions can be performed, we will show that anything that can be built using the basic constructions is constructible both by ruler and compass and by origami. Contrasting the two systems will help the student understand the difference between postulates and constructions. The postulates are, in fact, constructions, but simple ones that require no instruction. In this case students can see that two different sets of postulates can lead to the same constructions or theorems.

▷ **Exercise 6.** Fold the perpendicular bisector as directed.

▷ **Exercise 7.** (1) Let AB be the given line and C the point that lies on AB.
(2) Using Origami Postulate 5, fold through C so that B (or A) falls on the line AB.

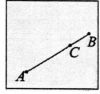 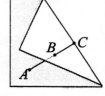 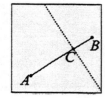

▷ **Exercise 8.** (1) Let AB be the given line and C the point that does not lie on AB.

(2) Using Origami Postulate 5, fold so that C lies on the crease while point B (or A) falls on line AB.

 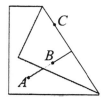 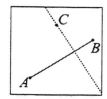

▷ **Exercise 9.** (1) Let $\angle ABC$ be the given angle.

(2) Using Origami Postulate 4, fold so that line AB falls on top of line CB. The crease thus formed bisects the angle.

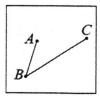 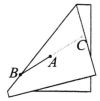 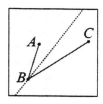

Most students find Exercises 10 and 11 a bit more difficult than 6-9, but with a little experimenting, they will figure out how to do these constructions.

▷ **Exercise 10.** (1) Let $\angle BAC$ be the given angle and DE the given line segment.

(2) Fold so that line DE lies on top of the line AC. You may need to extend your lines to make this clearer. Note that the points are unlikely to land on top of each other. (The case of parallel lines is easy. In the case of intersecting lines, you are extending the lines so that they intersect and then bisecting the angle formed.)

(3) Without unfolding, fold along AB and AC. These folds will form the desired angle with the line DE. Note that the vertex of the angle may not be at point D.

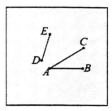 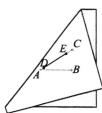 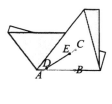 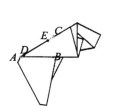 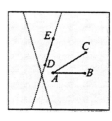

▷ **Exercise 11.** Fold through B so that A falls on line AB. Label the point where A falls as C. Fold through C so that A falls on line AB. Label the point where B falls as D and where A falls as E.

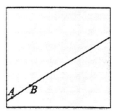 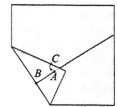 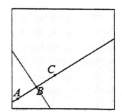 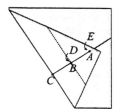 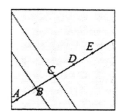

Exercises 12–15 involve the mechanics of folding regular polygons with origami. Most students quickly find one solution in Exercise 12 but find Exercise 13 more difficult. After completing Exercise 12, they should be allowed to use standard square origami paper. Tell them to try to fold the equilateral triangle so that the lower edge of the origami paper forms the base, and point out that the top vertex will not lie on the upper edge but will lie on the perpendicular bisector of the base. For Exercise 14, the instructor may have to point out that a hexagon can be divided up into six equilateral triangles.

▷ **Exercise 12.** There are several ways to do this, but here's one: first, fold line BC, then erect two perpendicular lines at B and C as shown. Bisect $\angle ABC$ and $\angle DCB$ to form the diagonals of the square. We then have a square with $AB = BC = CD = DA$.

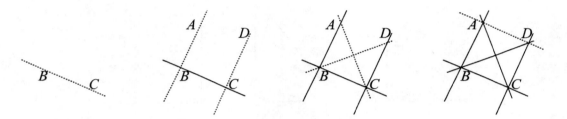

▷ **Exercise 13.** Let $ABCD$ be a square piece of origami paper. Fold it in half as shown below, then fold through D so that corner C lies on the mid-line. The distance from D to the point on the dashed line underneath C is equal to the distance from D to C. Repeat for the other side to get the third equal side.

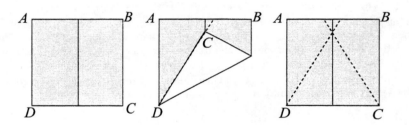

▷ **Exercise 14.** There are many ways of doing this, all based on the previous exercise. Here is one, from Sundara Row's book. Fold a square sheet of origami paper $ABCD$ in half and then in fourths as shown below, forming lines EF and GH, intersecting at O. Fold again so that AD falls on EF, and BC falls on EF, forming lines IJ and KL. Fold through O so that G falls on IJ, and again through O so that H falls on KL. Fold through E so that A falls on IJ, through E so that B falls on KL, through F so that C falls on KL, and through F so that D falls on IJ. The hexagon is outlined below:

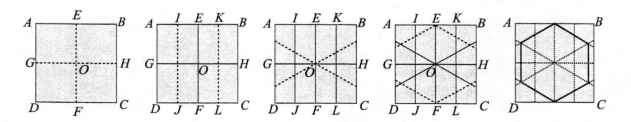

34

▷ **Exercise 15.** Here's a neat way to do this: fold a sheet of origami paper in fourths, then bisect the interior angles to get eighths. Fold up the sheet along these creases to form a wedge as shown and bisect the right angle. Bisect the angle again, and unfold to get an octagon.

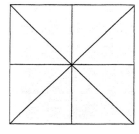   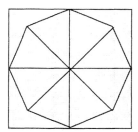

In parallel with the ruler and compass development, Exercises 16 and 17 first show that Construction 7 divides a line segment (the edge of the origami paper in this case) by the golden ratio, and then uses this construction to make a regular pentagon. Emphasize that the vertex L in the construction of the pentagon in the text will not lie on the edge of the origami paper.

▷ **Exercise 16.** (a) Since $\triangle BAE$ is a right triangle and $AB = 1$ and $AE = \frac{1}{2}$, $BE^2 = 1 + \frac{1}{4} = \frac{5}{4}$, so $BE = \frac{\sqrt{5}}{2}$.
(b) $EA = \frac{1}{2}$ since it is half of $AD = AB = 1$. Since we folded so that AE lay over EG, $EA = EG = \frac{1}{2}$.
(c) Note that $BH = BG = BE - EG = \frac{\sqrt{5}}{2} - \frac{1}{2} = \frac{\sqrt{5}-1}{2}$.
(d) $\frac{AB}{BH} = \frac{1}{\frac{\sqrt{5}-1}{2}} = \frac{1+\sqrt{5}}{2} = \phi$

▷ **Exercise 17.** Construct a pentagon using the directions.

Haga's theorem applies the Pythagorean Theorem and similar triangles to divide the edges of the square in rational proportions. These are investigated in Exercises 18–22. These exercises and the accompanying text can be omitted without loss of continuity.

▷ **Exercise 18.** Fold a piece of origami paper as shown.

▷ **Exercise 19.** Note that $\angle A$, $\angle B$, $\angle D$, and $\angle EMF$ are all right angles. Thus $\angle BME + \angle BEM = \angle BME + \angle AMF = \angle AMF + \angle AFM = \angle DHG + \angle DGH = 90°$. Thus, $\angle BME = \angle AFM = \angle DHG$, and $\angle BEM = \angle AMF = \angle DGH$, and thus the triangles EBM, MAF, and GDH are all similar.

▷ **Exercise 20.** By the Pythagorean Theorem, $x^2 + (\frac{1}{2})^2 = (1-x)^2 = 1 - 2x + x^2$. Thus, $BE = x = \frac{3}{8}$ and $CE = 1 - x = \frac{5}{8}$. The triangle BEM has sides $\frac{3}{8}$-$\frac{1}{2}$-$\frac{5}{8}$, in proportion 3-4-5.

▷ **Exercise 21.** Triangle AMF will also have sides in proportion 3-4-5, or 1-$\frac{4}{3}$-$\frac{5}{3}$. Since the shorter side $AM = \frac{1}{2}$, $AF = \frac{2}{3}$ and $FM = \frac{5}{6}$.

▷ **Exercise 22.** Since $CH = MF = \frac{5}{6}$, $DH = \frac{1}{6}$. The triangle DHG has proportions 3-4-5 or $\frac{3}{4}$-1-$\frac{5}{4}$, so $DG = \frac{1}{8}$ and $HG = \frac{5}{24}$.

Exercises 23–25 concern another nice application of paper folding, again applying similar triangles. These exercises can also be omitted.

▷ **Exercise 23.** (a) Use Origami Postulate 4, laying AB on top of CD.
(b) Use Origami Postulate 1 to fold through points M and D.
(c) Use Origami Postulate 5 to fold through E so that point C falls on BM.

▷ **Exercise 24.** Fold an $8\frac{1}{2}$ by 11 inch piece of paper in thirds as shown.

▷ **Exercise 25.** (a) Since AD is parallel to BC, $\angle DAE = \angle MCE$ and $\angle ADE = \angle EMC$. Also, $\angle AED = \angle CEM$.
(b) Since the triangles are similar and $AD = 2CM$, $AE = 2CE$.
(c) By (a), $\angle JAE = \angle KCE$. $\angle AJE = \angle CKE = 90°$ and $\angle AEJ = \angle CEK$, so the triangles are similar.
(d) Since the triangles of (c) are similar and $AE = 2CE$, $JE = 2KE$, and thus $KE = \frac{1}{3}KJ$.

> *In this part of the text we discuss a crucial and subtle difference between the traditional ruler and compass tools and origami. Origami Postulate 6 has no counterpart with ruler and compass, but allows one to solve classical problems that are not amenable to ruler and compass. Duplication of the cube and construction of a regular heptagon are also possible with origami, but squaring the circle is not.*

▷ **Exercise 26.** Fold as directed.

▷ **Exercise 27.** Trisect an angle as directed.

3.4. Knots and Stars

This section begins with tying some knots, goes on to investigate star polygons, and ends by finding a relationship between the two types of activities. Begin by encouraging students to make the pentagonal knot pictured in the text. Exercise 1 should be easy for all students. Some students have described this as linking two AIDS ribbons. Exercise 2 is a little more difficult. Exercise 3 requires careful attention to the instructions. Attention should be drawn to the order of the folds. If the instructor prefers, Exercises 1–3 and 21–23 (those dealing with the knotted polygons) may be omitted.

▷ **Exercise 1.** Knot two strips of paper in a square knot to form a regular hexagon as shown.

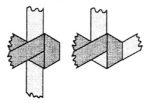

▷ **Exercise 2.** Knot a strip of paper to form a regular heptagon.

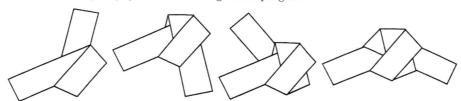

▷ **Exercise 3.** Tie an octagonal knot from a single strip of paper to make a knot as shown. Be careful to make the first fold precisely as pictured in the text.

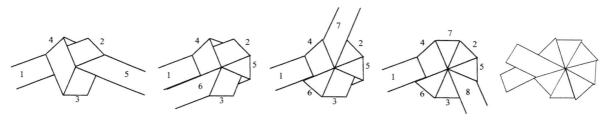

After making the knots of Exercises 1–3, move on to star polygons. Use the dot paper of Templates 3–8 in the Appendix. While the students seem to like (or at least don't mind) drawing the star polygons, this is another section where we hear "why are we doing this?" Remind your students that they are learning the process of mathematics. The results may not be something they will use on a daily basis, but they are learning to find patterns and express general results from studying examples. To do this, they need a sufficient number of examples to base their hypotheses on.

▷ **Exercise 4.** When you connect every third dot and every fifth dot you get a star with one strand. These two pictures are exactly the same in the end, though the points are connected in different orders. Every fourth dot gives four straight lines intersecting at the center. Every sixth dot gives the same picture as every other dot. Every seventh dot gives a regular octagon.

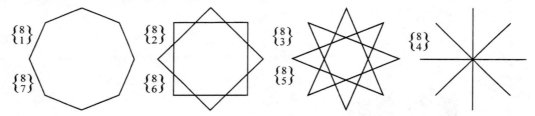

▷ **Exercise 5.** Note that $\left\{ {9 \atop 1} \right\} = \left\{ {9 \atop 8} \right\}$ is not pictured. These form regular nonagons.

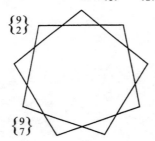
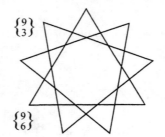
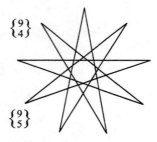

▷ **Exercise 6.** $\left\{ {8 \atop 1} \right\} = \left\{ {8 \atop 7} \right\}$, $\left\{ {8 \atop 2} \right\} = \left\{ {8 \atop 6} \right\}$, $\left\{ {8 \atop 3} \right\} = \left\{ {8 \atop 5} \right\}$; $\left\{ {9 \atop 1} \right\} = \left\{ {9 \atop 8} \right\}$, $\left\{ {9 \atop 2} \right\} = \left\{ {9 \atop 7} \right\}$, $\left\{ {9 \atop 3} \right\} = \left\{ {9 \atop 6} \right\}$, $\left\{ {9 \atop 4} \right\} = \left\{ {9 \atop 5} \right\}$

▷ **Exercise 7.** $\left\{ {n \atop k} \right\} = \left\{ {n \atop n-k} \right\}$

▷ **Exercise 8.** Also see the table of Exercise 10. Note that $\left\{ {12 \atop 1} \right\}$ is omitted as are duplicate figures.

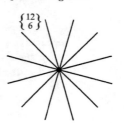

▷ **Exercise 9.** Also see the table of Exercise 10. Note that $\left\{{15 \atop 1}\right\}$ is omitted as are duplicate figures.

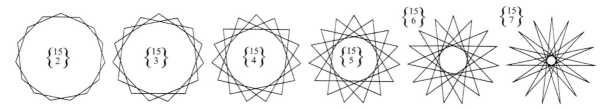

Encourage students to organize their findings for Exercises 10 and 11 in a table as shown below. This will help them analyze the patterns and find the rules for Exercises 12 and 13. Again, students will have particular trouble with the degenerate star polygons such as $\left\{{8 \atop 4}\right\}$ and $\left\{{12 \atop 6}\right\}$. Each cycle of these should be thought of as consisting of two legs: from the initial point to the opposite point and back again.

▷ **Exercise 10.**

Star Polygons

$\left\{{n \atop k}\right\}$	Revolutions	Regular/Compound	Cycles	Length
$\left\{{8 \atop 2}\right\}$	2	compound	2	4
$\left\{{8 \atop 3}\right\}$	3	regular		
$\left\{{8 \atop 4}\right\}$	4	compound	4	2
$\left\{{9 \atop 2}\right\}$	2	regular		
$\left\{{9 \atop 3}\right\}$	3	compound	3	3
$\left\{{9 \atop 4}\right\}$	4	regular		
$\left\{{12 \atop 2}\right\}$	2	compound	2	6
$\left\{{12 \atop 3}\right\}$	3	compound	3	4
$\left\{{12 \atop 4}\right\}$	4	compound	4	3
$\left\{{12 \atop 5}\right\}$	5	regular		
$\left\{{12 \atop 6}\right\}$	6	compound	6	2
$\left\{{15 \atop 2}\right\}$	2	regular		
$\left\{{15 \atop 3}\right\}$	3	compound	3	5
$\left\{{15 \atop 4}\right\}$	4	regular		
$\left\{{15 \atop 5}\right\}$	5	compound	5	3
$\left\{{15 \atop 6}\right\}$	6	compound	3	5
$\left\{{15 \atop 7}\right\}$	7	regular		

▷ **Exercise 11.** See the table of Exercise 10.

The next two exercises form the heart of this unit, and then Exercises 14 and 15 confirm that the student can apply the rules found. Many students will first guess that a star polygon is regular if the lower number does not divide the upper. Call attention to $\left\{{15 \atop 6}\right\}$. Organizing a chart of the compound star polygons will help make clear the rule that the number of cycles times their length equals the number of dots.

Students may not remember the phrase "no common factors" but will describe the situation. Others may have the right idea but use the wrong words (such as "no common multiples"). Again, one of the missions of this course is to teach them how to use such language precisely and correctly.

▷ **Exercise 12.** A star polygon $\left\{{n \atop k}\right\}$ is regular if n and k are relatively prime, that is, if they have no common factors. A star polygon $\left\{{n \atop k}\right\}$ is compound if n and k have a common factor $m > 1$, and then this common factor m is the number of cycles, and $\frac{n}{m}$ gives the length of these cycles.

▷ **Exercise 13.** A star polygon $\left\{{n \atop k}\right\}$ winds around the circle k times.

▷ **Exercise 14.** $\left\{{24 \atop 9}\right\}$ has three cycles of length 8.

▷ **Exercise 15.** $\left\{{21 \atop 2}\right\}$, $\left\{{21 \atop 4}\right\}$, $\left\{{21 \atop 5}\right\}$, $\left\{{21 \atop 8}\right\}$, and $\left\{{21 \atop 10}\right\}$ are regular star polygons.

Enlarging the drawings may help in Exercises 16 and 17. Work from the regular polygon nested at the center outward. The only rules needed are that vertical angles are equal and (from Section 1.2) that the angles in an n-sided polygon sum to $(n-2)180°$ and that each vertex angle of a regular n-sided polygon measures $\frac{(n-2)180°}{n}$.

▷ **Exercise 16.** The vertex angle of the star polygon $\left\{{8 \atop 3}\right\}$ is $45°$.

▷ **Exercise 17.** The vertex angle of the star polygon $\left\{{9 \atop 2}\right\}$ is $100°$, and the vertex angle for $\left\{{9 \atop 4}\right\}$ is $20°$.

▷ **Exercise 18.**

Vertex Angles

$n\downarrow$ $k\rightarrow$	1	2	3	4	Difference
5	$\angle\left\{{5 \atop 1}\right\} = 108°$	$\angle\left\{{5 \atop 2}\right\} = 36°$	$\bullet$	$\bullet$	72°
6	$\angle\left\{{6 \atop 1}\right\} = 120°$	$\angle\left\{{6 \atop 2}\right\} = 60°$	$\angle\left\{{6 \atop 3}\right\} = 0$	$\bullet$	60°
8	$\angle\left\{{8 \atop 1}\right\} = 135°$	$\angle\left\{{8 \atop 2}\right\} = 90°$	$\angle\left\{{8 \atop 3}\right\} = 45°$	$\angle\left\{{8 \atop 4}\right\} = 0$	45°
9	$\angle\left\{{9 \atop 1}\right\} = 140°$	$\angle\left\{{9 \atop 2}\right\} = 100°$	$\angle\left\{{9 \atop 3}\right\} = 60°$	$\angle\left\{{9 \atop 4}\right\} = 20°$	40°

After filling out the chart of Exercise 18, encourage the students to find rules for Exercises 19 and 20 that involve the quantity $180°$ or $360°$. This is usually enough of a hint for them to derive the necessary formulae, but if not, have them first express the numbers in the difference column of the table as $\frac{360°}{n}$. Try to lead them to realize that the vertex angle for $\left\{{n \atop k}\right\}$ is $180°$ minus k times this difference.

▷ **Exercise 19.** The difference between the vertex angle of $\left\{{n \atop k}\right\}$ and $\left\{{n \atop k+1}\right\}$ is $\frac{360°}{n}$.

▷ **Exercise 20.** The vertex angle of the star polygon $\left\{{n \atop k}\right\}$ is $180° - \frac{360°k}{n} = 180°\left(\frac{n-2k}{n}\right)$.

Now that the students have learned the language of star polygons, they should revisit the knots formed earlier: the order of the folds in the pentagonal knot is easily seen to be $\{\frac{5}{2}\}$. The hexagonal knot of Exercise 1 is related to the compound star polygon $\{\frac{6}{2}\}$ and the heptagonal knot of Exercise 2 is modeled on $\{\frac{7}{3}\}$. The instructional drawing for Exercise 3 makes the relation to the star polygon $\{\frac{8}{3}\}$ clear.

▷ **Exercise 21.** The sequence of folds forms a star polygon.

▷ **Exercise 22.** A nine-sided knot can be modeled after $\{\frac{9}{2}\}$ (which makes a wreathlike knot) or $\{\frac{9}{4}\}$ (which is quite like the seven-sided knot of Exercise 2).

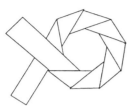   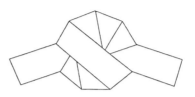

▷ **Exercise 23.** Model the eight-sided knot on $\{\frac{8}{2}\}$. This makes a very loose knot. Paper clips holding the loose ends together will help it hold its shape.

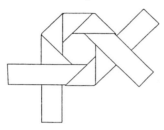

3.5. Linkages

Under the guise of studying mechanical linkages, basic geometric properties, especially similarity, are reinforced. Exercises 1–5 concern the variable-based triangle linkage. In general, students are not used to dealing with dynamic geometry, so actually building the linkages will help them keep in mind that some of the points are not fixed in position. Alternatively, dynamic demonstrations can be developed using the Locus command in The Geometer's Sketchpad®.

▷ **Exercise 1.** B draws a circle around A with radius AB.

▷ **Exercise 2.** E draws an ellipse.

▷ **Exercise 3.** D draws a straight line, perpendicular to AC.

▷ **Exercise 4.** (a) Triangle ABC is isosceles, so $\angle BAC = \angle BCA$.
(b) $\angle BAC + \angle BCA + \angle ABC = 180°$
(c) $\angle BAD = \angle BDA$
(d) $\angle BAD + \angle BDA + \angle ABD = 180°$
(e) $\angle ABD + \angle ABC = 180°$
(f) Using (a) and (b), $\angle ABC = 180° - \angle BCA - \angle BAC = 180° - 2\angle BAC$. Using (c) and (d), $\angle ABD = 180° - \angle BDA - \angle BAD = 180° - 2\angle BAD$. Now, use (e) to get $180° = \angle ABD + \angle ABC = (180° - 2\angle BAC) + (180° - 2\angle BAD) = 360° - 2\angle BAC - 2\angle BAD$. Thus, $\angle CAD = \angle BAC + \angle BAD = 90°$.

In the following exercise, we have made the perhaps unwarranted assumption that your students have some familiarity with the traditional ironing board or can find one to play with.

▷ **Exercise 5.** Traditional ironing boards use a variable triangle linkage, as shown below:

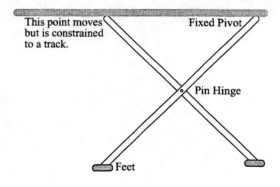

Exercises 6–18 concern parallelogram linkages. The similar triangles involved in the constructions give the scaling factor when the linkage is used to draw a figure. For Exercises 6–8, students should actually build the linkage and use it to trace a figure. For Exercises 9–12, they may first try to figure out the answer and then confirm it with the physical model. The actual linkage will be especially helpful for Exercise 11 (the first one with a negative scaling factor). In general, once one knows that the relevant triangles are similar, one can compute the scaling factor easily. Let F denote the fixed point, P the pencil point, and T the tracing point. The scaling factor will be $\frac{FP}{FT}$ where FX is positive if X is to the right of F and negative if X is to the left of F. Use this group of exercises to lead the students to this realization before trying the more advanced exercises (13–18).

▷ **Exercise 6.** (a) Note that in all configurations $BFED$ is a parallelogram. Thus, $\angle ADB = \angle AEC$ and $\angle ABD = \angle ACE$, so $\triangle ADB \sim \triangle AEC$.
(b) Since $AD = DE$, $AE = 2AD$ and by similar triangles $AC = 2AB$.
(c) 2 inches

▷ **Exercise 7.** The same figure scaled to be twice as large.

▷ **Exercise 8.** The same figure scaled to be half as large.

▷ **Exercise 9.** (a) Note that in all configurations $BFED$ is a parallelogram. Thus, $\angle ADB = \angle AEC$ and $\angle ABD = \angle ACE$, so $\triangle ADB \sim \triangle AEC$.
(b) Since $3AD = DE$, $AE = 4AD$ and the scaling factor is 4.

▷ **Exercise 10.** The same figure with scaling factor one fourth.

▷ **Exercise 11.** The orientation is reversed and $BC = 3AB$, so the scaling factor is -3.

▷ **Exercise 12.** $-\frac{1}{3}$

For Exercises 13–18, the use of a physical model is optional. By this time, the students should begin to understand the mathematical theory well enough to be able to predict the behavior of the linkage without actually building it, though they may still want to confirm that their hypotheses agree with reality.

▷ **Exercise 13.** The triangles AYB and AXC below are similar and since $AC = 4AB$, the scaling factor is 4.

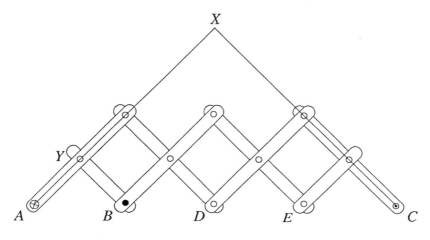

▷ **Exercise 14.** Note that some answers are not unique.

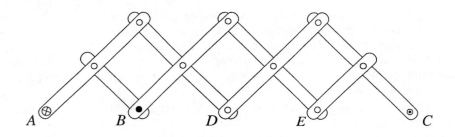

(a) Fix A, trace C, pencil B.

(b) Fix A, trace B, pencil E (or fix B, trace D, pencil C).

(c) Fix A, trace B, pencil D.

(d) Fix B, trace A, pencil E.

(e) Fix B, trace A, pencil C.

(f) Fix A, trace E, pencil C.

(g) Fix A, trace C, pencil E.

(h) Fix A, trace E, pencil D.

(i) Fix D, trace A, pencil E.

▷ **Exercise 15.** The triangles AYB and AXC are similar and since $AC = 4AB$, the scaling factor is 4.

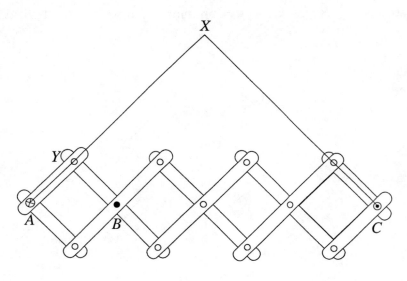

▷ **Exercise 16.**   The triangles AYB and AXC are similar and since $AC = 4AB$, the scaling factor is 4.

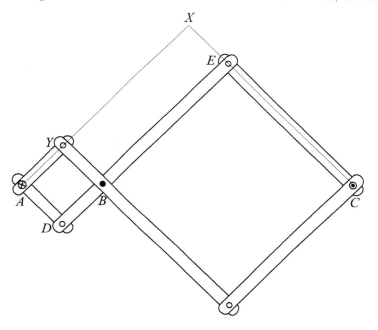

▷ **Exercise 17.**   The triangles AYB and AXC are similar and since $AC = 4AB$, the scaling factor is 4.

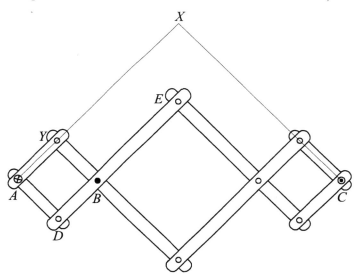

▷ **Exercise 18.**   Design three linkages.

Peaucellier's linkage is of historical importance as one of the first that converted circular motion (note that the locus of point A is a circle about point X) into linear motion.

▷ **Exercise 19.** B traces out a straight line perpendicular to XY.

Chapter 4. Tesselations

★ ★ 4.1. Regular and Semiregular Tilings
Dependencies: None
References: This section prefigures Section 7.3.

- Regular tilings
- Semiregular or Archimedean tilings
- Dual tilings

★ ★ 4.2. Irregular Tilings
Dependencies: Chapter 4.1

- Tilings by irregular polygons
- Reptiles
- Modification of tilings by translation, glide reflection, midpoint rotation, and side rotation
- Conway criterion for tiling
- Parquet deformations

★ ★ ★ 4.3. Penrose Tilings
Dependencies: Chapter 3.2, 4.1
References: Chapter 3.2 (basic knowledge of the golden ratio and the golden triangle only)

- Periodic and nonperiodic tilings
- Tiling with Penrose's kites and darts
- Inflation and deflation of tiling

This chapter and its three sections investigate tilings, first by regular polygons, then by modifications of these, and finally the nonperiodic Penrose tilings. The first section covers very traditional material. The students study the three regular tilings and then go on to explore the eight semiregular tilings. First, vertex conditions are discussed, and a list of candidates for possible semiregular tilings is generated. These are checked individually to find all possibilities. Last, a brief introduction to the concept of dual tilings is included. This subsection on dual tilings may be omitted without loss of understanding in the following sections.

The second section is devoted to the study of irregular tilings. First some examples of tilings by irregular polygons are introduced. Reptiles are defined with examples and exercises. Rules are given for the generation of Escher-style tilings from a basic tiling, using translation, glide reflection, or midpoint or side rotation. The Conway criteria are explained. Escher's Metamorphosis drawings are discussed.

Chapter 4.3 makes explicit the difference between the periodic tilings of Sections 4.1 and 4.2 and the nonperiodic Penrose tilings. Various rules for putting together Penrose kites and darts are explored, including the rules that give rise to the nonperiodic tilings. The process of inflation is explained and is used in an informal proof that these tilings are nonperiodic.

4.1. Regular and Semiregular Tilings

Stress to the students that any admissible tiling in these sections must meet at vertices and along edges: a vertex may not be placed in the middle of an edge. In Exercise 1, some students may note that any isosceles triangle (indeed, any triangle) can tile the plane. Reinforce the idea of a regular tiling if students raise this question.

Students are asked to investigate and draw a number of tilings in this section. In the investigation phase (Exercises 1–9) many students prefer to work analytically, using the vertex angles found in Exercise 2 and Rules 1–5 in the text. Some students prefer the more concrete approach of manipulating cardboard models of the polygons. For these students, templates for the polygons are given in the Appendix (Templates 9–21). These should be photocopied onto cardstock. Alternatively, instead of cutting out the templates, tracing paper may be used by laying it over each polygon and tracing to create a drawing of each possible tiling configuration. Students who choose to either manipulate cardboard models or trace the templates must be encouraged to check their work using the angle sums of Exercise 2.

▷ **Exercise 1.** The equilateral triangle, the square, and the regular hexagon can each tile the plane.

Students may need to be reminded of the formula from Chapter 1.2, in which it was found that each vertex of a regular n-sided polygon has angle measure $\frac{(n-2)180°}{n}$.

▷ **Exercise 2.**

Vertex Angles of Regular Polygons

Polygon	Sides	Angle
Triangle	3	60°
Square	4	90°
Pentagon	5	108°
Hexagon	6	120°
Heptagon	7	128.57°
Octagon	8	135°
Nonagon	9	140°
Decagon	10	144°
Dodecagon	12	150°
Pentakaidecagon	15	156°
Octakaidecagon	18	160°
Icosagon	20	162°
Tetrakaicosagon	24	165°

▷ **Exercise 3.** The largest number of polygons that can meet at a vertex is six, giving the tiling 3.3.3.3.3.3.

▷ **Exercise 4.** No, there cannot be four different polygons meeting at a vertex. The smallest sum of four different vertex angles is $60 + 90 + 108 + 120 = 378°$.

▷ **Exercise 5.** If there are four or more polygons at a vertex, then there must be duplicates, so that at least two are the same.

▷ **Exercise 6.** One cannot alternate n and m around a pentagon or any other odd-sided polygon. Thus, we cannot have this vertex configuration unless $n = m$.

The intent in Exercises 7–9 is to generate a complete list of candidates for tilings, and all results should be recorded in the table preceding Exercise 7 in the text to keep things orderly. At this point, do not try to draw these: these candidates will be checked in later exercises. Note that the order of the polygons does not matter at this point, but students should recognize that, for example, 3.9.18 and 18.3.9 are the same configuration.

If students need a hint for Exercise 7, ask them to think about using five of the angles listed in Exercise 2 and try to find various arrangements that will sum to 360°. Recall that by Rule 3 there must be some duplicates. Suggest that they start with four equilateral triangles and ask what polygon will make the sum of the angles 360°. Then ask for three triangles and two other polygons to complete the figure.

▷ **Exercise 7.** The vertex configurations 3.3.3.4.4 and 3.3.3.3.6 are possible tilings.

If students need help on Exercise 8, suggest that they start by using two equilateral triangles plus two other polygons. With this hint, most students will figure out the configurations 3.3.4.12 and 3.3.6.6. Then suggest that they use only one triangle plus three other polygons, but point out that Rule 3 says that there must be duplicates, so one of the nontriangle polygons must be repeated.

▷ **Exercise 8.** The vertex configurations 3.3.4.12, 3.3.6.6, and 3.4.4.6 are possible tilings.

If students can find the seven possibilities of Exercise 9 without going through the steps as laid out, that is fine and let them proceed to Exercise 10. Otherwise, proceed systematically using the hints given. In Exercise 9(a), point out that 3.3.n and 4.4.n are not viable since no angle from Exercise 2 will complete the sum to 360°. However 5.5.n will work since the student should be able to show you that the two pentagons give an angle sum of $108° + 108° = 216°$ and $360° - 216° = 144°$, which is the vertex angle for the decagon. After this example, students should be able to find the second vertex configuration of 9(a). In 9(b), restate that we are trying to find three polygons, one of which is a square, that sum to 360°, and so all they need to do is find two polygon angles that add up to 270°. In 9(c), we want two polygon angles that add up to 300°, so that they can be joined with an equilateral triangle.

▷ **Exercise 9.** (a) The vertex configurations 5.5.10 and 3.12.12 are possible tilings.
(b) The vertex configurations 4.6.12 and 4.5.20 are possible tilings.
(c) The vertex configurations 3.9.18, 3.8.24, and 3.10.15 are possible tilings.

The results of Exercises 7–9 and 10–14 are summarized in this table:

Vertex Configurations for Possible Tilings

Symbol	# Polygons	Reference	Tiling?
3.3.3.3.3.3	6	Exercise 3	yes
3.3.3.3.6	5	Exercise 7	yes
3.3.3.4.4	5	Exercise 7	yes, also 3.3.4.3.4
4.4.4.4	4	Exercise 1	yes
3.3.4.12	4	Exercise 8	no
3.3.6.6	4	Exercise 8	no, but 3.6.3.6 tiles
3.4.4.6	4	Exercise 8	no, but 3.4.6.4 tiles
6.6.6	3	Exercise 1	yes
4.8.8	3	Text	yes
3.7.42	3	Exercise 9	no
5.5.10	3	Exercise 9(a)	no
3.12.12	3	Exercise 9(a)	yes
4.6.12	3	Exercise 9(b)	yes
4.5.20	3	Exercise 9(b)	no
3.9.18	3	Exercise 9(c)	no
3.8.24	3	Exercise 9(c)	no
3.10.15	3	Exercise 9(c)	no

In Exercises 10–14, we check the list of possible tilings to see whether they extend beyond a single vertex to a tiling of the entire plane. Many students do not immediately realize the applicability of Rules 4 and 5, but use these with glee after seeing an example. Insist that students draw a reasonable section of each tiling by either specifying the number of tiles to be used or the area to be covered.

▷ **Exercise 10.**

  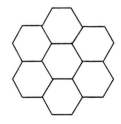

▷ **Exercise 11.** (a) Rule 4 eliminates 3.8.24, 3.9.18, 3.10.15, 4.5.20, and 5.5.10.

(b) 3.12.12 and 4.6.12 tile the plane, as shown:

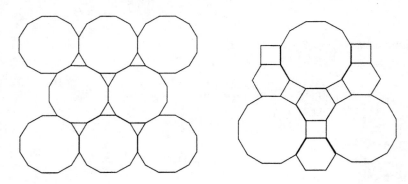

In Exercises 12–14 the order of the arrangement matters. Students need to pay particular attention to the example 3.4.4.6 (which fails) versus 3.4.6.4 (which tiles). Stress that each vertex must not only have the same polygons meeting, but that they must also meet in the same order.

▷ **Exercise 12.** 3.4.6.4 extends to cover the whole plane.

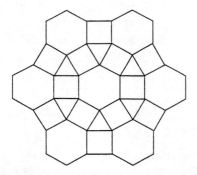

▷ **Exercise 13.** (a) Rule 5 eliminates 3.3.4.12 and 3.4.3.12.

(b) Rule 5 also eliminates 3.3.6.6 as a tiling, but the rearrangement 3.6.3.6 tiles the plane.

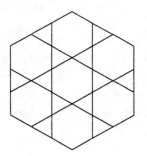

50

▷ **Exercise 14.** 3.3.3.4.4, 3.3.4.3.4, and 3.3.3.3.6 tile the plane.

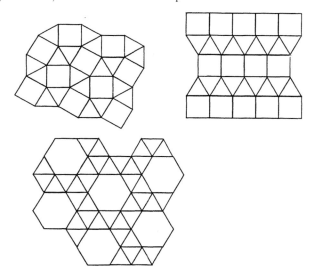

Note that the tiling 3.3.3.3.6 actually occurs in two forms: left-handed and right-handed as shown here. These forms are called enantiomorphic, from the Greek word meaning opposite. Technically, these are considered as different, since no rotation or translation of the plane can take one to the other, though a reflection of the plane will change one form into the other. We do not ask our students to distinguish between these.

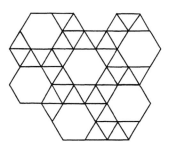 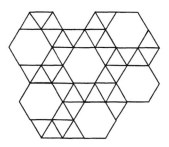

Some students are intimidated by the language of Exercises 15-17, but find the process easy enough in practice. You may need to ask them to find the center of a square and a hexagon, and then help them verbalize how they did it.

▷ **Exercise 15.** To find the center of gravity for a regular polygon with an even number of sides, connect opposite vertices. These lines will intersect at the center. Alternatively, connect the midpoints of opposite sides. This is illustrated below for the square and hexagon.

▷ **Exercise 16.** To find the center of gravity for a regular polygon with an odd number of sides, connect each vertex with the midpoint of the opposite side. These lines will intersect at the center. This is illustrated below for the triangle and pentagon.

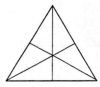

▷ **Exercise 17.** As we saw in Exercises 15 and 16, the line from the center to the midpoint of any side is perpendicular to that side. Therefore, the line connecting the centers of two polygons will intersect the shared edge at the midpoint, forming a 90° angle.

▷ **Exercise 18.** The dual tiling of 4.8.8 consists of irregular right isosceles triangles with angles 45°-45°-90°.

In Exercises 19–23, have the students draw these dual tilings over the tiling drawings of Exercises 10–14 using a different colored pencil. Some students will persist in drawing all of the lines of Exercises 15 and 16 and using these for the dual tilings. Instead, suggest that they simply place a colored dot at the approximate center of each polygon and then connect the dots only when the corresponding polygons share an edge.

▷ **Exercise 19.** The dual tiling of 3.3.3.3.3.3 is 6.6.6. The dual tiling for 4.4.4.4 is 4.4.4.4. The dual tiling for 6.6.6 is 3.3.3.3.3.3.

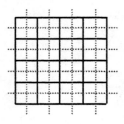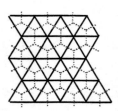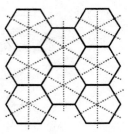

▷ **Exercise 20.** The dual tiling for 3.12.12 consists of 120°-30°-30° triangles. The dual tiling for 4.6.12 consists of 90°-60°-30° triangles.

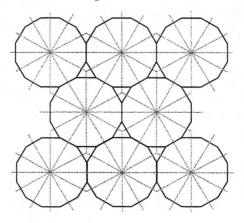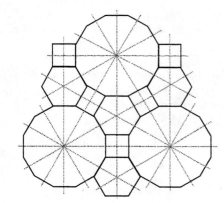

▷ **Exercise 21.** The dual tiling for 3.4.6.4 consists of 120°-90°-60°-90° quadrilaterals.

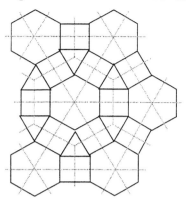

▷ **Exercise 22.** The dual tiling for 3.6.3.6 consists of quadrilaterals with angles 120°-60°-120°-60°.

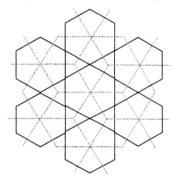

▷ **Exercise 23.** The dual tiling for 3.3.3.4.4 consists of pentagons with angles 90°-90°-120°-120°-120°. The dual tiling for 3.3.3.3.6 consists of 120°-120°-120°-120°-60° pentagons.

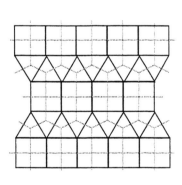 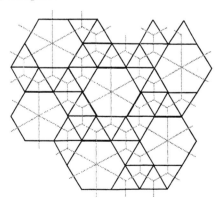

▷ **Exercise 24.** Each tile of the dual depends only on the vertex configuration. Since the configuration at each vertex is the same, each dual tile will be identical.

▷ **Exercise 25.** The tilings that have 3 polygons meeting at each vertex have duals formed by triangles, while those with four polygons have duals with quadrilaterals and those with five have pentagons. If n polygons meet at each vertex in the original semiregular tiling, each dual tile will have n sides.

4.2. Irregular Tilings

▷ **Exercise 1.** Two copies of any triangle can be put together to form a parallelogram, which then tiles the plane.

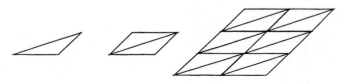

▷ **Exercise 2.** Two copies of any trapezoid can be put together to form a parallelogram, which then tiles the plane.

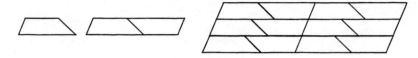

▷ **Exercise 3.**

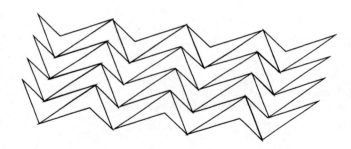

▷ **Exercise 4.** The trapezoid has angles 60°-120°-120°-60°.

The concept of similarity, used in solving Exercise 5, will recur in Section 9.1. Many students will not reorient the smaller rectangle before constructing the ratios and so will get $\frac{1}{x} = \frac{1}{2x}$. Asking them to sketch the smaller rectangle beside the larger one will usually help them get the order straight.

▷ **Exercise 5.** $\frac{1}{x} = \frac{2x}{1}$, so $x = \frac{1}{\sqrt{2}}$.

▷ **Exercise 6.**

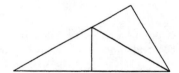

▷ **Exercise 7.** The 45°-45°-90° triangle:

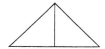

Students can use either cardboard models, tracing paper, or graph paper for Exercise 8. Many students will take only two copies of the parallelogram and put them together to form a larger parallelogram. Point out that while this figure has the right shape, it does not have the right proportions.

▷ **Exercise 8.**

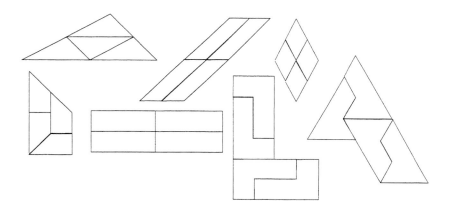

For Exercises 9–14, give extra credit if the student can form a somewhat artistic tiling or tell them you will display some of the drawings on the departmental bulletin board. The easiest way to generate these is by cutting a piece of cardboard in the shape of the designated grid (parallelogram, rectangle, or regular hexagon. Then cut a piece off one side and attach it to another side, using either translation, glide reflection, or rotation as indicated. For midpoint rotation, mark the midpoint of the side and cut a pattern that starts at the midpoint and ends at the corner, rotate and tape to the other half side. After creating the tile, lay it on a piece of paper and trace the outline, fitting together successive tiles.

For Exercises 9–14, first efforts should be done by hand, but if you have access to computers and the software package Tesselmania! students will enjoy trying more elaborate pictures. Most will be surprised at how difficult it is to make their shapes look like animals or anything else easily recognizable. (This is the voice of experience talking.) Make sure you have tried this before you turn your students loose. Template 22 of the Appendix can be copied onto cardstock to provide the basic tiles for Exercises 9–14.

▷ **Exercise 9.** Create an irregular tiling from a parallelogram grid, using translation of both pairs of parallel sides. See Template 22.

▷ **Exercise 10.** Create an irregular tiling from a hexagonal grid, using translation of all three pairs of parallel sides. See Template 22.

▷ **Exercise 11.** Create an irregular tiling from a rectangular grid, using glide reflection on both pairs of parallel sides. See Template 22.

▷ **Exercise 12.** Create an irregular tiling from an equilateral triangle grid, using midpoint rotation on each side. See Template 22.

▷ **Exercise 13.** Create an irregular tiling from a parallelogram grid, using a translation on one pair of parallel sides and a midpoint rotation on each of the other sides. See Template 22.

▷ **Exercise 14.** Create an irregular tiling from an equilateral triangle grid, using side rotation on one pair of sides and midpoint rotation on the other side. See Template 22.

▷ **Exercise 15.** This fails to tile the plane. Note that this will create a tiling if the angles of the rhombus are chosen to be 60°-120°-60°-120°, but otherwise it will not. If one tries to put the tiles together, a space is left that is too narrow to insert another tile.

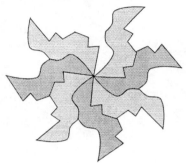

A source for additional exercises and test problems like Exercises 16–19 is Escher's notebooks, where he worked out examples of numerous tilings, only some of which were incorporated in his final prints. See Schattschneider's <u>Visions of Symmetry</u>.

▷ **Exercise 16.** The tiling of frogs (by Kevin Lee) is formed with a rectangular (or parallelogram) grid, using translation.

▷ **Exercise 17.** The tiling of dogs (by Kevin Lee) is formed from a grid of equilateral triangles by side rotation on a pair of sides (the rotation center is marked with a • where the tails of the dogs meet) and a midpoint rotation on the remaining side (with the rotation center marked with a ○).

▷ **Exercise 18.** The tiling of a crowd uses a rectangular (or parallelogram) grid, with translation on one pair of sides (right and left) and glide reflection on the other pair (top and bottom).

▷ **Exercise 19.** The tiling shown in M. C. Escher's *Reptiles* was formed from a hexagonal grid, using side rotation on pairs of adjacent sides.

Some students find the abstraction of Conway's criterion difficult to understand. However, almost all students will be able to find the translated segments of the tiling. Have them mark the points A, B, D, and E for Exercises 21 and 23, where AB and DE are translates. Then they only need to break AE and BD into two segments, each with a midpoint rotation. It is often easier to mark the midpoint rotation centers, and then go back to locate points C and F.

▷ **Exercise 20.**

▷ **Exercise 21.** Note that the answers are not unique.

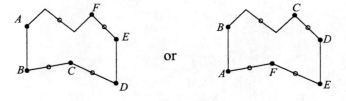

58

▷ **Exercise 22.**

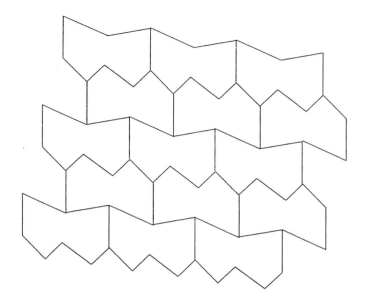

▷ **Exercise 23.** As in Exercise 21, the labeling is not unique.

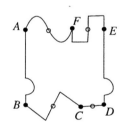

▷ **Exercise 24.**

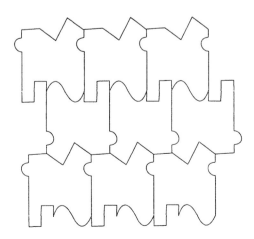

▷ **Exercise 25.**

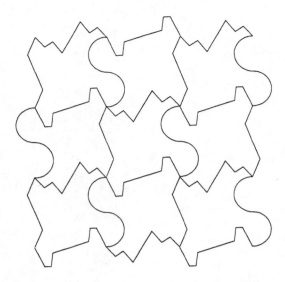

Exercises 26 and 27 are designed to test the student's understanding of Conway's criterion.

▷ **Exercise 26.**   You get a triangular tiling with midpoint rotation on each side.

▷ **Exercise 27.**   You get a trapezoidal tiling with parallel translation on one pair of opposite sides and midpoint rotation on the other two sides.

4.3. Penrose Tilings

For Exercises 4–12, each student will need a plentiful supply of the kite and dart tiles, marked with dots as in the text. A template for these is included in the Appendix (see Template 23). Photocopy the template onto cardstock and give each student four or five sheets. Ask the students to take them home and cut them out for the next class. Alternatively, sets of foam Penrose tiles can be purchased from Tesselations.

▷ **Exercise 1.** Here are two choices for a repeating region for the tiling 3.4.6.4 of Exercise 4.1.12. Note that each shaded region contains enough parts to make a hexagon, three squares (in each of the three orientations appearing in the tiling), and two triangles (vertex up and vertex down). Since the tilings of Exercises 4.2.11 and 4.2.14 were student generated, no solution is given.

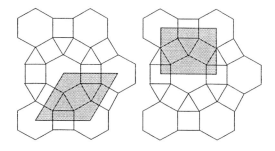

▷ **Exercise 2.**

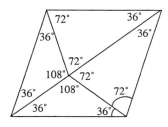

▷ **Exercise 3.** There are other solutions, but here is one:

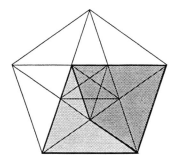

▷ **Exercise 4.** A periodic tiling can be formed if you do not match up the dots. Recall Exercise 4.2.3, where it was shown that any quadrilateral will tile the plane in a periodic manner. Thus, a periodic tiling can be formed using only darts if you do not match up the dots.

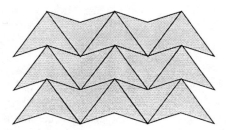

▷ **Exercise 5.** A periodic tiling can also be formed using only kites if you do not match up the dots.

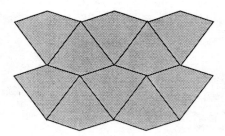

▷ **Exercise 6.** No. Since both the dots and the lengths of the edges must match, one will have to match up two dart wings. A third dart wing cannot fit in the gap between these while matching the dots.

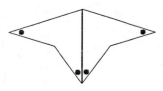

▷ **Exercise 7.** No. Since both the dots and the lengths of the edges must match, one will have to match up two kite heads. The gap between these is too small for a third kite head. A kite tail would fit, but the edge length is too long.

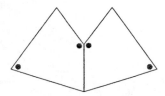

▷ **Exercise 8.** Note that the only possible configurations with kite heads if dots cannot match is either the rhombus, shown on the left, and the arrangement of four kites shown at the center. One can alternate strips of kites and darts as shown below on the right to form a periodic tiling combining these two configurations. Note that the dots are never next to dots.

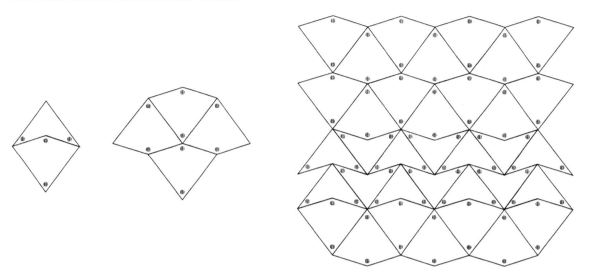

▷ **Exercise 9.** No. Consider one edge of a kite head (this is the shorter edge of the kite). This must be matched with either another short kite head edge or with the shorter edge of a dart. The first case, as pictured below on the left, leaves a 72° gap with short edges. A kite head is too big for this gap (144°), and the edges of a kite tail don't match the lengths of the sides forming the gap. The edges of a dart head don't match with the sides of the gap, and one cannot use the dart wings since the dots would match up. In the second case, a dart fits onto the kite making a rhombus as shown on the right. These rhombi must fit together so that the dots on the kites match, but this leaves a gap none of the tiles will fit.

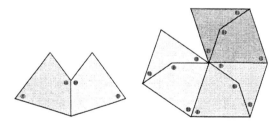

▷ **Exercise 10.** Yes, one can make an infinite periodic tiling as shown below:

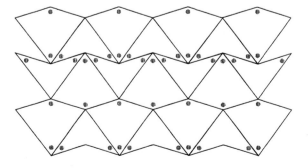

▷ **Exercise 11.** (a) Case 1: Suppose that two kite heads match along their shorter sides. The only way to fill the gap is with two darts, but then the dots will all match, as shown below:

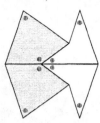

Case 2: Suppose two kite tails are put together so that the longer edges match. If you add two more kites at the top vertex as shown below, you will get one of the two pictures at the right. The first picture requires a dart to fill the gap, but then the dots will match between the dart and the neighboring kites. The second picture requires two darts and forms two rhombi, but note that the dots match on the darts.

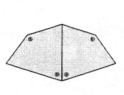 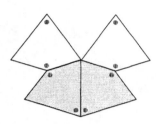 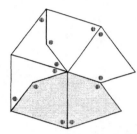

Case 2, continued (two kite tails match): If you add darts at the top of the two kites, you get rhombi as shown below on the left. To finish filling the gap, you can use two kite wings as shown in the second picture, but that causes the problem discussed in Case 1. You could also use two darts as shown in the third picture, but then the dots on the darts will match. Finally, you could use one kite and one dart, as shown in the fourth picture, but then the dots on the kite will match those on one of the darts.

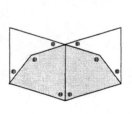 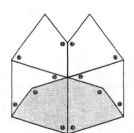 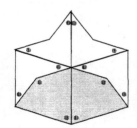 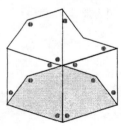

(b) If we have two darts meeting along an edge with the dots matching and if dots are not allowed to match between a kite and a dart, then the only tile that will fit into the dart tails are kites, forming two rhombi as shown on the left. To this, one can add another rhombus, leaving an impossible gap as shown in the second picture, or another kite. If one attaches a kite, then this leaves a gap that must be filled either with a dart (but then the dots on the dart and one of the kites match, as in the third picture) or a kite (but then the dots on the kites match as in the fourth picture).

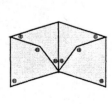 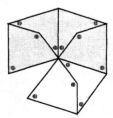 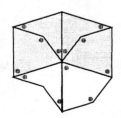 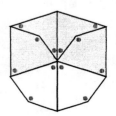

64

▷ **Exercise 12.** (a) If dots are allowed not to match only on kites, then you can get the periodic tiling of Exercise 5 if you use only kites. If you try to use any darts, then consider the gap at the dart tail. You can't fill this with two kites because the dots would then match on the kites as shown below on the left. You also can't fill this gap with darts since the dots would not match on the darts, as shown on the right.

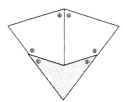 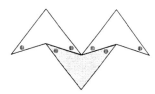

(b) If dots are allowed not to match only on darts and you use only darts, you can get the periodic tiling of Exercise 4. If you use any kites, you cannot put two kite heads together or the dots would match. Thus, you must put dart wings at the kite head, as shown below on the left. The remaining gap can only be filled by two kite tails, as shown at the center. At the head of either of these new kites, you can again only use a dart, but then the edges of this dart will not fit the edges of the dart already attached to the original kite, as shown below on the right.

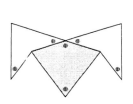 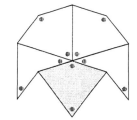 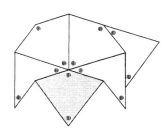

▷ **Exercise 13.** At most 2 kite heads, and at most 5 kite tails can come together at any vertex.

▷ **Exercise 14.** At most 5 dart heads, and at most 1 dart tail can come together at any vertex.

▷ **Exercise 15.** At most 4 kite wings can come together at any vertex. Note that even though five of the angle measures for the kite wings will fit, the edge lengths will not match for a fifth tile.

▷ **Exercise 16.** The names given are those bestowed by Conway.

 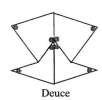  

Ace   Deuce   Jack   Queen

▷ **Exercise 17.** The empire of the ace is empty, since there are many ways to add the surrounding tiles. The empires for the deuce, jack and queen are shown below:

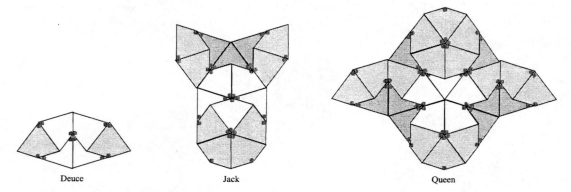

Deuce   Jack   Queen

▷ **Exercise 18.** Cut up each kite and dart into smaller kites and darts, precisely reversing the process of inflation.

▷ **Exercise 19.** Create your own Penrose tiling.

Chapter 5. Two-Dimensional Symmetry

★ **5.1. Kaleidoscopes**
Dependencies: None

- Mirror symmetry
- Hinged mirrors
- Three mirrors
- Kaleidoscopes

★ ★ **5.2. Rosette Groups: Point Symmetry**
Dependencies: None
References: Chapter 5.1

- Reflection and rotation
- Group notation and tables
- Cutting rosette patterns

★ ★ **5.3. Frieze Patterns: Line Symmetry**
Dependencies: None
References: Chapter 5.1, 5.2

- Line isometries: translation, reflection, rotation, glide reflection
- Generating frieze patterns
- Classification of frieze patterns
- Cutting frieze patterns

★ ★ ★ **5.4. Wallpaper Patterns: Plane Symmetry**
Dependencies: Chapter 5.3

- Lattices
- Generating wallpaper patterns
- Classification of wallpaper patterns

★ ★ ★ **5.5. Islamic Lattice Patterns**
Dependencies: Chapter 5.4
References: Chapter 4.1 (for Exercise 12 only)

- Generating lattice designs
- Classification of lattice patterns

This chapter and its five sections deal with symmetries in two dimensions. The first section, on kaleidoscopes, introduces some of these ideas in the context of playing with various configurations of mirrors. By means of these mirrors, one can explore both the reflectional symmetries of an object or artistic motif and patterns of repeated motifs. The section ends with instructions for building a simple kaleidoscope.

The second section, on rosette groups, introduces a more formal approach to the symmetries of a motif about a central point. The idea of composition is used in a concrete manner. The group theory implicit in this approach is not made overt, but could be introduced to more advanced students. Rosette groups are classified as either dihedral or cyclic, and so concrete examples of nonabelian groups are given and explored.

The third section of this chapter begins with a discussion of the isometries of the plane: translation, rotation, reflection, and glide reflection. Their use to generate frieze patterns is shown, along with the necessary modifications to preserve the linear character of the resulting strip patterns. The standard crystallographic notation as well as Conway's terminology is defined. Students are asked to classify patterns as well as draw their own examples. The section ends with an exploration of how one can generate frieze patterns by cutting strips of paper, which can be used to open the door to a discussion either of paper dolls or orbifolds.

The fourth section extends the generation and classification of patterns to the plane, in the form of the 17 wallpaper patterns. The crystallographic notation is defined. The role of the lattice in generating the patterns is discussed, and a variety of exercises leads the students through each pattern type.

The last section of the chapter explores a certain type of wallpaper pattern: the lattice patterns common in Islamic decoration. An algorithm for the generation of some simple examples of these patterns is given, and students are asked to draw several examples. The results are then classified as wallpaper patterns.

5.1. Kaleidoscopes

Inexpensive mirrors can be purchased from any art supply store or ordered from the sources given at the end of the section in the text. We have found that the shiny "transparent" tape works better than the matte "magic" tape that disappears when used on paper. The "magic" tape does not disappear on the mirrors and obscures the patterns. Most of the exercises require one or two mirrors. Only a few require three or four, and then students can share these. Exercises 1–3 explore very basic properties of mirror symmetry.

▷ **Exercise 1.** The line from the dot to its image is perpendicular to the mirror line.

▷ **Exercise 2.** The perceived distance from the dot to its reflection is 6 inches. The actual distance from the dot to its image is 3 inches.

For some reason, the question of Exercise 3 confuses some students. They will insist on comparing the angle from the line to the mirror with the angle from the line to the reflection.

▷ **Exercise 3.** The angles formed by the line with the mirror and its image with the mirror line are equal.

Encourage the students to stop and think and explore Exercise 4, instead of looking for a brief, quick answer. This is one of those questions that can stimulate an extended discussion and is accessible to all students, even the most mathematically challenged. However, students will often struggle to find the words to express their ideas.

▷ **Exercise 4.** A mirror does not actually reverse left and right, no more than it reverses up and down. The problem is that since the human face is approximately symmetric across the line dividing left from right, that we interpret the reversed image in the mirror as a rotated image, rather than a reflected one. This is made clearer by looking at an object without symmetry. What a mirror does is reverse front and back: if you are facing north and are looking into a mirror, then your image will be facing south.

Exercises 5–7 are straightforward, checking the students' grasp of the idea of a reflection or mirror line. Some students will not find all of the reflection lines, especially in Exercise 6(b), (g), and (i): they will tend to find the lines through the vertices but not through the midpoints of the sides, or vice versa. Make sure students know that shading matters in 6(c). The more extremely careful students will then worry about the somewhat pixelated shading pattern in 6(d). I tell them the spots should be solid gray but the printer couldn't do this correctly. They may also tell you (quite correctly) that 6(e) has no lines of reflection, since the "8" is not perfectly symmetric.

▷ **Exercise 5.** The line of reflection runs vertically.

▷ **Exercise 6.** Figures (a) and (c) have no lines of reflection, while figure (j) has infinitely many (any line through the center of the circle will be a line of reflection). Reflection lines for the other figures are shown below:

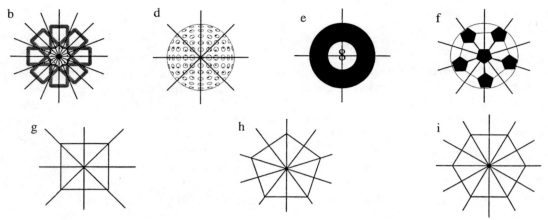

▷ **Exercise 7.** If n is even, there are n lines of symmetry—through pairs of opposite vertices and through the midpoints of opposite edges. If n is odd, there are n lines—from each vertex to the midpoint of the opposite edge.

> *In Exercises 8 and 9, two parallel mirrors are used, foreshadowing certain frieze patterns of Section 5.3. In Exercise 8 some students will not look past the first reflection. They will tell you the distance between reflections is 12 inches because they are comparing the first reflections in the two mirrors. Good students will tell you the distance depends on which dots you choose. Be prepared to ask for the shortest distance between any two images or to ask them for a general rule that applies to any two dots.*

▷ **Exercise 8.** The perceived distance between reflections of the dot is six inches, which is twice the distance from the dot to the mirror.

▷ **Exercise 9.** You should see an infinite progression of alternate left and right hands.

> *Exercises 10–19 use a hinged mirror, so have the students tape two mirrors together. These exercises explore the angles that one can use with a hinged mirror in order to get an unambiguous number of reflections of a motif. Remember to use clear tape. It will simplify things if you instruct your students to only consider angles less than 180°. Otherwise, each of the diagrams below for Exercises 11–13 can be considered to represent two angles. You should also encourage them to find distinct setups instead of the same angle positioned at a different corner.*

▷ **Exercise 10.** You should always see a circle.

▷ **Exercise 11.** The angles will all be multiples of 45°.

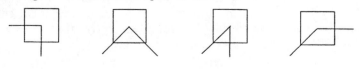

▷ **Exercise 12.**   The angles will all be multiples of 36°.

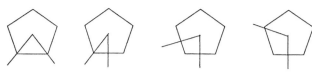

▷ **Exercise 13.**   The angles will all be multiples of 30°.

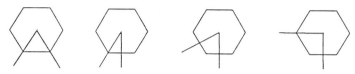

In Exercise 14, if you look into the mirrors from a position close to the right-hand mirror, you will see the picture on the left in the text. If you keep the mirrors in place, but move your eyes to a position close to the left-hand mirror, you will see the picture on the right. Make sure that the students can see both pictures and understand how moving their heads gives different views, since this is the visual ambiguity that we are looking for in Exercises 15–19. In Exercise 15, some students might not see the fractional lizard if their viewing point is such that the partial sector reflects empty space. Discussing Exercise 14 in class before they continue will encourage them to consider the view from several positions.

▷ **Exercise 14.**   You can see both pictures, depending on the viewing angle.

▷ **Exercise 15.**   For 60°, there are six lizards: three right-handed and three left-handed. For 72°, there are five lizards, but the number of right- and left-handed lizards varies with the viewing angle. For 90°, there are four: two right and two left. For 108°, there are three and a fractional lizard, with distortion from different viewing angles. For 120°, there are three, but the number of right- and left-handed lizards varies with the viewing angle. For 150°, there are two and a fractional lizard (from most viewpoints), with distortion from different viewing angles.

From Exercise 15, students will have found that angles of 60°, 90°, and 120° all give unambiguous views, while 72°, 108°, and 150° do not. From this, they should realize that angles of the form $\frac{180°}{k}$ can be used with a hinged mirror and an asymmetric motif, though some may have trouble abstracting to give the formula. It may help for them to draw a sketch, dividing the circle into wedges, each of which contains one copy of the motif, arranged to alternate left- and right-handed images.

▷ **Exercise 16.**   The angles that work are of the form $\frac{180°}{k} = \frac{360°}{2k}$ for k an integer and the number of lizards is $2k$, giving an equal number of left- and right-handed lizards.

▷ **Exercise 17.**   For 60°, there are six arrows; for 72°, five arrows; for 90°, there are four. For 108°, there are three and a fractional arrow; for 120°, there are three arrows. For 150°, there are two and a fractional arrow, with distortion from different viewing angles.

▷ **Exercise 18.**   The angles that work for a symmetrical figure are of the form $\frac{360°}{k}$ for k an integer and the number of arrows is k.

From Exercise 17, students will have found that all of the given angles except 150° angles give unambiguous views. From this, they could realize that angles of the form $\frac{360°}{k}$ can be used with a hinged mirror and a symmetric motif, though some may have trouble abstracting to give the formula. If they do not realize the pattern, encourage them to try angles like 80°. For the asymmetrical lizard, they needed to always generate an even number of motifs, so that right- and left-handed lizards will alternate around the circle. For a symmetric motif like the arrow, one can view an odd integer number of motifs arranged in a circle without ambiguity. When students tell you that Exercise 7 is identical to Exercise 15, suggest that they revisit the 72° pictures.

▷ **Exercise 19.** The angles $\frac{180°}{k}$ give you regular polygons. You can form all even-sided polygons using angles of this form by placing the mirrors so that they form an isosceles triangle with the line, and then the number of sides in the polygon will be $2k$. The odd-sided polygons can be formed by keeping one mirror perpendicular to the line and varying the angle of the other mirror.

If you did not do Section 4.1, Exercise 20 may be omitted, or one can accept a more informal answer. Suggest students use a very simple scribble that is clearly asymmetric so that drawing the pattern is easier. An "L" or hook shape works well.

▷ **Exercise 20.** You should see an extensive field of the tiling 3.3.3.3.3.3, with a scribble in each triangle.

▷ **Exercise 21.** Unless it happens to be a 45°-45°-90° isosceles triangle (which is unlikely), there is distortion: the triangles do not fit together to form a tiling.

▷ **Exercise 22.** The Coxeter triangles are 60°-60°-60°, 30°-60°-90°, and 45°-45°-90°.

▷ **Exercise 23.** The only Coxeter quadrilateral is a rectangle with angles 90°-90°-90°-90°.

The following exercise is, of course, optional, but students have enjoyed it, especially those majoring in elementary education. Students can decorate their kaleidoscopes using either colored markers or wrapping the whole thing in wrapping paper. The mirror assembly is the part that is most likely to give trouble. These should be cut as precisely as possible, polished to remove fingerprints, and taped securely together (on the outside nonmirrored side, of course). If the mirrors do not fit securely in the tube, a few sheets of paper rolled into a cylinder or small wedges should be placed between the tube and the mirrors until the fit is tight. If the mirrors are too large, the tube gets distorted but the image will be correct. The actual mirror width for a three-mirror kaleidoscope using an equilateral triangle arrangement of mirrors will be $\frac{\sqrt{3}}{2}$ times the diameter of the tube. Plastic food storage film can be used instead of the proposed clear rigid thin plastic, but the result is not as satisfactory. For the objects in the viewing chamber, fairly large objects work best. Tiny bits fall out of the viewing chamber into the space between the mirrors and the tube when the kaleidoscope is turned. Note that if the inner plastic disc is omitted then the objects may fall behind the mirrors.

▷ **Exercise 24.** Build a kaleidoscope.

5.2. Rosette Groups: Point Symmetry

Unfortunately, we were unable to convince our editor to allow us to print the text in color, and this is one of the sections that would be far more clear if color were used. The instructor is encouraged to redraw the pictures of the different configurations of the triangle on the chalkboard using colored chalk for the sides or on an overhead transparency with colored markers. For example, color edge AB red, BC blue, and AC yellow in each configuration. It is then much easier (unless one is color blind) to distinguish when two configurations are the same and when they differ. Start with a color-coded picture of the original triangle, labeled 1 (for identity). Use tracing paper to trace this again in colored chalk or on a second copy of the overhead transparency with the markers. Show the students how rotating the traced picture will align with the original after a rotation of 120°, but with the colored sides arranged differently. Draw this new colored configuration on the chalkboard and label it R. Then rotate another 120° until the traced triangle realigns with the original, but again with the colors arranged differently. Draw this configuration on the chalkboard and label it R^2. Use the traced triangle to show that a third rotation through 120° returns the triangle to its original position and coloring, so that $R^3 = 1$. Reiterate to the students that it does not matter if they rotate clockwise or counterclockwise as long as they are consistent, but that your life is much easier if they all rotate the same direction. Return the traced triangle to its original position over the identity triangle and reflect. Make sure the students understand that one is not simply turning the paper over, but performing a reflection across the vertical line bisecting the triangle, so that the top vertex returns to the top vertex and the bottom edge returns to the bottom edge. This gives a new coloring pattern, so draw this on the chalkboard and label it F. Using the traced triangle, go on to show them the configurations RF and R^2F and draw these on the chalkboard. Emphasize that RF stands for rotate first, then reflect across the vertical line. Some students will want to reflect through the same vertex (such as always through vertex A) each time instead of over the same line. Life is easier if you fix this problem early. Students should then be able to mimic your process using colored pencils and a scrap of tracing paper. Exercises 1–4 will show if they understand the procedure and should convince them that all possible configurations have already been given, so all they need to do is match up each end result with one of the standard six shown on the chalkboard.

▷ **Exercise 1.** A 120° clockwise rotation of the triangle is the same as R^2, the 240° counterclockwise rotation.

▷ **Exercise 2.** RF

▷ **Exercise 3.** R^2F

▷ **Exercise 4.** $FR = R^2F$, $FR^2 = RF$, and $RFR = F$

Exercise 5 can be done either using the color coding and a traced image, or using the table, or students can do it both ways to check their answers. If students are working in groups, suggest that different students use different methods to compare answers but that all students should understand each method. Emphasize that the table is used to compute, for example, FR by looking for the row of the first factor F and the column of second factor R, and then the entry in that row and column gives $FR = R^2F$. All answers must be given in the form of one of the six standard configurations. If students are in groups, someone will usually figure out the use of negative exponents but they will want confirmation. If they are working alone, you can explain this to the class as a whole or prepare for a lot of questions.

▷ **Exercise 5.** (a) $F(R^2F \cdot R) = F(RF) = R^2$
(b) $(RF \cdot RF) \cdot (RF \cdot RF) = 1$
(c) $FR^5FR^{10} = FR^2FR = R^2$
(d) $R^{-2}FR^2 = RFR^2 = (RF) \cdot R^2 = R^2F$
(e) $R^2FR^{-3}FR^2 = R^2F \cdot 1 \cdot FR^2 = R^2FFR^2 = R^2R^2 = R$

▷ **Exercise 6.** There are, of course, infinitely many correct answers, but look for a motif that has a 120° rotation and a reflection.

▷ **Exercise 7.** The angle of rotation is 60°, and six rotations return the figure to the original position.

Have the students generate the multiplication table for Exercise 8 by color coding the motif making each of the six legs a different color. Trace the figure and its colors on a scrap of tracing paper and rotate (preferably counterclockwise) until it realigns. Copy this new colored configuration and label it R, etc. Once one has pictures of all possible colored configurations $(1, R, R^2, R^3, R^4,$ and $R^5)$, the table is formed by listing all of these down the rows and across the columns. the rest of the table is easily filled in, and you will find that students need to refer to the colored pictures less often.

▷ **Exercise 8.**

$$C_6$$

	1	R	R^2	R^3	R^4	R^5
1	1	R	R^2	R^3	R^4	R^5
R	R	R^2	R^3	R^4	R^5	1
R^2	R^2	R^3	R^4	R^5	1	R
R^3	R^3	R^4	R^5	1	R	R^2
R^4	R^4	R^5	1	R	R^2	R^3
R^5	R^5	1	R	R^2	R^3	R^4

▷ **Exercise 9.** A correct figure is shown on the left. Tell the students to draw carefully. Student illustrations for C_6 often end up looking like the picture on the right, which only has symmetry group C_2. Sometimes this is only sloppiness, but sometimes this is a genuine lack of understanding.

▷ **Exercise 10.**

A motif with rosette group C_n will have a rotation of $\frac{360°}{n}$ and no reflections, while the group D_n indicates a rotation of $\frac{360°}{n}$ and at least one reflection line. A little experimenting should quickly convince students that if there is one line of reflection and an n-fold rotation, then each rotation of the motif will also rotate the reflection line to a new reflection line. Thus, if there is one reflection and an n-fold rotation, there must be n lines of reflection. A mirror can be used to determine whether a figure has a reflection, though, of course, this will not give the correct coloring. If you haven't discussed that the order of the rotation and the number of lines of reflection must match, many students will find only four lines of reflection for Exercise 11, as shown. Even if they know theoretically that there should be eight lines, some students will draw these four lines and double count them as eight (for example, by counting the vertical line twice: once north and once south).

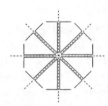

▷ **Exercise 11.** The figure must have eight lines of reflection, shown below on the right.

 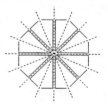

Some students may have trouble initially with the concept of D_1 and C_1. Tell them that this means there is no rotational symmetry, or that only a rotation through a full 360° will return the motif to its original position. One can also point out that they themselves (or most people) have rosette group D_1. Students will also want to label a figure both C_n and D_n. Emphasize that C_n means that the figure has an n-fold rotation without any reflections.

▷ **Exercise 12.**

$\top$

D₁

	1	F
1	1	F
F	F	1

▷ **Exercise 13.**

▷ **Exercise 14.**

▷ **Exercise 15.**

$\bot$

▷ **Exercise 16.** The square has rotations through 90° and four lines of reflection, and so symmetry group D_4.

▷ **Exercise 17.**

D₄: Symmetries of a Square

	1	R	R^2	R^3	F	RF	R^2F	R^3F
1	1	R	R^2	R^3F	F	RF	R^2F	R^3F
R	R	R^2	R^3	1	RF	R^2F	R^3F	F
R^2	R^2	R^3	1	R	R^2F	R^3F	F	RF
R^3	R^3	1	R	R^2	R^3F	F	RF	R^2F
F	F	R^3F	R^2F	RF	1	R^3	R^2	R
RF	RF	F	R^3F	R^2F	R	1	R^3	R^2
R^2F	R^2F	RF	F	R^3F	R^2	R	1	R^3
R^3F	R^3F	R^2F	RF	F	R^3	R^2	R	1

▷ **Exercise 18.**

77

For Exercises 19 and 20, I have students describe the symmetry in words as well as identifying the group to make sure they understand what the notation means. Most refer to the text for the D_3 table but will write out the others.

▷ **Exercise 19.** The figure on the left has symmetry group D_3, and the one on the right, C_3.

▷ **Exercise 20.** The figure on the left has symmetry group D_2, and the one on the right, C_4.

Exercises 21–24 explore the generation of rosette patterns by cutting. Students may be interested to learn that such pattern making is a common pastime in Japan, where it is known as kirigami (paper cutting), related to the more popular origami (paper folding). For paper discs, old fashioned coffee filters work well. These exercises are optional.

▷ **Exercise 21.** D_4

▷ **Exercise 22.** Fold the paper in sixths.

▷ **Exercise 23.** C_3

▷ **Exercise 24.** Slit the disc to the center and then wrap to form a cone so that the paper is four layers thick.

5.3. Frieze Patterns: Line Symmetry

In Exercises 1–6 we are trying to achieve two things: to familiarize the students with the basic isometries and their use in combination and to convince them that the seven frieze patterns given are indeed a complete list of all possibilities. Tracing the motif and applying the indicated isometries will give the end result. Stress that we are asking for the relationship between the original motif and the end result, not any intermediate positions, and that the answers in this series of exercises should be given as a single one of these six expressions: identity, translation, rotation (by 180°), reflection across the center line, reflection perpendicular to the center line, or glide reflection. Though not essential, I have my students "pick a direction and keep going." For example, they tend to put the rotation points inside the motif or just in front of it instead of on the center line that they reflect across. They also reflect across the same vertical line twice (yielding the identity) instead of reflecting across translates of the first vertical reflection line or rotate twice about the same point instead of rotating around translates of the original rotation point.

▷ **Exercise 1.** This gives a translation of the original motif. Note that if your distance of translation that is part of the glide reflection is 0, then this would give you the identity.

▷ **Exercise 2.** This gives a rotation of the motif by 180° about a point on the center line.

▷ **Exercise 3.** This gives a translation of the original motif.

▷ **Exercise 4.** This gives a rotation of the motif by 180° about a point on the center line.

▷ **Exercise 5.** This gives a reflection across a line perpendicular to the center line.

▷ **Exercise 6.** Let T indicate a translation, $F_{||}$ a reflection across the centerline, $F_\perp$ a reflection across the line perpendicular to the centerline, G a glide reflection, and R a rotation by 180°. Also, let 1 indicate that the object has returned to its original position. Note that by the chart below, combining any two of these actions does not result in any new patterns. The table is read by letting the row represent the first action, followed by the action in the column.

Composing Isometries

	T	$F_{||}$	$F_\perp$	G	R
T	T (or 1)	G	$F_\perp$	G	R
$F_{||}$	G	1	R (Ex. 2)	T (Ex. 3)	$F_\perp$ (Ex. 5)
$F_\perp$	$F_\perp$	R	1 (or T)	R (Ex. 4)	G
G	G	T	R	T (Ex. 1)	$F_\perp$
R	R	$F_\perp$	G	$F_\perp$	T (or 1)

We have, in fact, found that the following exercise is useful as well as entertaining. We have overheard students referring to physically jumping and spinning when they are trying to classify the patterns of Exercises 8–10.

▷ **Exercise 7.** Demonstrate the seven patterns.

While students may initially prefer Conway's hop-step-jump terminology, in practice the crystallographic notation is easier. We prefer to let them use whichever they choose and always give both terminologies on exam and quiz problems. To use the crystallographers' notation, think of filling in the blanks of $p \_ \_ \_$ one at a time. A mirror can be used to check whether a frieze has reflectional symmetry, but tracing paper works better. Have the students trace the pattern. To see if there is a reflection perpendicular to the center line, turn the traced image over, using a line perpendicular to the strip as the axis. See if the pattern on the tracing paper lines up with the original, perhaps after sliding it right or left. Emphasize that one does not simply turn the paper over haphazardly but must treat this as a reflection across the perpendicular line. If the patterns do match up, put an m in the first blank and if not, put a 1. To fill in the second blank, return the traced image to its position aligned with the original, then turn the paper over using the center line as the axis. If the pattern matches up with the first traced motif directly over the first motif of the original, then there is such a reflection. In doing this, emphasize that we are not allowed to slide the paper right or left: this is allowed in looking for a perpendicular reflection since there are infinitely many possible perpendicular lines to reflect across, but there is only one center line, so one must align the first motif. If there is a reflection across the center line, fill in the second blank with an m. If not, then slide the reflected traced frieze to the right and see if there is ever a point where the traced and original patterns match exactly. If so, then place a g in the second blank. If there is neither a reflection nor a glide reflection, put a 1 in the second blank. Return the traced pattern to the original position and rotate 180°. If the patterns match, possibly after sliding right and left (again because there are infinitely many possible rotation centers along the center line), then put a 2 in the last blank, and if not, put a 1. Note that if there is a reflection perpendicular to the center line and either a reflection across the center line or a glide reflection, then there must be a 2-fold rotation. There are no patterns of the form $pmm1$ or $pmg1$. Emphasize that patterns are infinite in both directions. Exercise 9(b) is cut off at the ends rather than changing patterns. Exercise 9(e) does not start with a square and end with a circle but alternates forever. Exercise 9(a) is a good one to do as an example. Many students will immediately see the vertical mirror line, but are surprised to see the same pattern when they flip across the horizontal line or rotate.

▷ **Exercise 8.** (a) $p1m1$ or jump
(b) $pmm2$ or spinning jump
(c) $p112$ or spinning hop
(d) $pm11$ or sidle
(e) $pmg2$ or spinning sidle
(f) $p111$ or hop
(g) $p1g1$ or step

▷ **Exercise 9.** (a) $pmg2$ or spinning sidle
(b) $p1m1$ or jump
(c) $pmm2$ or spinning jump
(d) $p112$ or spinning hop
(e) $p1g1$ or step

(f) *pmg*2 or spinning sidle

(g) *pm*11 or sidle

(h) *p*111 or hop

▷ **Exercise 10.** (a) *pm*11 or sidle

(b) *pmm*2 or spinning jump

(c) *p*111 or hop

(d) *pmg*2 or spinning sidle

(e) *p1g*1 or spinning hop

(f) *p*112 or step

(g) *p1m*1 or jump

▷ **Exercise 11.** Draw your own examples of each of the seven frieze patterns.

▷ **Exercise 12.** *p1g*1 or step

In Exercises 13–17, we investigate the generation of frieze patterns by folding and cutting. Cash register tape (we use paper tape 1 inch wide) works well, or students can cut strips of notebook paper, about an inch wide. If students do not understand the technical term "zigzag" in Exercise 13, tell them to fold the paper like an accordion. Emphasize that they should cut asymmetrical bits, so that any symmetries arise from the folding and rolling of the paper and not from the pattern they cut.

▷ **Exercise 13.** *pm*11 or sidle

▷ **Exercise 14.** *p*111 or hop (Note that flattening the cylinder gives the same pattern as folding the zigzag.)

▷ **Exercise 15.** *p1m*1 or jump

You will probably need to show the students how to make a Möbius band from a strip of paper for Exercise 16. Once one small Möbius band has been formed, the paper can be rolled around it to form a Möbius band several layers thick.

▷ **Exercise 16.** *p1g*1 or step

▷ **Exercise 17.** Form *pmm*2 (spinning jump) by folding the strip lengthwise and then in a zigzag. Form *p*112 (spinning hop) by a twisted zigzag (give the paper a half turn before overlapping). If you have ever wrapped boat lines round a deck cleat, this is the pattern you create (if you wrap the lines correctly). Form *pmg*2 (spinning sidle) by zigzagging alternately straight and twisted or by forming a Möbius band and folding perpendicular to the roll before you cut.

5.4. Wallpaper Patterns: Plane Symmetry

This is another section where color could have been used with advantage. Students should be encouraged to color-code reflection lines in red (these are shown as dashed in the text and in this manual) and glide reflection lines in blue (shown as dotted), as this makes them far clearer. There are far too many wallpaper patterns for comfort (17 in all), so this section might get either tedious or confusing. We have tried to vary the form of the exercises as much as we could, but there are still a lot of different patterns to go through. Further examples can be found using either samples of actual wallpaper (although one finds that glide reflections are rare, as are rotations of 60° and 120°) or Escher's tiling patterns (see especially Schattschneider's Visions of Symmetry). It may also help to give the students enlarged copies of some of the exercises (see Templates 24–28 in the Appendix) so that they have room to work.

▷ **Exercise 1.** The image after the reflection and the image after the glide reflection are related by a 180° rotation. Use Template 24 from the Appendix.

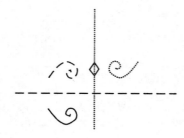

▷ **Exercise 2.** *pmg2* or spinning sidle

Exercises 3–5 will help students learn to identify properties of wallpaper patterns, such as finding a line of reflection or center of rotation. The argument in the text and Exercises 6 and 7 prove that wallpaper can only have rotations of 180°, 120°, 90°, or 60°.

▷ **Exercise 3.** Draw a line from one motif to the other connecting corresponding points. The mirror line will be the perpendicular bisector of this line.

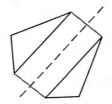

▷ **Exercise 4.** For the picture in the text, simply connect corresponding points on the images. These lines will intersect at their midpoints and this point will be the center of rotation. In general, draw the perpendicular bisectors of the lines connecting corresponding points on the images. The point where these perpendicular bisectors intersect is the rotation center:

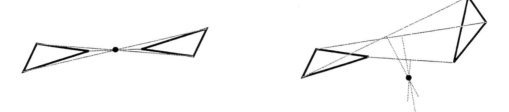

▷ **Exercise 5.** Connect corresponding points on the images. This should form an n-gon. Find the center of the n-gon by connecting opposite vertices for an even n-gon, or by connecting each vertex with the midpoint of the opposite side for an odd n-gon.

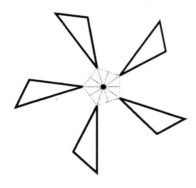

Make sure that students really understand the 5-fold argument in the text and precisely what one is proving there before you expect reasonable answers to Exercises 6 and 7. For a weaker class, either go over the 5-fold case in class or omit these exercises and merely talk about the final result.

▷ **Exercise 6.** Suppose that we had a 7-fold rotation point at point A. Let B be another 7-fold rotation point so that A and B are the closest two such points of all the 7-fold rotation centers. If B is rotated by $\frac{360}{7} = 51.4°$ about A, then we have another 7-fold rotation point C with $AB = BC$, since the wallpaper pattern is symmetric by rotation about A. Similarly, if A is rotated 51.4° around B, we get another 7-fold rotation point at D with $DB = AB$. But then C and D are closer to each other than A and B were.

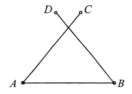

▷ **Exercise 7.** Applying the argument to 2-, 3-, or 4-fold rotation just gives C and D so that $CD = AB$ in the 2- and 4-fold cases, and points E and F so that $EF = AB$ in the 3-fold case.

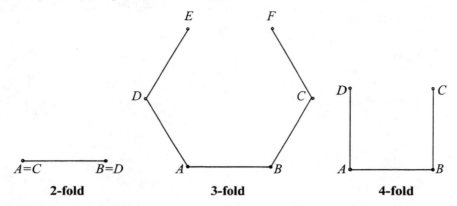

Make sure that students really understand the argument in the text about lining up reflections of a motif and precisely what one is proving there before you expect a reasonable answer to Exercise 8. For a weaker class, either go over the example in class or omit this exercise and merely talk about the final result.

▷ **Exercise 8.** On the left below is a picture of the basic motif and the dotted line of glide reflection. The horizontal arrow indicates the direction and distance that the reflected image will move as part of the glide reflection operation. The slanted arrow shows the other translation direction and distance (I have drawn this slanted rather than vertical to illustrate the most general case). We wish to show that the motifs occur directly over one another. For example, let us show that Motif d lines up with Motif b in the picture on the right. Motif a is glide reflected twice across line 1 to give Motif b. Motif a is also translated to Motif c and the line of glide reflection 1 is also translated to give the dotted line 2. The line of glide reflection 2 is also translated to line 3. However, Motif a can also be glide reflected across line 2: reflected across line 2 to land along line 3 and then translated the direction and twice the distance of the horizontal arrow, ending up at the position of Motif d directly over Motif b.

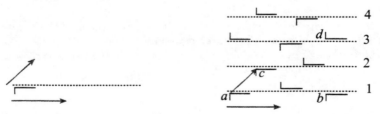

The rest of the exercises in this section are devoted to working through all 17 of the wallpaper patterns. We have tried to vary the exercises in doing these, having some where the students must generate the pattern for themselves and others where they analyze a given pattern. Throughout, the standard symbols and notation are used, so by the end, they should be comfortable using these correctly. Reflection lines should be marked in red and glide reflection lines in blue. Emphasize that the rotation symbols indicate the order of rotation: 2-fold for ♦ and ◇, 3-fold for ▲ and △, 4-fold for ■ and □, and 6-fold for ⬣ and ◯. These are drawn as solid black if they happen to fall on a line of reflection (colored red), and white if not. The basic cell and the lattice given by copies of the cell are chosen so that each cell contains copies of the motif in each orientation and so that the corners of the cell are centers of rotation (if any).

The wallpaper pattern exercises are ordered by the type of lattice. There are two patterns with a parallelogram lattice: **p111**, *which was the first example of the section, and* **p211**, *generated in Exercise 9.*

▷ **Exercise 9.** To form the pattern **p2**, add one more copy of the motif to the shaded cell by rotating the one shown 180° about the point marked at the center of the cell. Then stack copies of this basic cell to form a section of the wallpaper pattern, as shown below. Use Template 24 from the Appendix.

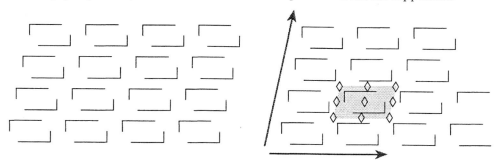

The wallpaper patterns that use a rectangular lattice are **p2mg** *(discussed as the second example of this section),* **p1g1, p1m1, p2gg,** *and* **p2mm.** *These are investigated in Exercises 10–15. In Exercise 10, one can think of the basic cell as a rubber stamp, and then copies of this stamp are repeated to fill the plane. Exercise 11 merely asks the student to identify the lines of reflection. Exercise 13 is a slightly more advanced version, where the student must find two different parallel families of lines of glide reflection, and then label centers of rotation (two nonparallel lines of glide reflection will induce a rotation) and shade the basic cell. Exercise 15 is the reverse of this, in which the basic cell, centers of rotation, and a single copy of the motif is given, and the student is asked to fill in the rest of the pattern. After completing the basic cell, this can be treated as repeats of a rubber stamp.*

▷ **Exercise 10.** This is **p1g1**, shown on the right with the given lines of glide reflection and a shaded basic cell. On the left is the final wallpaper pattern without annotations. Use Template 25.

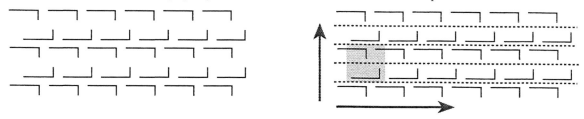

▷ **Exercise 11.** This is **p1m1**, with reflection lines shown as dashed and a shaded basic cell. Use Template 25.

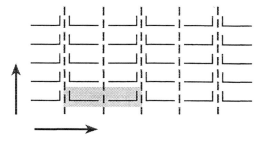

▷ **Exercise 12.** One row of the wallpaper pattern **p1m1** forms the frieze pattern *pm*11, or sidle.

▷ **Exercise 13.** Here is **p2gg** with glide reflection lines shown as dotted, ◊ marks at the rotation centers, and a shaded basic cell, with its corners at the rotation centers. Use Template 25 from the Appendix. Students would prefer a basic cell that does not cut the motif in pieces, so emphasize that corners of the cell must be at the rotation centers if any exist.

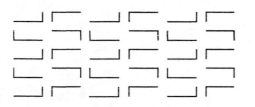 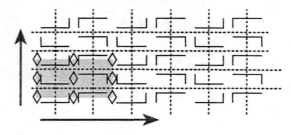

▷ **Exercise 14.** One row of **p2gg** forms the frieze pattern *p*112, or spinning hop.

▷ **Exercise 15.** Here is the completed **p2mm** pattern, shown on the right with the construction markings and without them on the left. Use Template 26 from the Appendix.

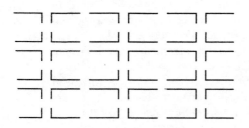 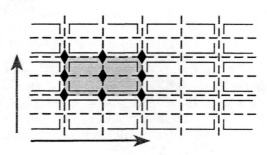

*Exercises 16 and 17 study the two wallpaper patterns with a lattice of rhombi: **c2mm** and **c1m1**. In Exercise 16, we ask the student to mark up a section of the pattern to show lines of reflection and glide reflection and 2-fold centers of rotation. The symbol ♦ should be used if a rotation center falls on a reflection line and ◊ if not. It will then be clear that the shaded cell was chosen to have ♦ marks at each corner, justifying the choice of a rhombic lattice. In Exercise 17, the process is reversed: a single motif, the basic cell, and the lines of reflection and glide reflection are given, and the student must generate the pattern.*

▷ **Exercise 16.** Use Template 26: **c2mm**

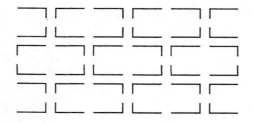 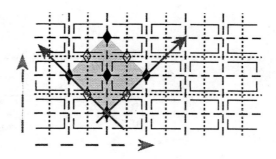

▷ **Exercise 17.** Use Template 26: **c1m1**

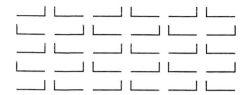
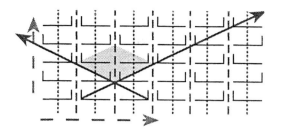

There are three wallpaper patterns using a square lattice, all of which contain 4-fold rotations: **p411**, **p4gm**, and **p4mm**. These are explored in Exercises 18–21. In Exercise 18, students must complete the basic cell and then fill in a section of wallpaper and mark the other rotation centers (there will be both 4-fold centers marked with a □ and 2-fold centers marked with a ◊). The wallpaper pattern of Exercise 19 is drawn at an angle rather than having the lines of reflection running horizontally and vertically. Students usually can find the two families of reflection lines without any trouble, and then will find two families of glide reflection lines parallel to the reflection lines. They may have trouble finding the other families of glide reflections. Exercise 20 shows that reflection lines meeting at a 45° angle force a 4-fold rotation center. This fact is then applied in Exercise 21 to generate the pattern **p4mm**.

▷ **Exercise 18.** Use Template 27: **p411**

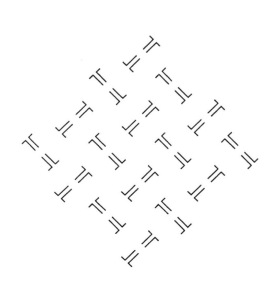

▷ **Exercise 19.** Use Template 27: **p4gm**

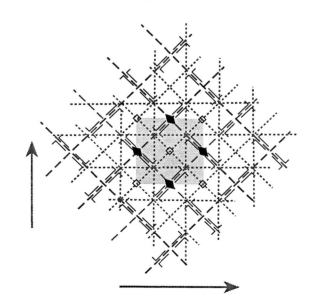

87

▷ **Exercise 20.** Use Template 27.

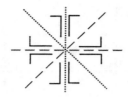

▷ **Exercise 21.** p4mm

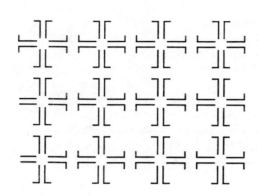

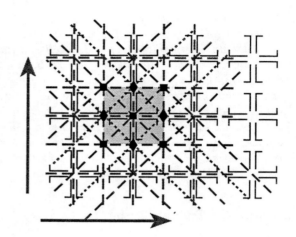

There are five wallpaper patterns with a hexagonal lattice: **p611** (the third example of the section), **p311**, **p3m1**, **p31m**, and **p6mm**. These are studied in Exercises 22–25. Students will have more difficulty with 3-fold and 6-fold centers of rotation than they did with 2-fold and 4-fold. In Exercise 22, one can have them trace the motif given on a scrap of tracing paper, then put their pencil point at one of the rotation centers and use it as an axis to rotate the motif to its new position. By doing this for each 3-fold rotation center, they will soon fill in the pattern. In Exercise 23 the patterns **p3m1** and **p31m** are studied: as the names imply, both have 3-fold rotation centers and both have reflection lines. One difference between the two is that **p3m1** has only ▲ rotation centers and **p31m** has both ▲ and △.

▷ **Exercise 22.** Use Template 28: **p311**

88

▷ **Exercise 23.** Use Template 28: **p3m1** is first,

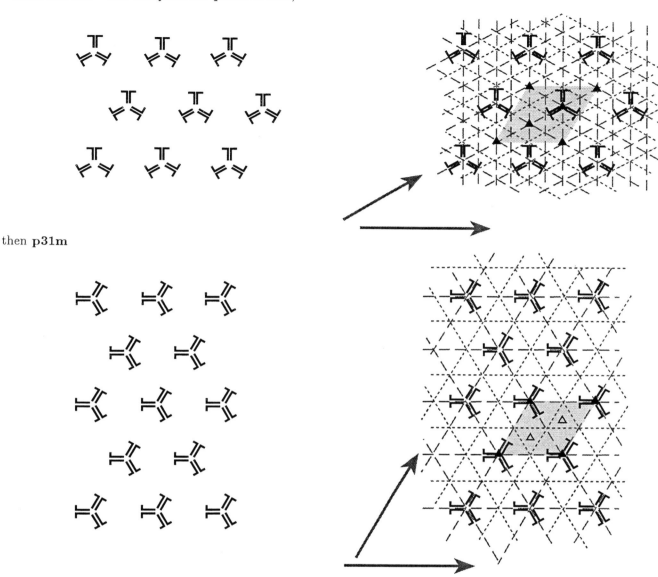

then **p31m**

*Exercise 24 shows that reflection lines meeting at a 30° angle force a 6-fold rotation center. This fact is then applied in Exercise 25 to generate the pattern **p6mm**.*

▷ **Exercise 24.** Use Template 28.

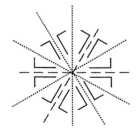

▷ **Exercise 25.** p6mm

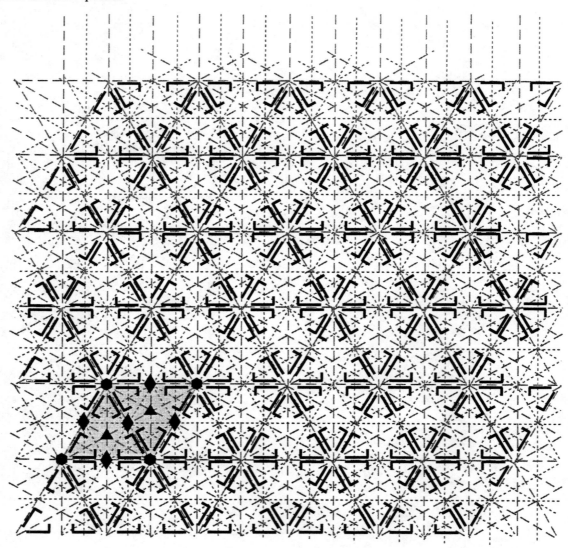

Note that if a pattern involves either a reflection or a glide reflection, then both left and right hands will appear. The flow chart on page 163 of the text will be helpful.

▷ **Exercise 26.**   (a) p111
  (b) **c2mm**
  (c) **p411**
  (d) **p1g1**
  (e) **c1m1**
  (f) **p2gg**
  (g) **p211**
  (h) **p2mm**
  (i) **p2mg**

(j) **p1m1**

(k) **p311**

(l) **p31m**

(m) **p4mm**

(n) **p4gm**

(o) **p611**

(q) **p3m1**

(r) **p6mm**

If you have access to software and computers, let students use them after creating examples by hand.

▷ **Exercise 27.** Draw your own examples of each of the 17 wallpaper patterns.

5.5. Islamic Lattice Patterns

In this section, we apply some of the techniques developed in previous sections to generate a new type of pattern. The Islamic lattice patterns are difficult to draw, but the results are beautiful. We distinguish between the design (the layout of the basic pattern) and the final interlaced pattern. The interlacing destroys any reflectional symmetry that the design has. Templates are provided in the Appendix for Exercises 4, 6, 10, and 13. Students will probably need several copies of each. Tell them to work very carefully or to expect a lot of changes to get them correct. Omit Exercise 12 if you did not cover Section 4.1.

▷ **Exercise 1.** The design has pattern **p4mm**, but the interlaced pattern is **p411**. The crossings eliminate the possibility of any reflectional symmetry.

▷ **Exercise 2.** The design has pattern **p6mm**, but the interlaced pattern is **p611**.

▷ **Exercise 3.** For a square grid, we can use any multiple of four, while for a triangular grid any multiple of three.

*In Exercises 4–9 and in the text following Exercise 7, we explore one of the choices made in designing a lattice pattern: the size and relative spacing of the circles. The patterns of page 173, Exercises 4 and 6, and the illustration at the top of page 176 all use a grid of circles arranged in a hexagonal grid with six dots for each circle. Thus the angles of reflection off these circles will be the same for all four of these patterns. The drawings for Exercises 4 and 6 show a great deal of similarity, but the lattice pattern of page 173 differs from these in having infinite strands. The design of page 176 cannot be extended to an interlace pattern. All four designs have wallpaper pattern **p6mm**, and the three interlaced patterns have wallpaper type **p611**.*

▷ **Exercise 4.** Use Template 29 from the Appendix.

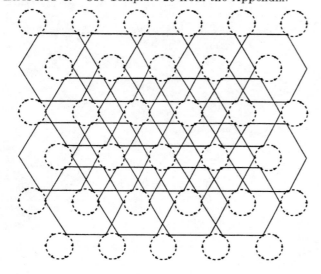

▷ **Exercise 5.** The design has pattern **p6mm**, but the interlaced pattern is **p611**.

▷ **Exercise 6.** Use Template 30.

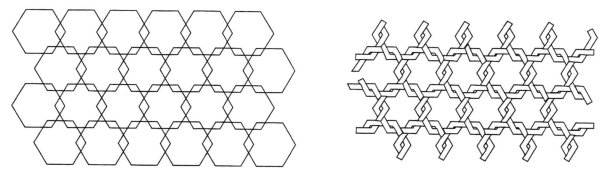

▷ **Exercise 7.** The design has pattern **p6mm**, but the interlaced pattern is **p611**.

▷ **Exercise 8.** The design has pattern **p6mm**.

▷ **Exercise 9.** The distance between the circles is the radius of the circles. In Exercise 4, the radius is larger than the distance between the circles, while in Exercise 6 the distance between circles is larger than the radius.

▷ **Exercise 10.** Use Template 31.

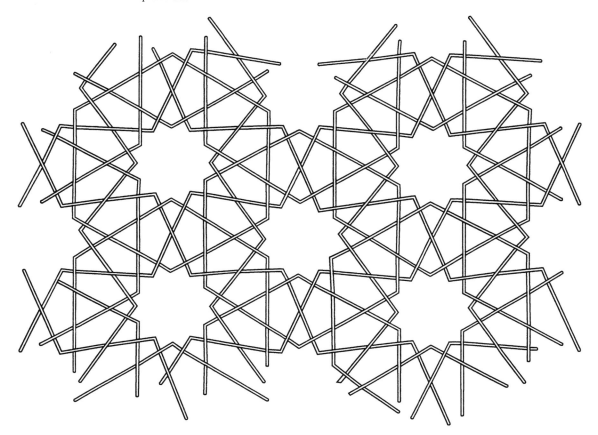

In Exercises 11–14, we extend the method to use two sizes of circles.

▷ **Exercise 11.** The design pattern is **p4mm**, and the interlaced pattern is **p411**.

▷ **Exercise 12.** Circles are arranged like the squares and octagons in the tiling 4.8.8.

▷ **Exercise 13.** Use Template 32.

▷ **Exercise 14.** The interlaced design in Exercise 13 is **p611**.

▷ **Exercise 15.** Bisect the 135° angles formed by the pattern. The circles must have centers where these bisectors meet.

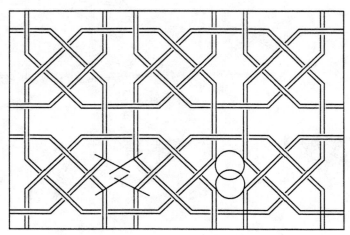

▷ **Exercise 16.** The interlaced pattern in Exercise 15 has wallpaper pattern **p411**.

▷ **Exercise 17.** This interlaced pattern has wallpaper type **p211**.

Chapter 6. Other Dimensions, Other Worlds

★ **6.1. Flatlands**
  Dependencies: None

- Abbott's <u>Flatland</u>
- Burger's <u>Sphereland</u>
- C. H. Hinton's <u>An Episode in Flatland</u>
- A. K. Dewdney's <u>The Planiverse</u>

★ ★ **6.2. The Fourth Dimension**
- **Dependencies:** Chapter 6.1

- Intersections of linear spaces
- Hypercube
- The fourth dimension in art

This chapter serves as a transition from the study of two-dimensional phenomena to higher dimensions. The concept of dimension is not studied formally until Section 13.1, but most students have a reasonably sound intuitive idea of dimension. This chapter, especially the first section, marks a dramatic change in emphasis. Abbott's <u>Flatland</u> asks the reader to use his imagination to figure out how life would be in a two-dimensional world, and, by analogy, in four dimensions. <u>Flatland</u> is commonly available, both in print and online, and we encourage everyone to read it. When we have taught this section, we always require students to write an essay on <u>Flatland</u>. Suggested topics might include:

a. *Write your own continuation or variation on life in Flatland.*
b. *Give a description of the ways in which a two-dimensional universe constrains the environment and its inhabitants.*
c. *Write a speculation on a fourth spatial dimension.*
d. *Describe the ways in which Abbott uses irony to relate life in Flatland with specific social problems of the era in which the book was written (1884).*

This section also discusses other works of two-dimensional literature. Our favorite, Dewdney's <u>The Planiverse</u>, has recently been reissued by Springer-Verlag, under the Copernicus imprint. Most of the exercises in the first section require students to figure out the mechanics and logistics of life in two dimensions.

The second section of this chapter focuses on phenomena in the fourth dimension. Students are impressed that mathematics can predict a lot of information about four-dimensional objects even when one cannot draw or even imagine them. This is an important lesson to learn, and the fourth dimension allows the students to experience this in action. The fourth dimension also has historical significance, both in its use as a metaphor in the spirituality movement at the turn of the last century and as inspiration for Cubist art.

6.1. Flatlands

Exercises 1 and 2, of course, only pertain if one has asked the students to read the book. We usually allow one class period to discuss the book after reading it and have found that most students have little concept of satire. Women, especially, tend to get quite indignant about their depiction as fragile, mindless, line segments. We have tried in the text to indicate what we know of Abbott's views on the education of women and other issues. The classroom discussion allows history and literature majors to help other students understand the cultural background of the period, while engineering and physics students enjoy figuring out the mechanics of life in two dimensions, so an hour can be spent quite profitably in discussion.

▷ **Exercise 1.** Read Abbott's Flatland.

▷ **Exercise 2.** It does seem that almost the whole of the culture of Flatland is devised to limit the threat of revolution from the lower but more numerous isosceles classes. The ruling powers, the polygonal and circle classes, limit access to education and execute irregularities. The religious life of Flatland, led by the circles, consists entirely of veneration for regularity and the preaching that one must submit to one's self-evident destiny as shown by one's configuration. Hope for eventual advancement is extended to the lower classes by a law of nature by which each succeeding generation becomes more regular, and the presence of this hope discourages revolt: "Had the acute-angled rabble been all, without exception, absolutely destitute of hope and ambition, they might have found leaders in some of their many seditious outbreaks." At times, the upper classes have found it necessary to subvert the leaders of a revolt, either by admitting them to the upper classes or by imprisonment: "By judicious use of this Law of Nature, the Polygons and Circles are almost always able to stifle sedition in its very cradle, taking advantage of the irrepressible and boundless hopefulness of the human mind. . . . It is generally found possible — by a little artificial compression or expansion on the part of the State physicians — to make some of the more intelligent leaders of a rebellion perfectly Regular, and to admit them at once into the privileged classes; a much larger number, who are still below the standard, allured by the prospect of being ultimately ennobled, are induced to enter the State Hospitals, where they are kept in honorable confinement for life; one or two alone of the more obstinate, foolish, and hopelessly irregular are led to execution." The removal of regular children from irregular parents and the adoption of the children by childless middle-class couples at once discourages the parents from rebelling against the middle class that the child has joined and enforces the separation of the classes.

For Exercises 3–5, there are not single correct answers. Instead, check to see if the answers the students figure out make sense and are workable in a two-dimensional world.

▷ **Exercise 3.** Abbot does not seem to have provided a way for Flatlanders to propel themselves. Since the atmosphere seems to have some substance, they could swim through it, if provided with hands or flippers, though the slight force of gravity would tend to pull them southward. Other means of propulsion are possible, through addition of physical features or appliances. More elaborate methods are possible and are detailed in Hinton's and Dewdney's two-dimensional models.

▷ **Exercise 4.** Nails will not work, since driving a nail into a line segment would disconnect it. Glue, perhaps with the added support of angle brackets, seems to be the best choice.

▷ **Exercise 5.** Their writing would probably be quite like Morse code, and all characters would be combinations of dots and dashes of varying lengths.

In Exercises 6–15, the student is asked first to explain phenomena in Flatland, and then to generalize these phenomena to higher dimensions.

▷ **Exercise 6.** The King saw a point appear, then become a line segment that gradually grew in size and then shrank to a point again before disappearing.

▷ **Exercise 7.** A 3 by 3 square moved 3 inches in a third direction will form a cube with volume 3^3.

▷ **Exercise 8.** A four-dimensional being would be able to see the insides of a three-dimensional being or dwelling.

▷ **Exercise 9.** First, one would see a point appear, then a small sphere, which would swell to a larger sphere, and then shrink to a point again before disappearing.

▷ **Exercise 10.** This depends somewhat on the angle at which the hypercube enters the three-dimensional space. If it enters so that a face is parallel to the space, first a square would appear, then a cube, which will remain constant in size, then become a square and finally disappear. See the illustration by Bragdon on page 199 of the text.

It is important that students not simply count the vertices, edges, and faces for the square and cube of Exercises 11 and 12, but understand how these are formed. For example, in the cube, two of the faces are formed by the initial and terminal positions of the square and the four side faces are formed by the movement of the edges of the square. Understanding this development is essential for Exercises 13 and 14 where one no longer has a drawing or physical model to rely on.

▷ **Exercise 11.** The square has four vertices representing the initial and terminal positions of the endpoints of the line segment, four edges, two of which represent the initial and terminal positions of the line segment and two of which are formed by the movement of the two endpoints of the line segment, and one two-dimensional face, formed by the movement of the line segment.

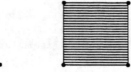

▷ **Exercise 12.** The square forms a cube, with eight vertices (four from the initial position of the square and four from the terminal square), 12 edges (four from the initial square, four from the terminal square and four formed by the movement of the four vertices of the square), six faces (two from the initial and terminal positions of the square and four formed by the movement of the four edges of the square), and one solid (formed by the movement of the single face of the square).

▷ **Exercise 13.** The hypercube will have 16 vertices (eight each from the initial and terminal positions of the cube), 32 edges (12 each from the initial and terminal cubes, plus eight formed by the movement of the cube's eight vertices), 24 faces (six each from the initial and terminal cubes, plus 12 formed by the movement of the cube's 12 edges), eight solids (two from the initial and terminal cubes and six from the movement of the cube's six faces), and one four-dimensional region.

▷ **Exercise 14.** The hyperhypercube will have 32 vertices (16 each from the initial and terminal positions of the hypercube), 80 edges (32 each from the initial and terminal hypercubes, plus 16 formed by the movement of the hypercube's 16 vertices), 80 faces (24 each from the initial and terminal hypercubes, plus 32 formed by the movement of the hypercube's 32 edges), 40 solids (eight each from the initial and terminal hypercubes and 24 from the movement of the hypercube's 24 faces), and 10 four-dimensional regions (one each from the initial and terminal hypercubes and eight from the movement of the hypercube's eight solids), and one five-dimensional region.

▷ **Exercise 15.** A four-dimensional being would be able to remove objects from locked boxes or safes without touching the door, or for that matter could remove one's appendix without surgery.

▷ **Exercise 16.** Simply use the third dimension to flip the dog over.

▷ **Exercise 17.** Each of the angles is approximately 120°, for a sum of 360°.

For Exercise 18, ask students to form the triangles out of something flexible: fingers or pipe cleaners, for example, instead of drawing on a piece of paper. This will lead them naturally to the desired answer for Exercise 19.

▷ **Exercise 18.** Bend *BC* up into the third dimension.

▷ **Exercise 19.** Triangles drawn on the surface of a ball or sphere will naturally have these properties.

There is no one correct answer for Exercise 20, but rather check to see if the solution that the student comes up with is feasible in two dimensions.

▷ **Exercise 20.** Hinton's Astrians cut down most of the trees they encounter while circling their earth. This would seem to violate basic ecological concerns, but such things do happen in the course of a war. A very athletic Astrian could climb a tree as shown below on the left. A rope ladder with a grapple hook at the end could be devised, as shown on the right:

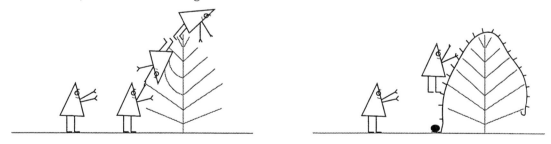

▷ **Exercise 21.** Yendred spelled backwards is Derdney, or Dewdney (remember that Alice has a slight speech impediment).

If students have trouble with Exercises 22 and 23, have them experiment with a bit of string that must remain confined to the desktop.

▷ **Exercise 22.** An Ardean would have to pinch the string, like pliers.

▷ **Exercise 23.** Knots do not exist in the plane. Ardeans would use clamps or pinchers to hold string in place.

> *The untying of knots is revisited in the next section with a more complete explanation. However, if students can understand that a four-dimensional being can remove an object from a sealed box, then they should be able to extrapolate this idea to untying a knot.*

▷ **Exercise 24.** Any knot in a four-dimensional universe can be untied, just by undoing the crossings where one strand passes over another. Thus, knots would not be of any use.

> *In Exercises 25 and 26 we again ask students to use their imaginations to find a solution to a two-dimensional problem. Any workable solution, the weirder the better, should be accepted.*

▷ **Exercise 25.** A bit of string can be looped around a heavy object to help tow it. Yendred at one point uses a balloon, again made with a bit of string. For very heavy objects, rigid circles or discs can be used as rollers.

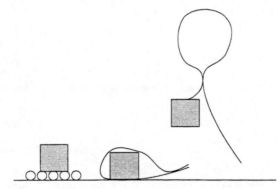

▷ **Exercise 26.** Drums and xylophones are quite easy to imagine, as is a one-stringed harp or piano.

> *A variety of physical models (sphere and torus) will help students to see the ways that the colored paths can intersect.*

▷ **Exercise 27.** On a sphere, a circle is formed by intersecting the sphere with a plane. Thus, the intersection of two circles on the sphere would be the intersection of the sphere and two intersecting planes. Since the intersection of these two planes is a line and the line would intersect the sphere at two points, the circles must intersect twice.

▷ **Exercise 28.** One such shape would be a torus, or doughnut.

6.2. The Fourth Dimension

▷ **Exercise 1.** Describe the location of the points relative to your classroom, after you have agreed on where the origin and axes are.

> *In Exercises 2–4, we are asking the students to reason by analogy. The instructor may need to draw their attention to the dimensions of the objects. For example, in the text of Exercise 2 we note that a point (zero-dimensional) cuts the one-dimensional line in half and that a one-dimensional line cuts the two-dimensional plane in half. In the exercise, the students must figure out that a two-dimensional plane cuts three-dimensional space in half, and three-dimensional space cuts four-dimensional space in half. These arguments are quite simple if one thinks of the dimensions explicitly.*

▷ **Exercise 2.** (a) The xy-plane cuts three-dimensional space in half.
(b) The three-dimensional space given by x, y, and z cuts four-dimensional space in half.

▷ **Exercise 3.** (a) The intersection of two nonparallel planes in the third dimension is a line.
(b) The intersection of two nonparallel three-dimensional spaces in hyperspace is a plane.

▷ **Exercise 4.** (a) A point.
(b) The empty set.
(c) The dimension of the intersection of a k-dimensional line or plane with an ℓ-dimensional line or plane in n-dimensional space is given by $k + \ell - n$, where a negative dimension indicates the null set.
(d) The empty set.
(e) A point.
(f) A line.

> *In Exercises 5–7 we investigate phenomena of four-dimensional space. The main tool is the formula of Exercise 4(c): the dimension of the intersection of a k-dimensional line or plane with an ℓ-dimensional line or plane in n-dimensional space is given by $k + \ell - n$.*

▷ **Exercise 5.** The first picture shows the original knot. In the second picture, one of the strands has been moved past another, reversing one crossing. This maneuver requires the fourth dimension. In the next picture, the loop has been rearranged, and in the last picture, a simple twist undoes the knot. The movement of a piece of the knot through the fourth dimension forms a subset of a plane (recall Exercise 6.1.11), and the intersection of this bit of plane and the rest of the knot is empty (since it has dimension $2 + 1 - 4 = -1$ by Exercise 4(c)).

▷ **Exercise 6.** Just as an object can be removed from a square on the plane by picking it up into the third dimension and lifting it out, a small, pointlike object can be lifted out of a box into the fourth dimension. The wall of the box is a plane, and a moving hand describes a linear path. Since $2 + 1 - 4$ is negative, there is no intersection.

▷ **Exercise 7.** Since a left glove is the mirror image of a right glove, one can pick it up into the fourth dimension and flip it over the mirror plane, as for the mongrel and pedigreed dogs in Burger's <u>Sphereland</u> in Exercise 6.1.16.

▷ **Exercise 8.** Sceptics would unbolt the tabletop from the base, slip the rings on and replace the top. Alternatively, the rings might be previously cut in two, and then glued carefully together around the table base.

▷ **Exercise 9.** Each gives $\chi = 1$.

In Exercises 10–13, we study three different models of the hypercube. Each has certain advantages and disadvantages. By the table on page 201 of the text, we know each is assembled from eight cubes, 24 faces, 32 edges, and 16 vertices, so the first task in familiarizing oneself with these is to find these components in each model.

▷ **Exercise 10.** Two of the cubes are illustrated in the text. Here are the other six, shown in parallel pairs.

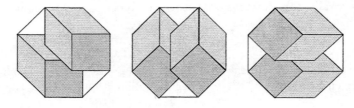

A three-dimensional model of the Schlegel projection at the top of page 202 may help, since students often fail to see the front and back cubes in the drawing. It may help to ask them to consider the Schlegel diagram for the cube.

▷ **Exercise 11.** The cubes can be described in pairs: outside and inside (on the left), right and left (center), top and bottom (right), and front and back (not illustrated).

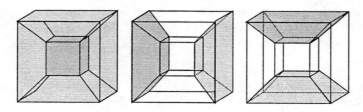

▷ **Exercise 12.** Cut out the net and tape it together to build a cube.

▷ **Exercise 13.** Glue together the faces marked with the same number. The faces on the back are identified similarly.

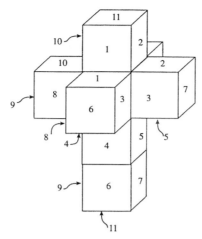

In order to figure out the pieces of the hypertetrahedron, one first needs to understand the progression from point to line to triangle to tetrahedron. The hypertetrahedron will look like a tetrahedron with a vertex suspended over it in the "ana" direction. Thus the number of vertices in the hypertetrahedron will equal the vertices in the tetrahedron plus one. The edges of the hypertetrahedron are either edges in the tetrahedron, or formed by connecting the new vertex with one of the old vertices from the tetrahedron. Since the tetrahedron has six edges and four vertices, the hypertetrahedron will have $6 + 4 = 10$ edges. Each face of the hypertetrahedron is either a face in the tetrahedron below or formed by connecting the new vertex to one of the edges of the tetrahedron. Since the tetrahedron has four faces and six edges, the number of faces for the hypertetrahedron will be $4 + 6 = 10$. Each solid three-dimensional region of the hypertetrahedron is either a solid in the tetrahedron or is formed by connecting the new vertex to one of the faces of the tetrahedron. Since the tetrahedron has one solid and four faces, the hypertetrahedron will have $1 + 4 = 5$ solids.

▷ **Exercise 14.**

n-Dimensional Triangular Figures

Dimension	Figure	v	e	f	s	t
1	Line segment	2	1			
2	Triangle	3	3	1		
3	Tetrahedron	4	6	4	1	
4	Hypertetrahedron	5	10	10	5	1

103

Chapter 7. Polyhedra

★ 7.1. Pyramids, Prisms, and Antiprisms
Dependencies: None

- Pyramids
- Skew versus right, regular versus irregular
- Nets
- Prisms
- Convexity
- Volume formulae
- Antiprisms

★ 7.2. The Platonic Solids
Dependencies: Chapter 7.1

- Platonic solids or regular polyhedra
- Dual polyhedra
- Schlegel diagrams
- Euler's formula
- Deltahedra
- Regularity for polyhedra

★ ★ 7.3. The Archimedean Solids
Dependencies: Chapter 7.1, 7.2
References: Chapter 4.1

- Archimedean solids or semiregular polyhedra

★ 7.4. Polyhedral Transformations
Dependencies: Chapter 7.1, 7.2, 7.3

- Truncation
- Snub polyhedra

★ ★ 7.5. Models of Polyhedra
Dependencies: Chapter 7.1, 7.2

- Cardboard models
- Wire-frame models
- Origami
- Plaited polyhedra
- Tetrahedral kites

★ ★ 7.6. Infinite Polyhedra
Dependencies: Chapter 4.1, 7.1, 7.2, 7.3

- Infinite regular polyhedra
- Cylindrical polyhedra
- Double-sided infinite polyhedra
- Sponges
- Close-packing, or space-filling, polyhedra

In this chapter we move to three dimensions to explore various families of polyhedra. The development is similar to that in Chapter 4. Although the material is technically independent, doing Section 4.1 before attempting Sections 7.3–7.6 will help the students by first exposing them to the ideas and techniques in an easier setting. In the first section, we begin with some of the most easily visualized polyhedra: the pyramids and prisms. Basic terminology (skew and right, regular and irregular, convexity) is introduced, as well as different ways of representing polyhedra (drawings, models, nets). The Euler characteristic is first used here. The volume formulae for prisms and for pyramids are derived. Antiprisms are defined and examples given.

The second section introduces the Platonic solids or regular polyhedra. Their nomenclature and the dual polyhedra are studied. These polyhedra are represented by models, drawings, nets, and Schlegel diagrams. Several visualization exercises are given, involving cross-sections of the polyhedra. An informal proof shows that any spherelike polyhedron has Euler characteristic $\chi = 2$. We ask the student to find the eight convex deltahedra. Finally, regularity of polyhedra is discussed, in terms of the examples generated thus far.

Section 7.3 moves on to the semiregular polyhedra, or Archimedean solids. This section proceeds in a manner analogous to Section 4.1, making use of many of the same rules and concepts. The students are asked, in the course of this section, to build models of all 13 semiregular polyhedra and to show that this list is complete. If the instructor prefers, one could provide models of these to study and omit all the model-making exercises. It should be noted that these physical models are useful in visualizing the relationships between the polyhedra in Section 7.4 and that having these models on hand is essential in the close-packing problems at the end of Section 7.6.

The next section studies the truncation operation, which helps one understand the standard nomenclature and the relationships among the polyhedra. The Euler characteristic is used extensively.

The fifth section is devoted to practical advice on building polyhedral models. This section can be read independently of the others, as long as one has a basic idea of the nomenclature for the regular polyhedra. There are no formal exercises. Instead, one can either treat this section as an extended project or suggest that students use the various techniques given to generate their own models of other polyhedra.

The last section of this chapter introduces several classes of infinite polyhedra. Again, the major means of studying these is the building and analysis of physical models. The double-sided polyhedra draw on the student's knowledge of the semiregular tilings. The section ends with some examples of close packing of polyhedra.

7.1. Pyramids, Prisms, and Antiprisms

If the students are working in groups, tell them that a single model for the group will suffice for Exercise 1. This model can then be used for the visualizations of Exercises 3 and 4. Templates for the polygons used in this and the following sections can be found in the Appendix. For this section, you will need equilateral triangles (Template 9 from the Appendix) and squares (Template 10) photocopied onto cardstock.

▷ **Exercise 1.** Build a model of a right square pyramid with equilateral sides as pictured in the text.

▷ **Exercise 2.** Consider the triangle formed by the diagonal of the base and two of the edges between the triangle sides. Using the Pythagorean Theorem, the diagonal of the base has length $\sqrt{2}$. Thus the height of the pyramid is one side of a right triangle with another side of length $\frac{\sqrt{2}}{2}$ and hypotenuse 1, so the height is $\frac{\sqrt{2}}{2} = .707$.

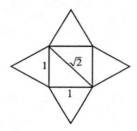 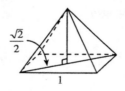

If students have trouble visualizing the cross-sections of Exercises 3 and 4, have them either dip their cardboard models into water and contemplate the water lines, or make the polyhedra out of clay and cut them as specified. Make it clear that we want the cut surface, not the remainder of the polyhedron.

▷ **Exercise 3.** The cross-sections are squares.

▷ **Exercise 4.** The cross-sections are trapezoids, except at the center where the cross-section is an isosceles triangle.

Exercise 5 should help students understand the object of Exercise 6. If they still have trouble, ask them to picture pyramids formed by other nets with varying isosceles triangles.

▷ **Exercise 5.**

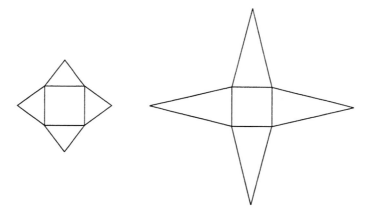

▷ **Exercise 6.** The isosceles triangles forming the sides must have altitude greater than $\frac{1}{2}$. If the altitude were exactly $\frac{1}{2}$, then the pyramid would lie flat in the plane instead of forming a three-dimensional solid. If the altitude is less than $\frac{1}{2}$, then the triangular sides do not touch.

Exercise 7 involves routine application of the Pythagorean Theorem, but also requires that one realize which edges of the net are identified in the model of the pyramid.

▷ **Exercise 7.**

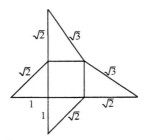

▷ **Exercise 8.** Build a model of a disphenoid using the net in the text.

Exercises 9–12 show if the student understands the rather cumbersome nomenclature for pyramids. A right pyramid must have its apex directly over the center of the base polygon, while a skew pyramid will have its apex anywhere else. A regular-polygon pyramid will have the regular polygon as the base and can either be skew or right. On the other hand, a regular right pentagonal pyramid (where regular describes the entire pyramid instead of only the base), for example, must have only regular polygons for the sides and the base, the apex directly over the center of the base, and a regular pentagonal base. Students may have trouble with the drawings since in any point of view other than directly above a regular polygon will not look regular, but rather foreshortened. Emphasize that we are not looking for great art, nor do we expect any formal knowledge of the rules of perspective at this point, but they should try to simulate a perspective effect of the pyramids and prisms.

107

▷ **Exercise 9.** Draw a right regular-hexagonal pyramid.

▷ **Exercise 10.** Draw a skew regular-hexagonal pyramid.

▷ **Exercise 11.** Draw a right irregular-hexagonal pyramid.

▷ **Exercise 12.** Draw a skew irregular-hexagonal pyramid.

If students have trouble figuring out Exercise 13, have them count faces, edges, and vertices for the square pyramid pictured in the text on page 209 and in their drawing for Exercise 9 and try to extrapolate from this information.

▷ **Exercise 13.** $f = n + 1$, $e = 2n$, and $v = n + 1$.

Students may be overwhelmed by the word "all" in Exercise 14. Tell them to start building and see what happens. This is one place where jumping in and trying lets them discover the answer fairly quickly.

▷ **Exercise 14.** Since the side faces must be equilateral, the only possibilities are the pyramids with triangular, square, or pentagonal bases. Note that if a hexagon were used as the base and the sides were equilateral, then the pyramid would lie flat instead of being three-dimensional.

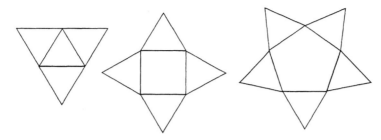

Exercises 15 and 16 examine the student's understanding of the nomenclature for prisms. Exercise 17 asks them to deduce the number of faces, edges, and vertices of an arbitrary prism from the examples in the text and exercises. Tell students to build a few more models if they don't see the pattern yet. Exercise 18 provides a contrasting result to Exercise 14.

▷ **Exercise 15.** Draw a right regular hexagonal prism and its net.

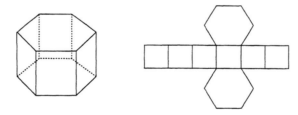

▷ **Exercise 16.** Draw a skew irregular hexagonal prism.

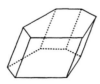

▷ **Exercise 17.** $f = n + 2$, $e = 3n$, and $v = 2n$

▷ **Exercise 18.** There are infinitely many: one for each regular polygon, with squares for the side faces.

The illustrations in the text should lead the students to figure out Exercises 19–21 with ease.

▷ **Exercise 19.** Two congruent right triangular prisms can be joined to form a rectangular box with $V = \ell wh$, so each right triangular prism has volume $V = \frac{1}{2}\ell wh$.

▷ **Exercise 20.** A wedge in the shape of a right triangular prism can be cut off one side of the skew rectangular prism and glued back on the other side. Thus the volume of the skew rectangular prism is the same as the rectangular box: $V = \ell wh$.

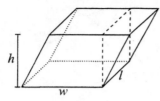 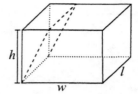

▷ **Exercise 21.** The volume of a pyramid depends only on the base and the height.

▷ **Exercise 22.** Cut the base of the pyramid up into n triangles. One way to do this is shown below. Then form a triangular pyramid using each of the base triangles as base and the pyramid vertex as top vertex.

Most students have some familiarity with pyramids and prisms, but will not have seen the antiprisms before. Note that every antiprism can be built from two identical components, each consisting of a polygon with congruent triangles attached along each edge. These two pieces are rotated (by half the interior angle of the central polygon) and then the triangles mesh like the teeth in a gear.

▷ **Exercise 23.** The antiprism with equilateral triangles for base and top faces and for the sides is the octahedron.

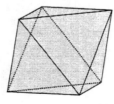

▷ **Exercise 24.** Here is the antiprism with squares for base and top faces.

▷ **Exercise 25.** $f = 2n + 2$, $e = 4n$, and $v = 2n$.

7.2. The Platonic Solids

To do all the exercises in this section, one would need 90 equilateral triangles, six squares, and 12 pentagons, ideally with the same edge length so that the models can be reused for the polyhedron-packing problems in Section 7.6. Templates for these can be found in the Appendix (Templates 9, 10, and 11): simply photocopy the templates onto the heaviest cardstock the machine will take and have students cut them out before you begin this section. Alternatively, one can save class time by providing prebuilt models, or use any of the readily available model-building sets, such as the one produced by Zometool. Nets for these polyhedra are also provided in Template 33. In any case, some sort of physical model, rather than relying solely on drawings, is desirable for many of the exercises. Some of these exercises ask the student to list physical attributes (such as number of faces, edges, and vertices) and some involve visualization (the Schlegel diagrams or figuring out cross-sections).

The nomenclature for the Platonic solids (except for the cube, which is only rarely referred to as the hexahedron) follows the Greek suffixes used for polygons in Section 1.2. We use the same Schläfli symbols (such as 4.4.4 for the cube) as we used in Section 4.1 for the regular and semiregular tilings.

▷ **Exercise 1.**   (a) Tetrahedron: four faces
(b) Octahedron: eight faces
(c) Icosahedron: 20 faces

(a)   (b) 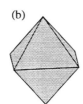 (c)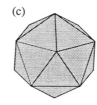

▷ **Exercise 2.**   Three squares; the cube (or hexahedron)

▷ **Exercise 3.**   Three pentagons; the dodecahedron

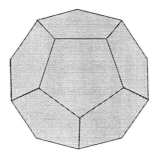

▷ **Exercise 4.**   Three hexagons tile the plane.

Students will find Exercise 5 easy but may have more difficulty with Exercise 6: reiterate that an antiprism has parallel and congruent top and bottom faces, joined by a band of equilateral triangles.

▷ **Exercise 5.** The tetrahedron is a triangular pyramid.

▷ **Exercise 6.** The octahedron is an antiprism with equilateral triangles for base and top.

▷ **Exercise 7.**

Platonic Solids

Polyhedron	Face Type	Symbol	f	e	v
Tetrahedron	triangle	3.3.3	4	6	4
Cube	square	4.4.4	6	12	8
Octahedron	triangle	3.3.3.3	8	12	6
Dodecahedron	pentagon	5.5.5	12	30	20
Icosahedron	triangle	3.3.3.3.3	20	30	12

If students miscounted in Exercise 7, they will, of course, have difficulty with Exercise 8: ask them to check their answers. Some will ask you if it's okay for a polyhedron to be its own dual.

▷ **Exercise 8.**

Duals

Polyhedron	Dual
Tetrahedron	Tetrahedron
Cube	Octahedron
Octahedron	Cube
Dodecahedron	Icosahedron
Icosahedron	Dodecahedron

Exercises 9 and 10 verify that the student understands the definition of a dual polyhedron. Exercise 11 is a bit of a trick: in Exercise 6 it was found that the octahedron is the antiprism with triangles for top and bottom faces, and the dual of the octahedron is the cube.

▷ **Exercise 9.** The dual of the right square pyramid with equilateral sides is a smaller upside down right square pyramid:

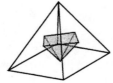

112

▷ **Exercise 10.** The dual of the right hexagonal prism with square sides is a double hexagonal pyramid:

▷ **Exercise 11.** This is the octahedron, and so its dual is the cube.

Some students have very accurate visualization abilities and will answer the questions of Exercises 12 and 13 effortlessly. Others may need to copy the nets, cut them out, and fold them up to see which form the desired polyhedron. One way to do Exercise 14 is to take the previously built models and cut them open to form a connected net.

▷ **Exercise 12.** No; yes; yes

▷ **Exercise 13.** Yes; no; yes

▷ **Exercise 14.** Nets for the octahedron, icosahedron, and dodecahedron can be formed by cutting open the models made earlier. There are many possible nets, but some are shown below:

Octahedron   Icosahedron   Dodecahedron

 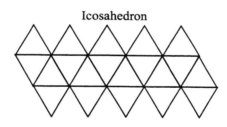 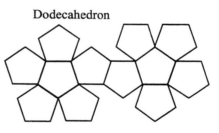

Schlegel diagrams can also be described as taking a wire-frame model with stretchy edges and stretching one face open to surround the others on a flat surface. In all cases, the outside edges of the Schlegel diagram form one of the faces of the polyhedron, and there should be the correct number of faces and the correct vertex configuration.

▷ **Exercise 15.** Draw the Schlegel diagram of the tetrahedron.

▷ **Exercise 16.** Draw the Schlegel diagram of the octahedron.

Exercises 17–22 are visualization problems. Some students can do these without effort. One can suggest that students who struggle with these take their models and dip them into a glass of water and consider the water line. Another alternative is to use clay and a knife.

▷ **Exercise 17.** Square

▷ **Exercise 18.** Rectangle

▷ **Exercise 19.** Triangle

▷ **Exercise 20.** Triangle

▷ **Exercise 21.** Rectangle

▷ **Exercise 22.** Triangle

▷ **Exercise 23.** Euler's formula should give $\chi = 2$ for each of the Platonic solids.

▷ **Exercise 24.** One face, two edges, and one vertex have been removed, so the net change in the Euler characteristic χ is 0.

▷ **Exercise 25.** One face, three edges, and two vertices have been removed, so the net change in the Euler characteristic χ is 0.

The most common mistake in doing Exercise 26 is to build a nonconvex polyhedron: one may not have six or more triangles meeting at any vertex. The names of these solids give some hint as to their structure: clearly a triangular dipyramid should be made of two triangular pyramids. The gyroelongated square dipyramid has two square pyramids joined by a belt of equilateral triangles. The snub disphenoid and triaugmented triangular prism are somewhat less transparent.

▷ **Exercise 26.** In building these, it helps to remember that at each vertex either three, four, or five triangles must meet and that not all vertices will have the same number of triangles. See the nets following.
(a) The triangular dipyramid: six equilateral triangles
(b) The pentagonal dipyramid: ten equilateral triangles
(c) The snub disphenoid or siamese dodecahedron: twelve equilateral triangles
(d) The triaugmented triangular prism: fourteen equilateral triangles
(e) The gyroelongated square dipyramid: sixteen equilateral triangles

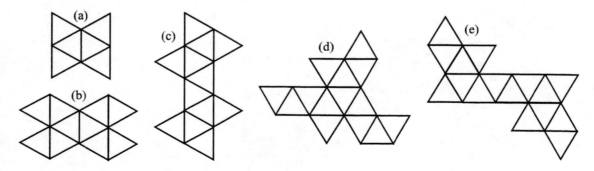

7.3. The Archimedean Solids

To build models of all of the Archimedean solids, one will need 200 triangles, 108 squares, 48 pentagons, 66 hexagons, six octagons, and 24 decagons. Templates for these can be found in the Appendix (Templates 9–12, 14, and 16). Alternatively, models can be built using the nets of Templates 34–38 enlarged and copied onto cardstock, cut out, and taped together. This section is modeled quite closely on the presentation of Section 4.1 of the semiregular or Archimedean tilings. The names of the polyhedra are given in the exercises, and this nomenclature will be explained in the following section. In addition to drawings of each of the Archimedean solids, these solutions also contain nets so one can see all of the polygons, but students are not asked to find these nets. Below is a table of all of the regular and semiregular convex polyhedra for reference, with names, Schläfli symbols, the number of polygons required with three, four, five, six, eight, or ten sides, the number of edges (e), and the number of vertices (v). We highly recommend the freeware software package KaleidoTile, by Jeffrey Weeks, but find physical models, though onerous to build, preferable.

Platonic and Archimedean Solids

Polyhedron	Symbol	3	4	5	6	8	10	e	v
Tetrahedron	3.3.3	4						6	4
Cube	4.4.4		6					12	8
Octahedron	3.3.3.3	8						12	6
Icosahedron	3.3.3.3.3	20						30	12
Dodecahedron	5.5.5			12				30	20
Truncated tetrahedron	3.6.6.	4			4			18	12
Truncated cube	3.8.8.	8			6			36	24
Cuboctahedron	3.4.3.4	8	6					24	12
Truncated octahedron	4.6.6		6		8			36	24
Rhombicuboctahedron	3.4.4.4	8	18					48	24
Great rhombicuboctahedron	4.6.8		12		8	6		72	48
Truncated dodecahedron	3.10.10	20					12	90	60
Icosidodecahedron	3.5.3.5	20		12				60	30
Truncated icosahedron	5.6.6			12	20			90	60
Rhombicosidodecahedron	3.4.5.4	20	30	12				120	60
Great rhombicosidodecahedron	4.6.10		30		20		12	180	120
Snub cube	3.3.3.3.4	32	6					60	24
Snub dodecahedron	3.3.3.3.5	80		12				150	60

Exercises 1–3 derive basic rules that the vertex configuration of any polyhedron must follow. These rules are quite similar to those found in Section 4.1 and will be used extensively in the exercises to eliminate possible vertex patterns for polyhedra.

▷ **Exercise 1.** Every semiregular polyhedron must have at least three polygons meeting at each vertex so that it doesn't make a two-dimensional figure, but no more than five so that the angles will add up to less than $360°$.

▷ **Exercise 2.** There are not four different types of polygons such that the sum of the angles is less than $360°$, since the four smallest vertex angles, all different, are $60° + 90° + 108° + 120° = 378° > 360°$. Therefore, if a polyhedron has four or more polygons meeting at a vertex, then some must be duplicates.

▷ **Exercise 3.** If one had a vertex configuration of the form $k.n.m$ where k is odd and $n \neq m$, then at vertex A of the k-sided polygon, we would have $k.n.m$. Vertex B shares the k- and n-sided faces, so we add an m-sided face, which is shared by vertex C, where we add an n-sided face and so on alternately. However, if k is odd, we cannot alternate n- and m-sided faces.

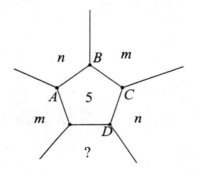

▷ **Exercise 4.** Build a snub cube, 3.3.3.3.4.

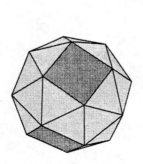 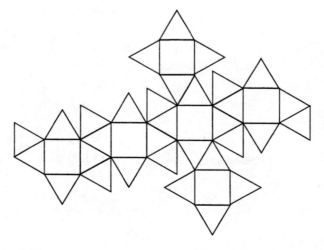

116

▷ **Exercise 5.** Build a snub dodecahedron, 3.3.3.3.5.

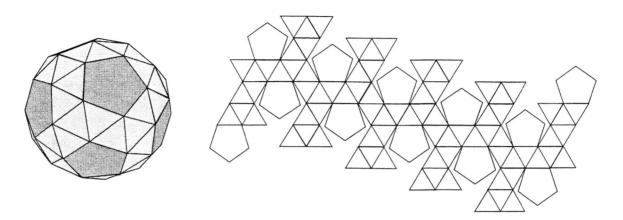

Like the tiling 3.3.3.3.6, the snub cube and the snub dodecahedron occur in two enantiomorphic forms, which are related to each other by reflection. The snub cubes are illustrated below. These can be thought of as left-handed and right-handed. We do not usually ask our students to distinguish between these.

▷ **Exercise 6.** At any vertex of the top n-gon, one has two triangles with edges shared with the adjacent edges of the n-gon. A third triangle, with one edge shared with the bottom n-gon, meets these two triangles, as shown below:

▷ **Exercise 7.** Build a cuboctahedron, 3.4.3.4.

 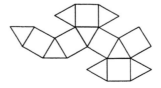

117

▷ **Exercise 8.** Build an icosidodecahedron (sometimes spelled "icosadodecahedron"), 3.5.3.5.

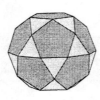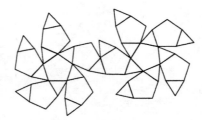

▷ **Exercise 9.** The pattern 3.6.3.6 gives a tiling of the plane.

▷ **Exercise 10.** The vertex configurations 3.4.3.5, 3.4.3.6, and 3.5.3.6 violate Rule 5.

▷ **Exercise 11.** The configuration 3.5.5 can be rewritten as 5.3.5, which violates Rule 4. Since 3.n.n for n odd can be rewritten as n.3.n, it also violates Rule 4 if $n \neq 3$.

▷ **Exercise 12.** Build a truncated tetrahedron, 3.6.6.

▷ **Exercise 13.** Build a truncated cube, 3.8.8.

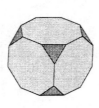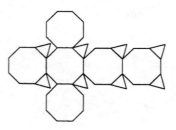

▷ **Exercise 14.** Build a truncated dodecahedron, 3.10.10.

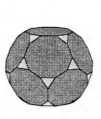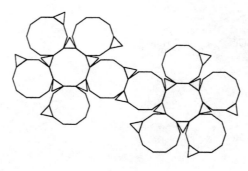

▷ **Exercise 15.** Build a rhombicuboctahedron, 3.4.4.4.

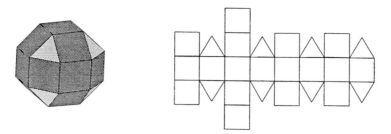

In Exercise 15, note that there is another polyhedron, called the pseudorhombicubocta-hedron, or Miller's solid, which also has Schläfli symbol 3.4.4.4 and is pictured below. This can be built by taking the top cap of the rhombicuboctahedron and rotating it by 45°. Some students may build this polyhedron instead. These are distinct, since the rhombicuboctahedron clearly has a mirror plane (as we will see in Section 8.1) missing in the pseudorhombicuboctahedron, and it is also generated by truncation of the cuboctahedron (as will be seen in Section 7.4). Technically, the pseudorhombicuboctahedron is not semiregular, since a rotation by 90° about the center of certain of the square faces does not return the figure to itself.

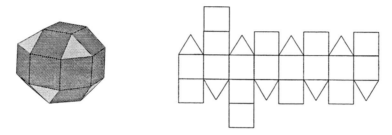

▷ **Exercise 16.** Patterns such as 3.4.4.5 and 3.4.4.6 violate Rule 5.

▷ **Exercise 17.** Rhombicosidodecahedron (sometimes spelled "rhombicosadodecahedron"), 3.4.5.4.

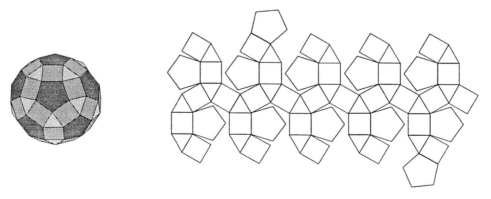

▷ **Exercise 18.** The patterns $3.n.4.n$ for $n > 5$ will give an angle sum of at least $60° + 120° + 90° + 120° > 360°$, and $3.4.n.4$ for $n > 5$ gives an angle sum of at least $60° + 90° + 120° + 90° \geq 360°$. Thus neither can form a semiregular solid.

▷ **Exercise 19.** The patterns $4.4.n.n$ and $4.4.n.m$ for $n, m > 4$ will have an angle sum of at least $90° + 90° + 108° + 108° > 360°$.

▷ **Exercise 20.** The pattern 4.n.n for n > 4 and odd can be rewritten as n.4.n, which violates Rule 4.

▷ **Exercise 21.** Build a truncated octahedron, 4.6.6.

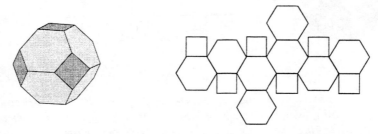

▷ **Exercise 22.** 4.8.8 forms a tiling and 4.n.n for n > 8 and n even will have an angle sum of more than 360°.

▷ **Exercise 23.** 4.n.m for n ≠ m and either n or m odd can be rewritten as either n.m.4 (if n is odd) or m.4.n (if m is odd), both of which violate Rule 4.

▷ **Exercise 24.** Build a great rhombicuboctahedron, 4.6.8 (also called the rhombitruncated cuboctahedron).

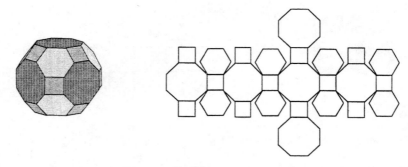

▷ **Exercise 25.** Build a great rhombicosidodecahedron, 4.6.10 (also called the rhombitruncated icosidodecahedron).

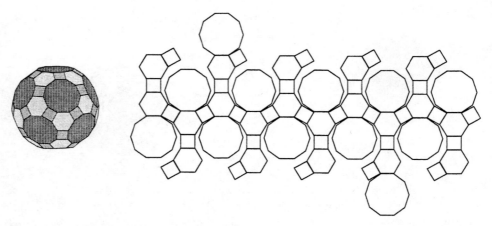

▷ **Exercise 26.** 4.6.12 gives a tiling of the plane, and 4.8.10 has an angle sum of more than 360°.

120

Note that the truncated icosahedron displays the pattern not only of a soccer ball, but also of the buckminsterfullerene molecule.

▷ **Exercise 27.** Build a truncated icosahedron, 5.6.6.

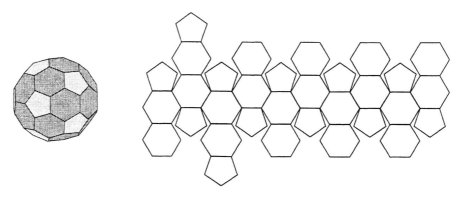

▷ **Exercise 28.** 5.n.n for $n > 6$ will have an angle sum of more than 360°.

7.4. Polyhedral Transformations

The nomenclature for the Archimedean solids was devised by Kepler, and this section will give some justification for this and will explicate how the various polyhedra are related.

In Exercise 1, make sure that the cube is cut by planes perpendicular to the axis of symmetry that runs from the vertex to the vertex diametrically opposite, so that the cross-sections formed by the cut are equilateral triangles. Also make sure that the cuts at each vertex are the same depth. The freeware program Kaleidotile, by Jeffrey Weeks, is excellent for demonstrating the truncations, though it does not display the snub polyhedra.

▷ **Exercise 1.** Make a cube out of clay, and perform the series of truncations.

▷ **Exercise 2.** In truncating the vertices of an octahedron, squares will replace the vertices and hexagons replace the faces. At first these will be irregular hexagons, but as the squares enlarge, the hexagons become regular.

▷ **Exercise 3.** Halfway through the truncation process a truncated octahedron is formed. When the slices meet, a cuboctahedron is formed.

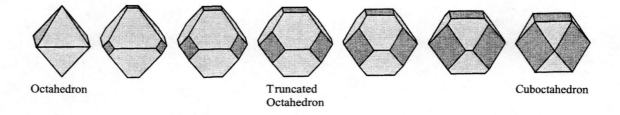

Octahedron   Truncated   Cuboctahedron
                        Octahedron

Ideally, students will try to understand how each vertex, edge, and face is formed from the original octahedron in Exercise 4, rather than merely counting them on a model. Exercises 6, 8, 10, 13, 15, and 17 are quite similar, so some time spent explaining Exercise 4 will help in these later exercises.

▷ **Exercise 4.** For the truncated octahedron, each of the six vertices of the octahedron gives four new vertices, so $v = 24$. Each vertex of the original octahedron gives four new edges in addition to the 12 original ones, so $e = 36$. We have the eight original faces plus six new ones replacing the original vertices, so $f = 14$. For the cuboctahedron, the vertices of the truncated octahedron merge in pairs, so $v = 12$. The original edges of the octahedron disappear, so $e = 24$, but the same number of faces shows as for the truncated octahedron, so $f = 14$.

▷ **Exercise 5.** Halfway through the truncation process a truncated tetrahedron is formed, and when the slices meet an octahedron is formed.

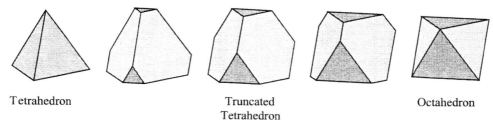

Tetrahedron   Truncated   Octahedron
                       Tetrahedron

▷ **Exercise 6.** For the truncated tetrahedron, each of the four vertices of the tetrahedron gives three new vertices, so $v = 12$. Each vertex of the original tetrahedron gives three new edges in addition to the six original ones, so $e = 18$. We have the four original faces plus four new ones replacing the original vertices, so $f = 8$. For the octahedron, the vertices of the truncated tetrahedron merge in pairs, so $v = 6$. The original edges of the tetrahedron disappear, so $e = 12$, but the same number of faces shows as for the truncated tetrahedron, so $f = 8$.

▷ **Exercise 7.** Halfway through the truncation process a truncated dodecahedron is formed, and when the slices meet an icosidodecahedron is formed.

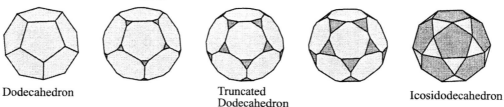

Dodecahedron   Truncated   Icosidodecahedron
                        Dodecahedron

▷ **Exercise 8.** For the truncated dodecahedron, each of the 20 vertices of the dodecahedron gives three new vertices, so $v = 60$. Each vertex of the original dodecahedron gives three new edges in addition to the 30 original ones, so $e = 90$. We have the 12 original faces plus 20 new ones replacing the original vertices, so $f = 32$. For the icosidodecahedron, the vertices of the truncated dodecahedron merge in pairs, so $v = 30$. The original edges of the dodecahedron disappear, so $e = 60$, but the same number of faces shows as for the truncated icosahedron, so $f = 32$.

▷ **Exercise 9.** Halfway through the truncation process a truncated icosahedron is formed and when the slices meet an icosidodecahedron is formed.

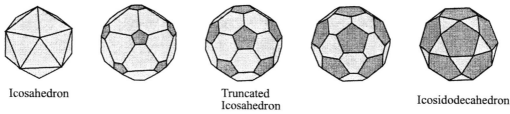

Icosahedron   Truncated   Icosidodecahedron
                       Icosahedron

▷ **Exercise 10.** For the truncated icosahedron, each of the 12 vertices of the icosahedron gives five new vertices, so $v = 60$. Each vertex of the original icosahedron gives five new edges in addition to the 30 original ones, so $e = 90$. We have the 20 original faces plus 12 new ones replacing the original vertices, so $f = 32$. For the icosidodecahedron, the vertices of the truncated icosahedron merge in pairs, so $v = 30$. The original edges of the icosahedron disappear, so $e = 60$, but the same number of faces shows as for the truncated icosahedron, so $f = 32$.

▷ **Exercise 11.** The cuboctahedron is halfway between the octahedron and the cube, and the icosidodecahedron is halfway between the icosahedron and the dodecahedron. The names are thus compounds of the two Platonic solids involved.

▷ **Exercise 12.** dodecahedron ⟷ truncated dodecahedron ⟷ icosidodecahedron ⟷ truncated icosahedron ⟷ icosahedron

> *Actually, truncating the vertices of a cuboctahedron does not give a semiregular polyhedron, but rather the polyhedron shown below on the right, in which the cuts form rectangles rather than squares. Inflating these rectangles into squares gives the great rhombicuboctahedron, also known as the rhombitruncated cuboctahedron.*

▷ **Exercise 13.** Each of the 12 vertices of the cuboctahedron is replaced by four, so the great rhombicuboctahedron has $v = 48$. The great rhombicuboctahedron has the 24 edges of the cuboctahedron, plus four more for each of the original vertices, so $e = 72$. It has faces corresponding to each of the 14 faces of the cuboctahedron, plus one for each of 12 the original vertices, so $f = 26$.

▷ **Exercise 14.** When the squares meet, the hexagons become triangles and the octagons become squares, forming the rhombicuboctahedron.

▷ **Exercise 15.** The rhombicuboctahedron has $v = 24$, $e = 48$, and $f = 26$.

> *Again, truncating the vertices of the icosidodecahedron would give rectangles, instead of squares, but if these are slightly inflated, one gets the semiregular solid known as the great rhombicosidodecahedron, or rhombitruncated icosidodecahedron.*

▷ **Exercise 16.** icosidodecahedron ⟷ great rhombicosidodecahedron ⟷ rhombicosidodecahedron

Icosidodecahedron   Great   Rhombicosadodecahedron
                        Rhombicosadodecahedron

▷ **Exercise 17.** For the great rhombicosidodecahedron, $v = 120$, $e = 180$, and $f = 62$. For the rhombicosidodecahedron, $v = 60$, $e = 120$, and $f = 62$.

▷ **Exercise 18.** $f = 12 + 12 \cdot 5 + 20 = 92$, $v = 12 \cdot 5 = 60$, so $e = 150$

▷ **Exercise 19.** When you snub a tetrahedron, an icosahedron is formed.

7.5. Models of Polyhedra

There are no exercises in Section 7.5, but rather technical details on a variety of types of polyhedral models. Cardboard models are inexpensive and easy to build. For the purposes of a physical model to study in the other sections of this chapter, thin cardstock and tape work fine, but if one wants more permanent models, one should use heavier acid-free bristol board and go to the trouble of taping on the inside of the polyhedra or gluing the edges together. This isn't too much more trouble until the last few pieces. The books by Magnus Wenninger (we reference only the one that contains the Platonic and Archimedean solids) show such cardboard models brought to their highest level. Wire-frame models are more durable and beautiful, but assume that one knows how to solder. Low-budget equivalents can be made using drinking straws and string and are useful for investigating the rigidity of polyhedra. The origami models are perhaps the most satisfying, and we have found that many students enjoy making these. We have included patterns for some of the Platonic solids, using a variety of origami styles. We have tried to use the traditional origami notation, so that students can try to build the models they can find in other text devoted exclusively to origami. We particularly recommend the book by Tomoko Fusé. The plaited polyhedra are fun to braid. Templates 39 and 40 contain the patterns for the plaited polyhedra from the text enlarged to a useful size. The book by Hilton and Pedersen is very enjoyable for all levels of students and investigates the mathematics of folding strips of paper. It contains other patterns for plaited polyhedra. The article by Alexander Graham Bell remains quite readable and is interesting as a period piece immediately preceding the flight of the Wright brothers. The kites are easy to build and sometimes even fly.

7.6. Infinite Polyhedra

There is, of course, no one correct answer for Exercise 1, but in all cases the student should end up with an infinite polyhedron with five squares meeting at each vertex. One of the purposes of this section is to show that the Schläfli notation, which has performed so well up to now (with the exception of the pseudorhombicuboctahedron), is useless for infinite ~polyhedra.

▷ **Exercise 1.**

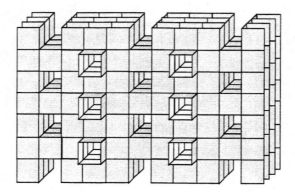

▷ **Exercise 2.** This polyhedron can be denoted as 6.6.6.6. The spaces enclosed by the polyhedron and outside the polyhedron are identical. Below on the left is a section of truncated octahedra stacked up, and on the right, a piece of the infinite regular polyhedron.

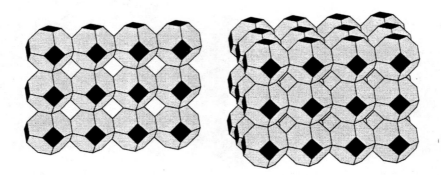

126

▷ **Exercise 3.** This polyhedron can be denoted by 6.6.6.6.6.6. The spaces enclosed by the polyhedron and outside the polyhedron are identical. Below on the left is a single layer of truncated tetrahedra, and on the -right, another layer of reversed truncated tetrahedra is added. This process is repeated forever.

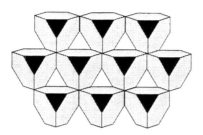 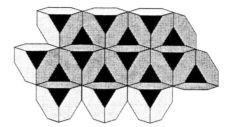

▷ **Exercise 4.** The infinite square cylinder can be denoted by 4.4.4.4. The spaces enclosed by the polyhedron and outside the polyhedron are clearly not identical.

▷ **Exercise 5.** This polyhedron (a finite section is shown below) can also be denoted by 4.4.4.4.

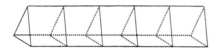

▷ **Exercise 6.** This polyhedron (a finite section is shown below) can also be denoted by 4.4.4.4.

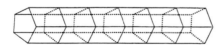

▷ **Exercise 7.** Below is a section of a cylindrical antiprismatic polyhedron built by stacking up four square antiprisms. This would be denoted $3.3.3.3.3.3 = 3^6$.

▷ **Exercise 8.**   Below is a section of another cylindrical polyhedron, this one built by stacking up alternately square prisms and square antiprisms. This would be denoted $3.3.3.4.4 = 3^34^2$.

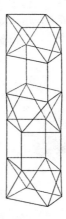

▷ **Exercise 9.**   Below is a net for the cylindrical square antiprismatic polyhedron.

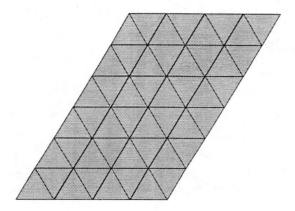

▷ **Exercise 10.**   The triangulated pentagonal cylinder would be denoted $3.3.3.3.3.3 = 3^6$. Note that a slight twist is necessary so that the triangles match up edge to edge.

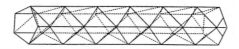

▷ **Exercise 11.**   This cylindrical polyhedron is made by alternating strips of squares and triangles. This would be denoted $3.3.3.4.4 = 3^34^2$.

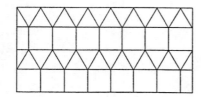
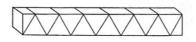

▷ **Exercise 12.**   Cut out the pattern of triangles and tape the sides together. This would be denoted $3.3.3.3.3.3 = 3^6$.

▷ **Exercise 13.** One can replace all the squares in the tiling 4.6.12 by tunnels to get a double-sided polyhedron 4.4.6.12; all the hexagons by tunnels to get 4.4.4.12; or all the dodecagons to get 4.4.4.6.

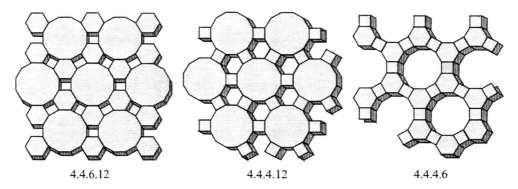

4.4.6.12   4.4.4.12   4.4.4.6

▷ **Exercise 14.**

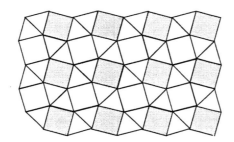

▷ **Exercise 15.**

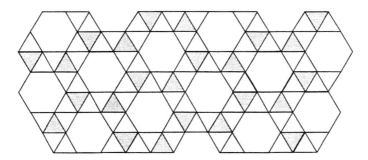

▷ **Exercise 16.** This is the multiple-layered infinite polyhedron built from the tiling 4.8.8 by deleting half of the octagons and building tunnels alternately to the layer above and the layer below.

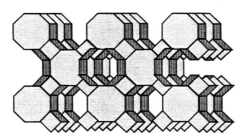

▷ **Exercise 17.**

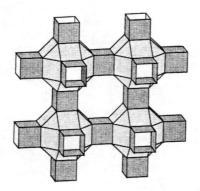

▷ **Exercise 18.** Only the truncated octahedron close-packs by itself:

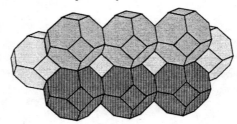

Truncated
Octahedron

▷ **Exercise 19.** To close-pack tetrahedra and octahedra, you will need two tetrahedra for every octahedron. Join two tetrahedra and an octahedron as shown below, and then stack these assemblies.

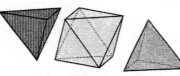

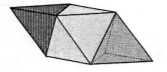

Two Tetrahedra and an Octahedron

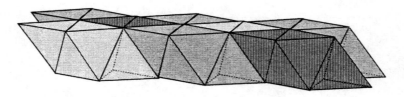

▷ **Exercise 20.** To close-pack octahedra and truncated cubes, you will need equal numbers of both. The octahedra fill the spaces left between the truncated cubes.

Octahedron

Truncated Cube

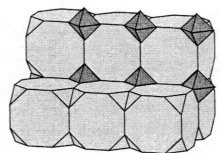

130

▷ **Exercise 21.** To close-pack rhombicuboctahedra, tetrahedra, and cubes you will need as many cubes as rhombicuboctahedra and twice as many tetrahedra. First stack the rhombicuboctahedra, and then fill the gaps with the cubes, as shown in the partially complete center illustration. Finally, fill in the corners with the tetrahedra, as shown on the right.

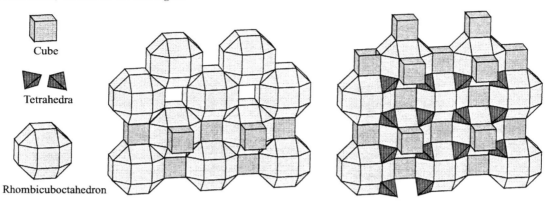

Cube

Tetrahedra

Rhombicuboctahedron

▷ **Exercise 22.** To close-pack cuboctahedra, truncated octahedra, and truncated tetrahedra, you will need as many cuboctahedra as truncated octahedra and twice as many truncated tetrahedra.

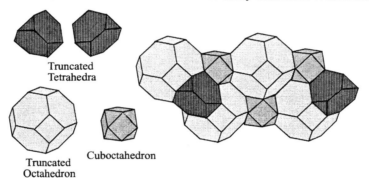

Truncated
Tetrahedra

Truncated
Octahedron

Cuboctahedron

Chapter 8. Three-Dimensional Symmetry

★ ★ **8.1. Symmetries of Polyhedra**
Dependencies: Chapter 7.1, 7.2, 7.3, 7.6
References: Chapter 5.2, 5.3

- Axes of rotation
- Planes of reflection
- Isometries in three dimensions
- Rotary reflection
- Translation
- Glide reflection
- Screw rotation

★ ★ ★ **8.2. Three-Dimensional Kaleidoscopes**
Dependencies: Chapter 7.2, 8.1
References: Chapter 5.2, 5.3, 7.1, 7.3

- Orthoschemes for the cube, octahedron, and tetrahedron

In this chapter, we investigate symmetries in three dimensions, building on the experiences in two dimensions in Chapter 5 and the examples of three-dimensional objects constructed in Chapter 7. While these isometries do form a group, we have chosen not to explore the group structure. There are seven isometries in three-dimensional space. We met five of these (the identity, rotation, reflection, translation, and glide reflection) in Chapter 5, and the two others particular to dimensions greater than two (rotary reflection, screw rotation) are exemplified in some of the polyhedral examples of Chapter 7. It is shown that any isometry can be expressed as a composition of reflections.

In Section 8.2, we apply the notion of generating a polyhedron by reflections of a fundamental region (or orthoscheme) to build what might be called a three-dimensional kaleidoscope: a wedge built of mirrors. Looking into the wedge generates the illusion of looking at the whole polyhedron. Figuring out how the orthoscheme is formed requires a thorough understanding of the reflection planes, their intersections, and many applications of the Pythagorean Theorem.

8.1. Symmetries of Polyhedra

In order to do the problems of this section, it is helpful to have models of the cube, tetrahedron, octahedron, dodecahedron, and icosahedron. Exercises 1–5 discuss the rotation axes for the tetrahedron and the cube in detail, and in Exercise 6 the students are expected to use the experience gained to repeat the process of determining rotation axes and their order for the other Platonic solids. From Chapter 5, students are familiar with centers of rotation in the plane. One may wish to discuss how in three dimensions one rotates around a line, like an axle or hinge, perhaps demonstrating with a globe. Thus, instead of using a point as the center of rotation, one looks for a line. This line does not move under the rotation, but spins in place.

▷ **Exercise 1.** The tetrahedron has three more 3-fold axes of rotation, for a total of four: one for each vertex.

▷ **Exercise 2.** The tetrahedron has two more 2-fold axes of rotation, for a total of three: one for each pair of edges.

▷ **Exercise 3.** The cube has two other 4-fold axes, for a total of three: one for each pair of opposite faces.

▷ **Exercise 4.** This is a 3-fold axis of the cube, with a rotation angle of 120°. There are three other such axes, for a total of four: one for each pair of diametrically opposed vertices.

▷ **Exercise 5.** This is a 2-fold axis of the cube, with a rotation angle of 180°. There are five other such axes, for a total of six: one for each pair of opposite edges.

The answers for the first two rows of the table of Exercise 6 have already been found in the preceding exercises, and students should at this point be comfortable with the process of searching for axes of rotation and identifying their order. Encourage the use of models for this. Remind them that an axis of rotation can pass through a vertex, an edge (but then the axis can only pass through the midpoint of the edge), or a face (and in this case the axis will pass through the center of the face). Once the table is completed, the similarities of the rotations for dual polyhedra is striking. This will be discussed in Exercise 10. If students mention it now, one can ask them to recall the relationship between the cube and the octahedron and between the icosahedron and the dodecahedron.

▷ **Exercise 6.**

Rotations of Platonic Solids

Polygon	2-Fold Axes	3-Fold Axes	4-Fold Axes	5-Fold Axes
Tetrahedron	3	4	0	0
Cube	6	4	3	0
Octahedron	6	4	3	0
Dodecahedron	15	10	0	6
Icosahedron	15	10	0	6

In Exercises 7–10, we explore planes of reflection, first for the tetrahedron and the cube, and then for the other Platonic solids. From Chapter 5, students are familiar with lines of reflection in the plane. One may wish to discuss how in three dimensions one reflects across a plane, like a mirror. Thus, instead of using a line of reflection or mirror line, one looks for a mirror plane. This plane does not move under the reflection, but everything else reverses across it.

▷ **Exercise 7.** The tetrahedron has five other planes of reflection, for a total of six: one for each edge.

▷ **Exercise 8.** The cube has nine mirror planes: three of the first type pictured parallel to each pair of opposite faces, and six of the second type, one for each pair of diametrically opposed edges.

The answers for the first two rows of the table of Exercise 9 have already been found in Exercises 7 and 8, so one needs only to repeat the process of identifying mirror planes for the other Platonic solids. Again, the similarities for dual polyhedra are striking.

▷ **Exercise 9.**

Reflections of Platonic Solids

Polygon	Mirror Planes
Tetrahedron	6
Cube	9
Octahedron	9
Dodecahedron	15
Icosahedron	15

At this point, students should have noticed that dual polyhedra have the same numbers of rotations and reflections. One can refer them to the illustration of the nested dual cube and octahedron (page 218 of the text) and ask them to locate the rotation axes and reflection planes in the picture. With this hint, most students will realize that the duals have not only the same number of rotation axes and mirror planes, but in fact have exactly the same rotation axes and mirror planes when one is nested inside the other in the prescribed manner. Reinforce the idea that they are making significant mathematical discoveries on their own.

▷ **Exercise 10.** Dual polyhedra have the same symmetries.

Ideally, one would also have on hand models of the truncated Platonic solids, cubocta-hedron, and icosidodecahedron for Exercises 11 and 12. However, at this point students should be able to figure out the isometries by visualizing from a clear drawing (for example, the drawings on pages 231 and 232 of the text).

▷ **Exercise 11.** Truncated forms have the same symmetries as the parent polyhedra.

▷ **Exercise 12.** The cuboctahedron has the same symmetries as the cube and the octahedron. The icosi-dodecahedron has the same symmetries as the icosahedron and the dodecahedron.

Since the snub forms are more difficult to visualize than the truncated forms, for Exercise 13 it is very helpful to have models on hand.

▷ **Exercise 13.** The snub cube has the same rotational symmetries as the cube but does not have any reflectional symmetry. The snub dodecahedron has the same rotational symmetries as the dodecahedron but does not have any reflectional symmetry.

The rotary reflection is an isometry that does not exist in two dimensions. Again, demon-strating with a model may be helpful. In Exercise 14, one might also point out that in the example above the exercise, the three points on the top disc are spaced 120° from each other, and the angle of the rotary reflection is 60°. Then recall that the interior angle for a pentagon is 72°.

▷ **Exercise 14.** The plane of reflection is parallel to both the base and the top face and lies midway between the two. The axis of rotation is perpendicular to this plane and runs through the center of the base and top. The angle of rotation is $36° = \frac{360°/5}{2}$.

To visualize translations and glide reflections in three dimensions, it would be helpful to have models of some of the infinite polyhedra, though one can make do with the drawings of Section 7.6 in the text. In Section 5.3, we experimented with translations and glide reflections in a single direction, generating frieze patterns. In Section 5.4, we saw that translations and glide reflections in two directions gave rise to wallpaper patterns covering the plane. The infinite polyhedron illustrated on page 254 of the text has translations in three directions.

▷ **Exercise 15.** All of the double-sided infinite polyhedra (such as the one illustrated on page 258 of the text) have translations in two directions.

▷ **Exercise 16.** Some of the double-sided infinite polyhedra have glide reflections (including the one shown on page 258 of the text), as does this infinite polyhedron:

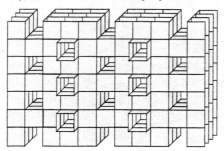

We have found that students have more trouble visualizing the screw rotation, so we have included Exercises 17 and 18, giving two different ways of building a model of the tetrahelix. Once either of the models is built, it is easy to see the action of the screw rotation. If students are not familiar with the "mountain fold"-"valley fold" terminology from origami, introduce it quickly, explaining that a mountain fold forms a ridge facing you, while a valley fold forms a crease or groove away from you. Template 41 repeats Exercises 17 and 18 with larger drawings, which can be photocopied for the class.

▷ **Exercise 17.** Build the model of the tetrahelix as directed. (See Template 41.)

▷ **Exercise 18.** Build the model of the tetrahelix as directed. (See Template 41.)

The remainder of this section explores the idea of breaking down any isometry into a composition of reflections. This should help consolidate the student's knowledge of the seven three-dimensional isometries. The text explores two of the more basic isometries: translation and rotation. Since the other isometries were described in terms of these, it is then easy to determine how any isometry can be rewritten as some number of reflections.

▷ **Exercise 19.** We have shown that rotation and translation can each be expressed as the composition of two reflections. The identity can be thought of as a reflection in zero planes or as two reflections in the same plane (so that everything is reflected and then reflected right back into its original position). Rotary reflection is the composition of a rotation and a reflection, and so is the result of three reflections (two for the rotation and then the reflection). Glide reflection can be expressed as a reflection followed by a translation and so can be written as three reflections. Screw rotation is a rotation followed by a translation and so can be written as four reflections (two for the rotation and then two for the translation).

Recall that the text states that any isometry of a finite polyhedron contains at least one fixed point, and that translation, glide reflection, and screw rotation acted on certain infinite polyhedra. Thus, the isometries in question in Exercise 20 are the identity, reflection, rotation, and rotary reflection. Then apply the findings of Exercise 19.

▷ **Exercise 20.** The symmetries with at least one fixed point are the identity (zero reflections), reflection, rotation (two reflections), and rotary reflection (three reflections).

8.2. Three-Dimensional Kaleidoscopes

The computations of this section may at times be a bit tedious, but they are well worth the trouble if you have capable students. In building the mirrored orthoschemes, measure angles and lengths very carefully and tape as neatly as possible. Foamcore makes a more satisfactory model, but the edges should be mitered to fit nicely, and in order to calculate the dihedral angles one would require a knowledge of trigonometry, so we consciously decided to omit those calculations. Nets for the orthoschemes are provided in Templates 42–44 in the Appendix, for those who wish to skip all the calculations. I have a perfectly beautiful polished steel orthoscheme for a Kepler star polyhedron (a stellated dodecahedron), sold as Pentakis: Sixtyfold Kaleidoscope, made and copyrighted by Caspar Schwabe of Switzerland, who has also built similar large structures for museum displays.

A cube placed in the mirror assembly as in the text should reflect and show another larger cube, which appears to be made of eight of the small cubes:

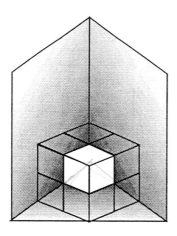

▷ **Exercise 1.** You should see what appears to be an octahedron.

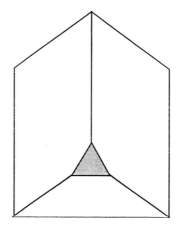
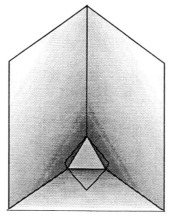

▷ **Exercise 2.** You should see what appears to be a cuboctahedron.

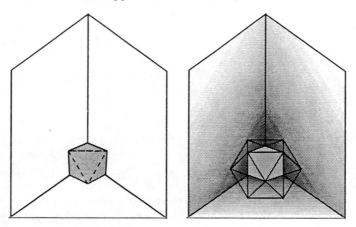

In Exercises 3–5, we derive the necessary measurements for the orthoscheme, or basic reflecting building block, for the cube. Each exercise depends on the results of the previous one, so one must take care.

▷ **Exercise 3.** The plane cuts the 1 by 1 cube in half. Applying the Pythagorean Theorem, we find that the diagonal edge has length $\sqrt{2}$.

▷ **Exercise 4.** This plane cuts the rear 1 by 1 square shown above in Exercise 3 in half along the diagonal, which has length $\sqrt{2}$. It also cuts the front diagonal 1 by $\sqrt{2}$ rectangular face in two, and we apply the Pythagorean Theorem again to find that this edge has length $\sqrt{3}$.

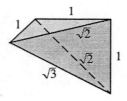

▷ **Exercise 5.** The net summarizes and confirms the calculations of Exercises 3 and 4.

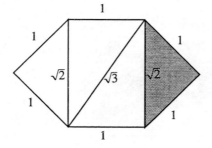

In Exercises 6–8, we build and view the completed orthoscheme. Template 42 for the cubic orthoscheme can be found in the Appendix. The instructions call for building a small cardboard orthoscheme and a larger similar mirrored one. For the mirrored wedge, leave off the face shaded in the solution for Exercise 5 for the viewing window. An interesting variation is to build the large mirrored orthoscheme but cut off the tip (cut along the dotted lines on the template). If one covers the small aperture thus created by colored translucent paper or film, one gets the illusion of an entire cube floating at the bottom of the wedge.

▷ **Exercise 6.** Build the orthoscheme out of cardboard.

▷ **Exercise 7.** Build the orthoscheme out of mirrors, omitting the face shaded in the net shown in the solution for Exercise 5.

▷ **Exercise 8.** You should see a three-dimensional cube.

Exercises 9–15 develop the orthoscheme for the octahedron. The process parallels that for the cube, but more of the steps are left to the student to figure out. In the text, it was noted that the reflection planes divide the cube into 48 congruent wedges. Since the octahedron is the dual of the cube and therefore has the same reflection planes, it is also divided into 48 wedges. A model may help to visualize the intersections of the planes. One can also use Template 43 of the Appendix.

▷ **Exercise 9.** The reflection planes cut the octahedron into 48 congruent wedges.

▷ **Exercise 10.** As in Chapter 8.1, these dual polyhedra have the same symmetries.

▷ **Exercise 11.** Note that either diagonal of the central square in the octagon has length $\sqrt{2}$ so that the interior edges of this wedge have lengths $\frac{\sqrt{2}}{2}$.

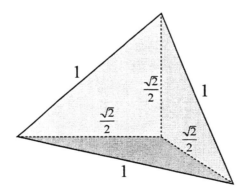

▷ **Exercise 12.** The base of this wedge is one half of the isosceles right triangle with legs $\frac{\sqrt{2}}{2}$ and hypotenuse 1 shown as the base of the wedge of Exercise 11. Therefore, the new base is an isosceles right triangle with legs $\frac{1}{2}$ and thus hypotenuse $\frac{1}{\sqrt{2}} = \frac{\sqrt{2}}{2}$. The right wall we already know to have sides $\frac{\sqrt{2}}{2}$-$\frac{\sqrt{2}}{2}$-1, and the left wall has two known sides: $\frac{1}{2}$ and $\frac{\sqrt{2}}{2}$. Applying the Pythagorean Theorem, we find that the third edge of the left wall (along the outside) has length $\frac{\sqrt{3}}{2}$. See the illustration on the following page.

139

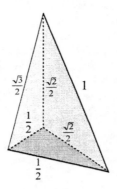

▷ **Exercise 13.** The base of this wedge is the same as the one of Exercise 12, and so has sides $\frac{1}{2}$-$\frac{1}{2}$-$\frac{\sqrt{2}}{2}$. Now consider the equilateral triangle ABC shown below on the left. This forms the front face of the octahedron and each side has length 1. It is cut by the planes along the lines AD and CE as shown. We wish to find the lengths of the edges CF and DF, since the front face of this wedge is $\triangle CDF$. Note that $\triangle CDF$ is similar to $\triangle ADB$, and from our previous calculations we know that $AB = 1$, $BD = CD = \frac{1}{2}$, and $AD = \frac{\sqrt{3}}{2}$. Therefore, $\frac{CF}{AB} = \frac{CD}{AD}$, so $\frac{CF}{1} = \frac{1/2}{\sqrt{3}/2}$ and so $CF = \frac{1}{\sqrt{3}} = \frac{\sqrt{3}}{3}$. Similarly, $\frac{DF}{DB} = \frac{CD}{AD}$, so $\frac{DF}{1/2} = \frac{1/2}{\sqrt{3}/2}$, so $DF = \frac{1}{2\sqrt{3}} = \frac{\sqrt{3}}{6}$. The left wall of the wedge is thus found to be a right triangle with one leg of length $\frac{\sqrt{3}}{6}$ and hypotenuse $\frac{1}{2}$. Using the Pythagorean Theorem, we find that the last leg of this triangle has length $\frac{1}{\sqrt{6}} = \frac{\sqrt{6}}{6}$.

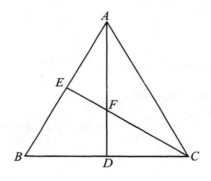

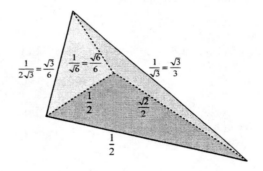

▷ **Exercise 14.** Laying out the walls of the wedge calculated in Exercise 13, we can get the net shown below. Obviously, there are other ways of unfolding, but any solutions will involve the same four triangles.

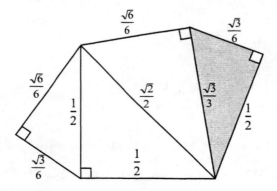

▷ **Exercise 15.** You should see an octahedron.

140

In Exercises 16–21, we build an orthoscheme for the tetrahedron. See also Template 44 of the Appendix.

▷ **Exercise 16.** The vertical planes cut the tetrahedron into six pieces.

▷ **Exercise 17.** The floor of the wedge is the same as the floor of the wedge pictured in the text, and so is a triangle with sides $\frac{1}{2}$, $\frac{\sqrt{3}}{3}$, and $\frac{\sqrt{3}}{6}$. Picture the vertical plane that slices through the rear vertex and the front face of the tetrahedron. This is pictured on the left as triangle ABC, and from our previous computations we know that $AB = 1$, $BC = AC = \frac{\sqrt{3}}{2}$. This triangle is cut by the vertical plane along edge AE, which has been given to have length $AE = \frac{\sqrt{6}}{3}$ and we also know that $CE = \frac{\sqrt{3}}{6}$. The newest plane cuts this triangle along the dotted line CD and we need to find CF and EF. Note that CD is perpendicular to AB, and D is the midpoint of AB. Therefore $AD = BD = \frac{1}{2}$, and we compute, using the Pythagorean Theorem, $CD = \frac{\sqrt{2}}{2}$. Also CD bisects $\angle BCA$. Therefore, $\triangle CEF$ is similar to $\triangle CDB$. Thus, $\frac{EF}{BD} = \frac{CE}{CD}$, so $\frac{EF}{1/2} = \frac{\sqrt{3}/6}{\sqrt{2}/2}$, and thus $EF = \frac{\sqrt{3}}{6\sqrt{2}} = \frac{\sqrt{6}}{12}$. Similarly, $\frac{CF}{BC} = \frac{CE}{CD}$, so $\frac{CF}{\sqrt{3}/2} = \frac{\sqrt{3}/6}{\sqrt{2}/2}$, and thus $CF = \frac{1}{2\sqrt{2}} = \frac{\sqrt{2}}{4}$. The remaining edge, formed along the outer wall of the left edge of the wedge, is computed by noting that this is the hypotenuse of a right triangle with edges $\frac{\sqrt{3}}{3}$ and $\frac{\sqrt{6}}{12}$, and so has length $\sqrt{\frac{3}{8}} = \frac{\sqrt{6}}{4}$.

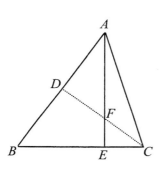
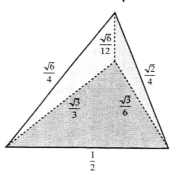

▷ **Exercise 18.**

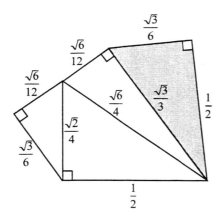

▷ **Exercise 19.** Build the orthoscheme out of cardboard.

▷ **Exercise 20.** Build the orthoscheme out of mirrors, omitting the face shaded in the net for the solution for Exercise 19.

▷ **Exercise 21.** You should see a tetrahedron.

141

Chapter 9. Spiral Growth

★ **9.1. Spirals and Helices**
  Dependencies: None
  References: Chapter 3.2 (some facts about the golden triangle and the golden ratio)

- Archimedean spirals
- Gnomons
- Gnomonic growth
- Golden spiral and Fibonacci numbers
- Polar coordinates
- Other spirals: hyperbolic, elliptic, and logarithmic
- Helices

★ **9.2. Fibonacci Numbers and Phyllotaxis**
  Dependencies: None
  References: Chapter 9.1

- Fibonacci numbers
- Phyllotaxis

This chapter is independent of the preceding chapters, except for a few facts about the golden ratio from Section 3.2, which could be quickly gone over in class if that section has not been studied. In the first section, we discuss several spirals and helices. Many examples of gnomons are given. We also discuss the phenomenon of gnomonic growth in the logarithmic spiral.

In Section 9.2, we discuss the properties and different representations of the Fibonacci numbers. Their prevalence in natural structures is discussed and explained informally.

9.1. Spirals and Helices

In Exercise 1, if the string on the drawing pencil is too tight, the student will not get a spiral, since in this case the string will unwind from one pencil and wind onto the other. If the student has wound a lot of string several thicknesses thick around the stationary pencil, then the relationship of Exercise 2 will not hold. Suggest that they wind the string up the pencil only one layer thick (as in a helix).

▷ **Exercise 1.** Draw an Archimedean spiral using this method.

▷ **Exercise 2.** The distance between adjacent coils should be approximately $2\pi r$, where r is the radius of the fixed pencil. To see this, imagine that the moving pencil starts at the position due north of the fixed pencil. When the pencil returns to the due north position after one revolution around the spiral, the string has been unwound one turn, or $2\pi r$.

Students using graph paper may have difficulty with Exercise 3. Many will start with a right triangle with legs going horizontally and vertically. Their second pass around the spiral will be one square bigger in each direction which does not give the same distance between lines along the hypotenuse. See the incorrect picture below on the right.

▷ **Exercise 3.** Draw a triangular Archimedean spiral.

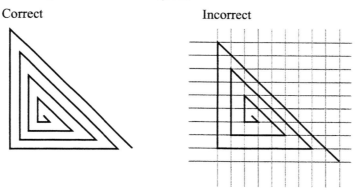

Correct   Incorrect

In Exercises 4–10, you will have to emphasize to your students that the gnomon is the shaded portion: the part that must be added to the original to make a similar but larger figure.

▷ **Exercise 4.** Here are some possible solutions (there are infinitely many).

Make sure that the students understand that in choosing a gnomon, proportions as well as general shape must be preserved. For example, in Exercise 5 we have shown two incorrect but common solutions.

▷ **Exercise 5.**   Here is one possible correct solution and two incorrect ones.

Correct

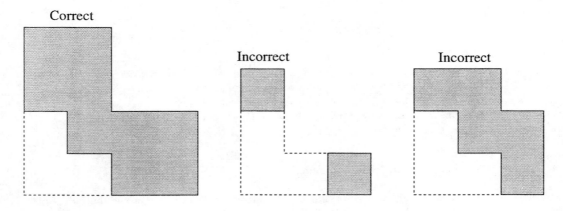

In Exercises 6–10, we use the proportionality properties of similar figures and some elementary algebra to find the desired quantities. These problems are arranged to be increasingly difficult. In Exercise 6, make sure that students orient the figures correctly for the proportions. It may help to have them redraw the original figure (the small white rectangle, rotated 90°) next to the larger figure (composed of the white rectangle together with a gray one in the text). If students do not compare the correct parts in this exercise, they will get the proportions $\frac{x}{2} = \frac{x}{1}$. Make sure that they consider long and short sides of the rectangles rather than horizontal and vertical sides. Once students understand Exercise 6, they should have no difficulty with Exercise 7. In Exercise 9, you may have to remind your students of the proportions of the 30°-60°-90° triangle.

▷ **Exercise 6.**   Since the larger rectangle with long side of length 2 and short side of length x is similar to the shaded rectangle, which has long side x and short side 1, we have $\frac{x}{2} = \frac{1}{x}$, and so $x = \sqrt{2}$.

▷ **Exercise 7.**   Since the larger rectangle with long side of length $1 + x$ and short side of length 1 is similar to the white rectangle, which has long side 1 and short side x, we have $\frac{1}{x+1} = \frac{x}{1}$. This simplifies to the equation $x^2 + x - 1 = 0$, which has positive solution $x = \frac{\sqrt{5}-1}{2}$.

▷ **Exercise 8.**   Since the larger triangle with height of length x, width 5, and hypotenuse $y + 3$ is similar to the white triangle, which has corresponding sides 4, 3, and 5, we have $\frac{x}{5} = \frac{4}{3}$, so $x = \frac{20}{3}$. Similarly, we have $\frac{y+3}{5} = \frac{5}{3}$, so $y + 3 = \frac{25}{3}$ and $y = \frac{16}{3}$. An alternate solution uses the similarity of the gray triangle to the smaller one, to obtain the proportions $\frac{4}{3} = \frac{y}{4}$ and $\frac{5}{3} = \frac{x}{4}$ and the same final answers.

If students do not recall the proportions of the 30°-60°-90° triangle, remind them that two such triangles placed back to back form an equilateral triangle with each side of length 1. Thus the hypotenuse of one of the 30°-60°-90° triangles is 1, the shorter leg has length $\frac{1}{2}$, and the Pythagorean Theorem can be applied to find the altitude.

▷ **Exercise 9.** Since $\alpha = 60°$ and $\beta = 30°$, the large triangle is similar to both the shaded triangle and the smaller white triangle. The standard 30°-60°-90° triangle has height $\frac{\sqrt{3}}{2}$, base $\frac{1}{2}$, and hypotenuse 1. Considering the larger triangle, we have $\frac{x}{1} = \frac{\sqrt{3}/2}{1/2}$, so $x = \sqrt{3}$. Considering the smallest triangle, we have $\frac{z}{1} = \frac{1/2}{1}$, so $z = \frac{1}{2}$. Considering the largest triangle again, we have $\frac{y+z}{1} = \frac{1}{1/2}$, so $y = 2 - z = \frac{3}{2}$.

▷ **Exercise 10.** A 45°-45°-90° triangle is its own gnomon.

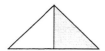

Two ways of generating logarithmic spirals are given in Exercises 11 and 12. It doesn't matter if these are drawn clockwise or counterclockwise.

▷ **Exercise 11.**

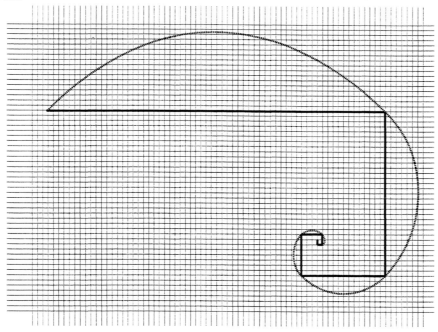

In Exercise 12, students must be consistent in choosing which corners to connect. Connecting the outer corners of the squares works. So does connecting the corners where the square meets the next larger square.

▷ **Exercise 12.**

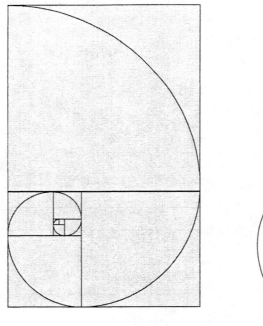 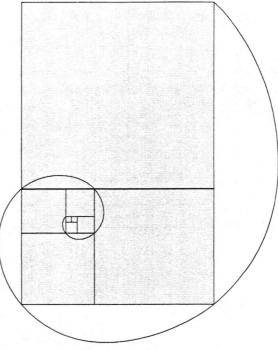

Most students will figure out the pattern for the Fibonacci numbers, but may need help figuring out how to write the recursive formula. Answering in sentence form is also acceptable.

▷ **Exercise 13.**   The Fibonacci sequence begins as follows: $1, 1, 2, 3, 5, 8, 13, 21, 34, 55, 89, 144, 233, 377, 610,$ 987. Note that $f_{n+1} = f_n + f_{n-1}$. In words, each term is the sum of the previous two.

If you did not cover Chapter 3.2, you will need to tell the students that the limit of the ratios in Exercise 14 is called the golden ratio and is designated by ϕ. Note that $\phi = \frac{1+\sqrt{5}}{2} \approx 1.61803398875$. If students do not recognize the limit, compute a few more terms. The sequence converges quite slowly.

▷ **Exercise 14.**   The ratios appear to converge to the golden ration ϕ.

Ratios

$\frac{2}{1}$	$\frac{3}{2}$	$\frac{5}{3}$	$\frac{8}{5}$	$\frac{13}{8}$	$\frac{21}{13}$	$\frac{34}{21}$
2.000000	1.500000	1.666667	1.600000	1.625000	1.615385	1.619048
$\frac{55}{34}$	$\frac{89}{55}$	$\frac{144}{89}$	$\frac{233}{144}$	$\frac{377}{233}$	$\frac{610}{377}$	$\frac{987}{610}$
1.617647	1.618182	1.617977	1.618056	1.618026	1.618037	1.618033

If your students are familiar with polar coordinates, you may omit Exercise 15 and ask them to do further exercises similar to Exercise 16, such as plotting hyperbolic, parabolic, and logarithmic spirals. Use polar graph paper or Template 45 in the Appendix.

▷ **Exercise 15.**

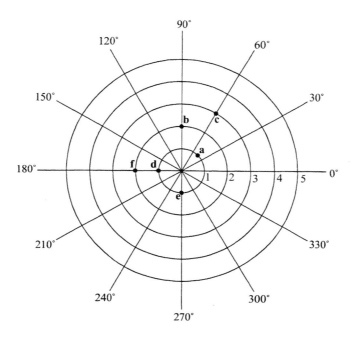

▷ **Exercise 16.** Draw the spiral $r = \frac{1}{2}\theta = \frac{\pi}{360}\Theta$. Note that the spiral crosses the horizontal axis to the right of the origin at the points π, 2π, 3π, 4π, and so on.

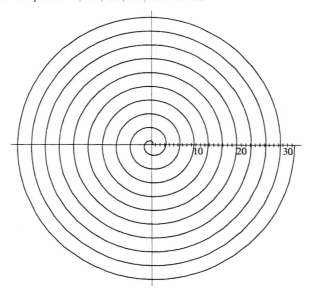

147

9.2. Fibonacci Numbers and Phyllotaxis

▷ **Exercise 1.** After 12 months there will be 377 pairs of rabbits, or 754 individuals.

Although Fibonacci's original problem begins with the sequence 1, 2, 3, 5, ..., it is common in any modern treatment to begin the sequence 1, 1, 2, 3, 5, ... The first two numbers of such a sequence are called the seed numbers, and from these all the other terms follow. Note that the answer to Exercise 1 is actually the fourteenth number in the sequence, rather than the twelfth.

▷ **Exercise 2.** The first 13 Fibonacci numbers are 1,1, 2, 3, 5, 8, 13, 21, 34, 55, 89, 144, 233. Note that $f_{n+1} = f_n + f_{n-1}$ (that is, each term is the sum of the previous two).

The pattern for the sums of Fibonacci numbers should be reasonably clear if one carries the computations out far enough, though some students may have a little trouble expressing this algebraically. Some students will see the initial sums 1, 2, 4 and jump to the conclusion that you get 1, 2, 4, 8, 16, 32, ... Others will add the sum from the previous row instead of the next Fibonacci number, such as $1 + 1 + 2 + 4$ instead of $1 + 1 + 2 + 3$ and so get the same incorrect sequence. Make sure that they understand the notation f_n and that they add carefully.

▷ **Exercise 3.** $f_1 + f_2 + \cdots + f_n = f_{n+2} - 1$

Sums of Fibonacci Numbers

f_1	1	1
$f_1 + f_2$	1+1	2
$f_1 + f_2 + f_3$	1+1+2	4
$f_1 + f_2 + f_3 + f_4$	1+1+2+3	7
$f_1 + f_2 + f_3 + f_4 + f_5$	1+1+2+3+5	12
$f_1 + f_2 + f_3 + f_4 + f_5 + f_6$	1+1+2+3+5+8	20
$f_1 + f_2 + f_3 + f_4 + f_5 + f_6 + f_7$	1+1+2+3+5+8+13	33
$f_1 + f_2 + f_3 + f_4 + f_5 + f_6 + f_7 + f_8$	1+1+2+3+5+8+13+21	54
$f_1 + f_2 + f_3 + f_4 + f_5 + f_6 + f_7 + f_8 + f_9$	1+1+2+3+5+8+13+21+34	88
$f_1 + f_2 + f_3 + f_4 + f_5 + f_6 + f_7 + f_8 + f_9 + f_{10}$	1+1+2+3+5+8+13+21+34+55	143

If you chose not to cover Section 9.1, then the limit of the terms of Exercise 4 may not be apparent. In this case, you can ask students to first note that the answers are all ratios of successive Fibonacci numbers and then to quickly compute decimal forms for the next few such ratios. After ten or so terms, the limit should be clear to those students who recall Section 3.2. If you did not cover this section, you will have to inform your students that the limit of the ratios is called the golden ratio and is designated by ϕ. Note that $\phi = \frac{1+\sqrt{5}}{2} \approx 1.61803398875$. For Exercise 5, students may argue that there is always one more term to the right of the equation $x = 1 + \frac{1}{x}$ when one substitutes the continued fraction for x. Be prepared to discuss infinity.

▷ **Exercise 4.** The numbers formed are ratios of Fibonacci numbers, with limit ϕ, as was seen in Exercise 9.1.14.

(a) $1 + \frac{1}{1} = 2$

(b) $1 + \frac{1}{1+\frac{1}{1}} = \frac{3}{2} = 1.5$

(c) $1 + \frac{1}{1+\frac{1}{1+\frac{1}{1}}} = \frac{8}{5} = 1.6$

(d) $1 + \frac{1}{1+\frac{1}{1+\frac{1}{1+\frac{1}{1}}}} = \frac{13}{8} = 1.625$

(e) Note that $1 + \frac{1}{1+\frac{1}{1+\frac{1}{1}}} = \frac{5}{3} = 1.666$. The infinite continued fraction will be the limit of the numbers computed above, and will be the golden ratio ϕ.

▷ **Exercise 5.** The continued fraction satisfies $x = 1 + \frac{1}{x}$ since

$$\text{if } x = 1 + \cfrac{1}{1+\cfrac{1}{1+\frac{1}{\cdots}}}, \text{ then } x = 1 + \cfrac{1}{1+\cfrac{1}{1+\frac{1}{\cdots}}} = 1 + \cfrac{1}{1+\cfrac{1}{1+\frac{1}{\cdots}}} = 1 + \frac{1}{x}$$

For Exercises 6, 8, 10, and 12, use weed flowers and nonhybrid plants. Even then, not all plants will exhibit the Fibonacci numbers. Really expensive hybrid pineapples may not exhibit Fibonacci growth patterns. Expect to have to explain the notation of the Lucas sequence of Exercise 7.

▷ **Exercise 6.** Count the petals of at least five different types of flowers. The number of petals is often a Fibonacci number (though sometimes one will find twice a Fibonacci number, or a Lucas number).

▷ **Exercise 7.** (a) The Lucas sequence is 2, 1, 3, 4, 7, 11, 18, 29, 47, 76, 123, 199, 322, 521, 843, . . .
(b) The limit of the ratio of successive members of the Lucas sequence $\frac{g_n}{g_{n-1}}$ is also ϕ.

▷ **Exercise 8.** The numbers of parastichies for a pineapple should be Fibonacci numbers.

▷ **Exercise 9.** The numbers of parastichies for a pine cone should be Fibonacci numbers.

▷ **Exercise 10.** This should be approximately 90°.

▷ **Exercise 11.** The numbers of parastichies for a sunflower should be Fibonacci numbers.

▷ **Exercise 12.** This should be approximately 90°.

▷ **Exercise 13.** This should be approximately the ratio of successive Fibonacci numbers.

▷ **Exercise 14.** Note that while primordium #2 must be placed as shown, primordia #3 and #4 may be reversed.

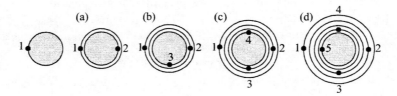

(e) There are several possible choices for where to insert primordium #5, but in all cases primordium #5 will always be shaded by the earlier primordia.

In Exercises 15–17, each dot should be placed slightly farther from the origin than the preceding one. This is most easily done using polar graph paper (or use Template 45 in the Appendix). The illustration in the text at the top of page 298 and those shown below show points distributed at the given angles and so that the distance from the origin to each point increases linearly, and thus the points can be thought of as points on an Archimedean spiral at the given angles. A more accurate model of growth would distribute the points on a parabolic (or Fermat) spiral.

▷ **Exercise 15.** Spacing 30 points at an angle of 180° gives the picture below:

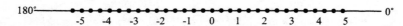

▷ **Exercise 16.** Spacing 30 points at an angle of $.6(360°) = 216° = -144°$ gives the picture below:

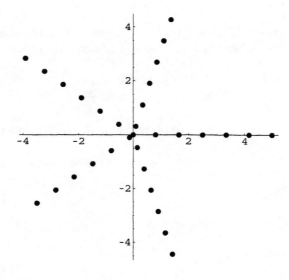

▷ **Exercise 17.** Spacing 30 points at an angle of $.7(360°) = 252° = -108°$ gives the picture below:

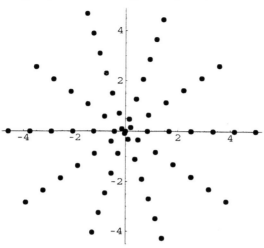

Chapter 10. Drawing Three Dimensions in Two

★ ★ **10.1. Perspective**
   Dependencies: None

- Parallel lines in perspective
- One-point perspective
- Two-point perspective

★ **10.2. Optical Illusions**
   Dependencies: None
   References: Chapter 10.1

- Illusions of length and size
- Illusions of parallel lines
- Illusions of three dimensions
- Impossible figures

This chapter is independent of the preceding chapters, and the two sections are also largely independent of each other. Either Chapter 6 or Chapter 10 (in whole or in part) can be used as a transition from the two-dimensional phenomena of Chapters 2–5 to the three-dimensional geometry of Chapters 7 and 8. The first section of this chapter is devoted to the mechanics and underlying principles of perspective drawing. This could lead to a discussion of projective geometry, but we have not chosen to pursue this.

The second section discusses various types of optical illusions. We have concentrated our attention on the more geometric of these and have, of course, entirely omitted the illusions that make use of color.

10.1. Perspective

In Exercises 1 and 2, we experiment with lines of sight and mirrors. This lays the ground-work for the study of perspective, in which one tries to mimic the effect of lines of sight in three dimensions to create a representation in two dimensions.

▷ **Exercise 1.** Consider the line formed from a key part of your face (such as the top of your head or your chin) to the image of that part in the mirror, and the line from that part of the mirror image to your eye. These two lines form equal angles with the mirror plane. Thus $\triangle ABC$ is congruent to $\triangle DEC$, and $\triangle DEF$ is congruent to $\triangle HGF$, so $AC = CD$ and $DF = FH$. Since $AD = BE$ and $DH = EG$, it follows that the size of the real face, BG, is twice the size of the image, CF.

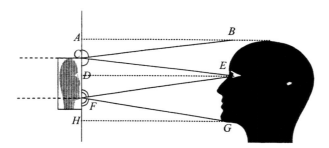

▷ **Exercise 2.** The mirror must be three feet tall. Assuming that it is four inches from this person's eyes to the top of his head, the top of the mirror must be 5 feet 10 inches from the floor.

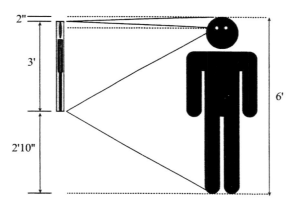

▷ **Exercise 3.** Families of parallel lines that are parallel to the ground line will never intersect.

153

In Exercises 4 and 5, the process in the text for drawing perspective views of a square tiled floor and railroad tracks is extended to a hexagonal tiling and to drawing a circle in perspective.

▷ **Exercise 4.** Note that there are three obvious families of nonhorizontal lines in the hexagonal tiling: the vertical lines and two diagonal families: to the right and to the left. All of these lines divide the object plane into a tiling of equilateral triangles. Draw these lines on the object plane. The principal vanishing point V is chosen on the picture plane directly below the center of the section of the tiling. The other vanishing points, V_1 and V_2 are chosen on the horizon determined by V and equidistant from V on either side. There are nine vertical lines drawn on the tiling in the object plane. Draw nine lines in the picture plane, each with one endpoint directly below one of the vertical object plane lines and all with the other endpoint at V. There are ten diagonal lines in each direction in the object plane. The ones that slant up to the left correspond to ten lines in the picture plane, each with one endpoint directly below the bottom endpoint of one of the object plane lines and the other endpoint at V_1. Repeat for the lines that slant up to the right and V_2. All of these lines in the picture plane determine a perspective view of an equilateral triangle tiling. Use this to draw the desired perspective view of the hexagonal tiling. Under the main drawing are small summary illustrations of the key steps in this process.

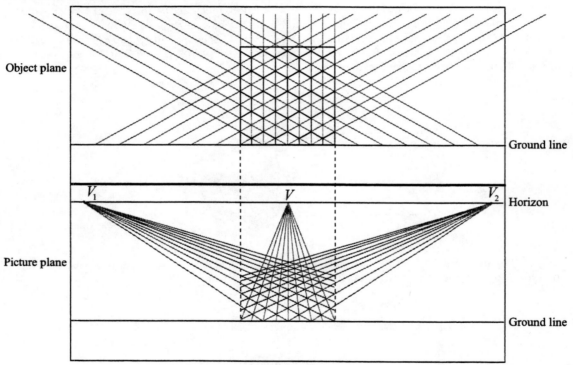

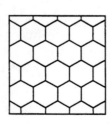

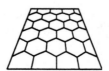

154

Many students are so used to seeing perspective drawings that they don't notice it. Show students a perspective drawing of a circle and ask them if it is a circle and how they might verify this. Also, considering the perspective drawing of the circle below without the framing square or the grid makes the difference between an actual circle and a perspective view of a circle clear.

▷ **Exercise 5.** Draw the circle on a grid of squares. This grid involves three families of nonhorizontal lines: vertical, right diagonal, and left diagonal. As in Exercise 4, draw these lines in the object plane and their counterparts in the picture plane. The vertical lines end at the centered vanishing point V, the right diagonals end at V_2 and the left diagonals at V_1, which is symmetric with V_2. This gives a grid of perspective squares in the picture plane. Use this grid and the way that the circle meets the grid of squares to draw the perspective circle.

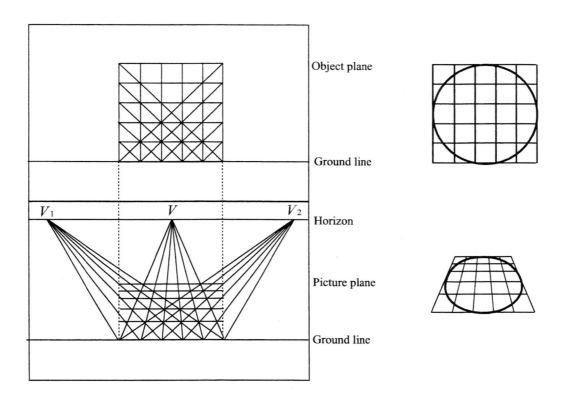

In Exercises 6 and 7, we see how two renaissance artists applied their knowledge of perspective in their art. Use tracing paper over the reproductions in the text, outlining the frame of the picture and a few key features.

▷ **Exercise 6.** Piero della Francesca's *Flagellation*: use the ceiling beams and floor tiles to locate the vanishing point.

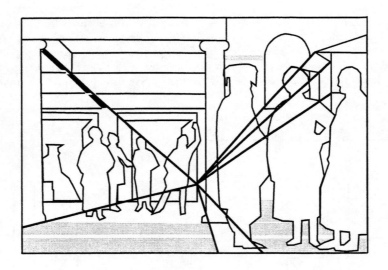

▷ **Exercise 7.** Paolo Uccello's *Night Hunt*: use the logs in the foreground to locate the vanishing point.

In Exercise 8, the student is asked to draw a one-point perspective view of a box, using the technique outlined in the text.

▷ **Exercise 8.** First draw the picture plane directly below the object plane pictured. Choose a horizon and a ground line on the picture plane. Then drop vertical lines from the viewpoint and the four points A', B', C', and D' where the dashed lines (from the corners of the bottom face $ABCD$ of the box to the viewpoint) meet the picture plane. The vanishing point V will lie on the horizon directly below the viewpoint. The two corner points A and B represent the bottom front corners: draw lines from the corresponding points A'' and B'' on the ground line to the vanishing point V. Locate the two bottom rear corners, C'' and D'', where the vertical lines from C' and D' meet the lines connecting points A'' and B'' to V. Now transfer the height directly to the diagram: draw the front face of the box as a rectangle with two corners at A'' and B'' and the height as specified. Connect the top front corners to the vanishing point. Use these lines to locate the top rear corners. The box is illustrated on the right without the construction lines.

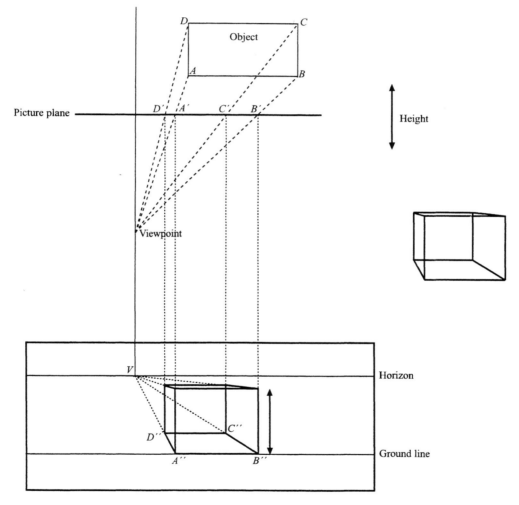

In Exercises 9–14, we ask the student to draw a number of different two-point perspectives, and see the effects of changing various parameters: the positions of the picture plane, the eye, and the ground line. If your students are struggling, do one part of each of Exercises 9, 11, and 13 together as an example.

157

▷ **Exercise 9.** Draw two-point perspective views of the box below using the three different positions of the picture plane shown. The key step is locating the vanishing points: draw a right angle with vertex on the line through the viewpoint E with sides parallel to the sides of the box. The intersection of the sides of this angle with the picture plane give the vanishing points.

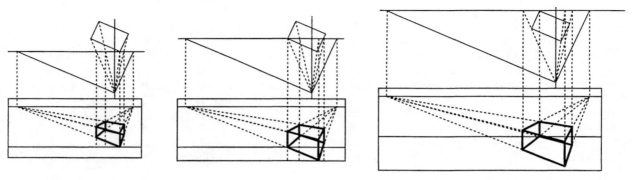

▷ **Exercise 10.** Moving the picture plane only reduces or enlarges the picture.

▷ **Exercise 11.** Draw two-point perspective views of the box below using the three different positions of the eye shown.

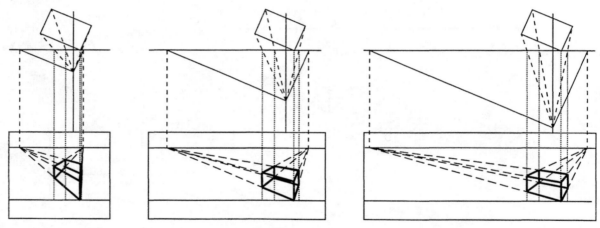

▷ **Exercise 12.** Moving the viewpoint or the eye changes the angle at which the object is viewed, resulting in a more or less oblique, or raking, angle of the sides.

▷ **Exercise 13.** Draw one-point perspective views of the box shown. In the pictures below, we have only drawn the visible faces. The front face is palest gray, the top face medium, and the bottom face the darkest. Since the view is from straight on, the sides are not visible in any of the views.

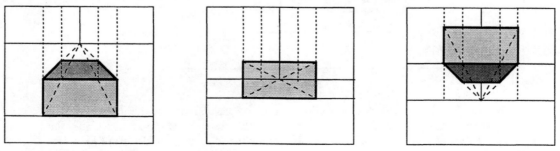

▷ **Exercise 14.** Moving the ground line changes the view from below or above the object.

10.2. Optical Illusions

Students will need either a ruler and compass or appropriate software to draw many of the illusions in the exercises of this section. Exercises 1–4 explore the Müller-Lyer illusion, asking the students to consider varying the component parts to see the effect on the illusion. It should be noted that response to these and other illusions is somewhat individual. Personal differences, including astigmatism and native culture, will affect how one sees these. Some psychologists have tried to quantify the results but none seem to agree.

▷ **Exercise 1.** Although the horizontal line segments are actually the same length, the bottom one looks as if it were longer.

▷ **Exercise 2.** For most people, smaller angles seem to exaggerate the effect.

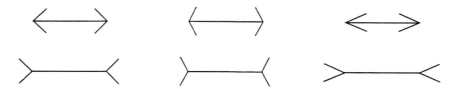

▷ **Exercise 3.** For most people, longer fins seem to exaggerate the effect.

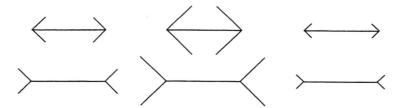

▷ **Exercise 4.** Here are two possible answers: the first involves some horizontal lines;

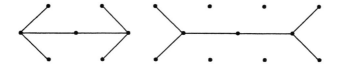

but the second doesn't. In this one, convince yourself that the distance along the center between the arrows is the same.

159

Exercises 5–7 explore the Ponzo illusion and various permutations of this. Again, the student is asked to try varying the components and to observe the apparent changes in the results.

▷ **Exercise 5.** Convince yourself by measuring the diameters that the two circles are actually the same size.

▷ **Exercise 6.** (d) To most observers, vertical lines work as well as circles, but for some, adding more lines or circles seems to detract from the illusion.

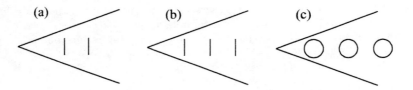

For Exercises 7 and 10, if you have access to The Geometer's Sketchpad or similar software, students can easily compare and contrast several examples. If not, consider doing a demonstration and letting students compare their reactions as the angle changes or the circles grow.

▷ **Exercise 7.** (c) Larger circles do not seem to make a difference, but the illusion is best with smaller acute angles.

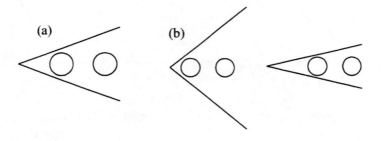

Exercises 8–10 explore the Titchener circle illusion and various permutations of this. Again, the student is asked to try varying the components and to observe the apparent changes in the results. Exercise 9 refers to ruler and compass constructions as in Chapter 3.1, but this exercise may be omitted without loss of continuity.

▷ **Exercise 8.** Convince yourself by measuring the diameters that the two center circles are actually the same size.

▷ **Exercise 9.** First construct a hexagon as in Chapter 3.1. Find the midpoints of all of the sides and draw circles with centers at the vertices of the hexagon and radius one-half of a side, thus tangent to each other at the midpoints. Draw another circle with center at the center of the hexagon and radius one half the distance from this center to any vertex of the hexagon. See the illustration.

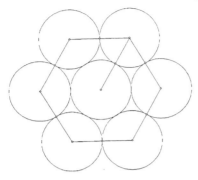

▷ **Exercise 10.** The illusion seems to be least effective when the surrounding circles are about the same size as the inner circle and when the surrounding circles are far away from the inner circle. Note that the larger outer circles are not required to touch.

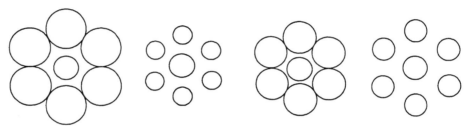

Exercises 11 and 12 explore Zöllner's illusion of parallel lines and various permutations of this. Again, the student is asked to try varying the components and to observe the apparent changes in the results, changing parallel lines to appear as skew and skew lines to appear as parallel.

▷ **Exercise 11.** The lines in Zöllner's illusion are actually parallel, as can be seen by using a ruler.

▷ **Exercise 12.** We can make the skew lines appear to be parallel by adding short intersecting slanted lines:

In Exercise 13, we ask the student to apply variations on Zöllner's illusion to make it appear that lines bend as indicated.

▷ **Exercise 13.** Here are some possible solutions.

(a) Draw a square and a field of circles so the sides of the square seem to bow out.

(b) Draw a pair of parallel lines and a field of other lines to make the parallel lines seem to bend toward each other at the center.

(a)

(b)

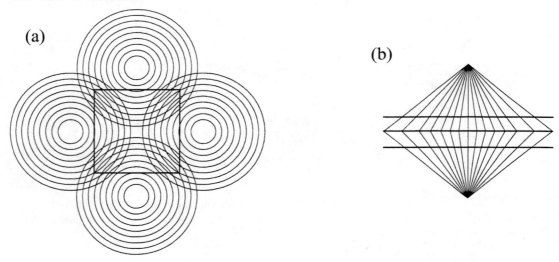

In Exercise 14, we ask the student to make use of the standard ways of representing lines that cross in three dimensions in a two-dimensional drawing. Most students learned to interpret this convention at so early an age that they do not recognize that it is a formal convention: a culturally accepted shorthand representing something that really cannot be accurately portrayed on a piece of paper.

▷ **Exercise 14.** Many such sketches are possible. Here is one simple one:

In Exercises 15–17, we explore the Necker cube: another standard way of representing three-dimensional objects in a two-dimensional drawing. Have your students consider the drawing of the Necker cube at the bottom of page 322 until they can make it pop back and forth between the two interpretations (with the dot at the upper right front corner, and at the upper right rear corner). It is interesting to ask them to describe the mental process that happens as one changes from one view to the other: an almost audible mental click seems to happen. Again, this is a conventional means of portraying the three-dimensional cube and students from some cultures will not see the effect.

▷ **Exercise 15.** In the picture on the left, the dot appears to be at the upper front right corner, while in the second picture the dot is at the upper right rear corner.

(a) 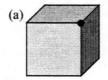   (b)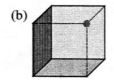

162

▷ **Exercise 16.** You should get six cubes counting one way and seven counting the other. When only six cubes are counted, note that there are enough bits left over to make a seventh cube.

▷ **Exercise 17.** Three cubes or five? The illustration was made by cutting the bottom row of cubes off the picture in the text.

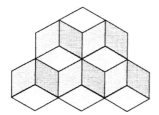 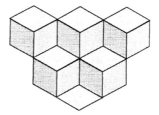

Note that if you remove the top row of cubes, then there are five cubes no matter how you count them.

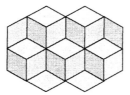 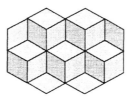

In Exercise 18, we ask the student to build an Ames room. This is an assignment most suitable for a group project or for one student to do as extra credit to show to the rest of the class. Use the blueprints, suitably enlarged, to build the model, remembering that the floor and ceiling will not be parallel. These blueprints are repeated as Template 46 in the Appendix. Cut a pinhole viewing window at the indicated position. Foamcore (available from most architectural supply stores) is suitable for the construction, joined with tape or glue. Outlining the doors and windows with tape or marker pen will add to the effect. For a more elaborate (and therefore more convincing) room, draw and color the floor (either with a checkerboard tile pattern or linearly to mimic floorboards), suitably graduating the width and length of the tiles or boards. Cut out the windows and use tracing paper to mimic frosted glass. Paint the walls a medium shade and the ceiling a lighter shade. Dolls can be used to illustrate the apparent-size illusion.

▷ **Exercise 18.** Make a model of an Ames room.

In Exercise 19, we ask the student to use the idea from the Borromini colonnade and their understanding of perspective to design a corridor that appears shorter than it really is.

▷ **Exercise 19.** Taper the sides in, and if there are columns or any other vertical design element, place them gradually closer together down the corridor.

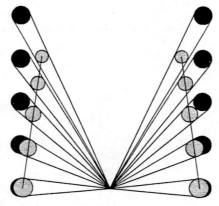

In Exercises 20–22, we ask the student to explore impossible figures in words, models, and drawings. These are two-dimensional representations of what appear to be three-dimensional objects that cannot actually exist in three dimensions. All of these are made by taking representations of pieces of three-dimensional objects and putting these pieces together in a way that contradicts the "front" and "back" indicators implicit in the drawing. Remind your students that in Exercise 20 you expect grammatically correct, complete sentences. In Exercise 21, we ask the student to build a model. For this, one can use pieces of square dowel, which is available at larger hardware stores. Cut sections and glue together neatly as shown in the picture on the right accompanying the exercise on page 327 of the text. Seen from a particular angle, in a generally diffused light (so that shadows will not serve as clear indications of direction), this will look like the tribar. Escher has a number of other drawings that exploit this phenomenon, and these are a rich source for classroom investigation.

▷ **Exercise 20.** (a) For the first figure, the tribar, each corner looks okay by itself. However, at corner 1, face A is in the foreground, B in the middle, and C is in the background. At corner 2, A is closer to the viewer than C, which is closer than B. At corner 3, C is closest, then B, then A. It is these relationships concerning which face is closest to the viewer that cannot be reconciled.

(b) For the middle figure, called the devil's trident, note that region A can be interpreted either as a surface of the figure or as part of the background. Since this ambiguity cannot be resolved, the figure is impossible.

(c) The third figure involves confusions similar to those in (a) concerning which faces lie closest to the observer. At corner 1, A is in front of face B, but at corner 2, B lies in front of A.

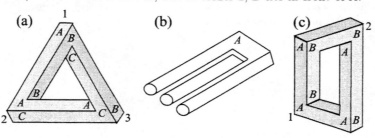

▷ **Exercise 21.** Build a model of the tribar.

▷ **Exercise 22.** Create your own drawing of an "impossible object."

164

Chapter 11. Shape

★ **11.1. Noneuclidean Geometry**
Dependencies: None

- Elliptic geometry
- Hyperbolic geometry
- Poincaré disk model for hyperbolic geometry

★ ★ **11.2. Map Projections**
Dependencies: None
References: Chapter 11.1

- Map projections
- Distortion of area, length, angle, shape, and points
- Common map projections

★ ★ **11.3. Curvature of Curves**
Dependencies: None

- Tangent lines
- Osculating circles
- Curvature
- Mean curvature
- Gaussian curvature

★ ★ ★ **11.4. Curvature of Surfaces**
Dependencies: Chapter 11.1, 11.3

- Angular deficit
- Descartes's formula
- Angle sum and area for spherical polygons
- Gauss-Bonnet formula for the sphere
- Angle deficit and Gaussian curvature

★ ★ ★ **11.5. Soap Bubbles**
Dependencies: Chapter 11.1, 11.3, 11.4

- Soap films
- Double bubbles
- Soap films on polyhedral frames
- Minimal surfaces

This chapter discusses the property of shape, beginning with a discussion of the three types of geometry: euclidean, elliptic, and hyperbolic. Students are asked to experiment with variations on the known euclidean relationship between circumference and area to develop physical models for these noneuclidean geometries. The formulae for angle sums of polygons is contrasted with the euclidean formulae.

The second section is devoted to a brief introduction to the problems of mapping the earth onto paper. The section begins with exercises demonstrating the personal biases given to maps by their creators. Since no flat map can accurately reflect the earth without distortion, there is a discussion of the five major types of distortion found in maps: distortion of area, length, angle, shape, and points. The simpler common map projections, including cylindrical projections, the orthographic projection, the stereographic projection, and the gnomonic projection, are investigated for these types of distortion. The section ends with a discussion of other mapping projections, including the Mercator projection and one by Buckminster Fuller.

Section 11.3 introduces the concept of curvature by means of tangent or osculating circles. Students can measure the radii of these circles using circle templates, and so find the curvature of a curve at various points. The principal curvatures of a surface are defined, and then the mean and Gaussian curvatures are defined in terms of these.

The next section expands on the idea of curvature for a surface. This section begins with a discussion of angular deficit for polyhedra and then Descartes's formula is proved. Students are asked to deduce the relationship between area and angle sum for spherical polygons. The Gauss-Bonnet formula confirms their hypothesis. The section ends with a discussion of the relationship between angular deficit and Gaussian curvature.

The last section is devoted to soap bubbles and soap films. The tendency of soap films to naturally conform to the surface of minimal area is discussed and demonstrated. The angles formed by intersecting soap films is investigated. The chapter ends with some illustrations of modern minimal surfaces.

11.1. Noneuclidean Geometry

This section has worked quite well for our students. Don't let them rush through Exercises 1-4. It is important that they use these opportunities to get a feel for the two noneuclidean geometries and how the geometry changes the relationship between area and circumference. Let the students experiment with the clay until they figure out how to comply with the given conditions.

▷ **Exercise 1.** Add ripples along the perimeter, without stretching the diameter.

▷ **Exercise 2.** Gather the perimeter together (think of a drawstring bag) without shrinking the diameter. This will bump the center up.

▷ **Exercise 3.** Taping five equilateral triangles together at each vertex will form a shape that closes back on itself: the icosahedron.

▷ **Exercise 4.** Taping seven equilateral triangles together at each vertex will form a shape that forms a floppy, ripply, infinite expanse, sort of like infinite kale. Note that it is possible to let some of the edges close back together as we did in building the infinite polyhedra. This would form tunnels or doughnut holes, but is not necessary.

In Exercises 5-7, the student is asked to confirm and consolidate the findings from the initial group of exercises.

▷ **Exercise 5.** In elliptic geometry, the circumference is too small for the area (compared to euclidean geometry). In hyperbolic geometry, the circumference is too large compared with the area.

▷ **Exercise 6.** Elliptic

▷ **Exercise 7.** The area of a circle in elliptic space will be less than πr^2, while in hyperbolic space, the area will be greater than πr^2.

> *For Exercise 8, it is again important that students spend some time thinking and, ideally, arguing with their peers about how to define a straight line on a noneuclidean surface. We suggest making use of their models from Exercises 1–4 and a useful-sized ball. Supply large rubber bands or string for the students to use to experiment. In Exercise 9, we ask the students to apply their ideas to an elliptic surface.*

▷ **Exercise 8.** Another definition might be that a line is formed by a bit of string stretched tight along the surface or the path of a light beam.

▷ **Exercise 9.** On a sphere, lines are great circles, circles passing around the fattest part of the globe, such as the equator.

> *In Exercises 10–13, we investigate other properties of lines in elliptic geometry. Two of the properties investigated contradict Euclid's axioms: on a sphere one can find two points (antipodal points) that do not determine a unique line, and parallel lines do not exist.*

▷ **Exercise 10.** There are infinitely many lines (great circles) passing through any pair of antipodal points (points directly opposite one another, like the North and South Poles).

▷ **Exercise 11.** Latitude lines are not lines, but circles in elliptic geometry, since they describe the set of all points at a fixed distance from the North or South Pole. They do not form the shortest path between two points.

▷ **Exercise 12.** No, any two lines on the sphere must intersect at two antipodal points.

▷ **Exercise 13.** Parallel lines do not exist on a sphere.

> *In Exercise 14, we ask the students to apply their findings from Exercise 8 to hyperbolic geometry. In Exercises 15–19, we discuss properties of lines in hyperbolic space. One property contradicts Euclid's axioms: there are infinitely many parallel lines through a point to a given line.*

▷ **Exercise 14.** Lines can be drawn on the hyperbolic model by laying a section out flat and using a ruler.

▷ **Exercise 15.** There is a unique line through any two points on the floppy surface. On your model, hold one point in each hand and pull the surface tight. Then the "shortest" and "straightest" path is the line.

▷ **Exercise 16.** Yes, it is pretty easy to draw two lines that never intersect.

▷ **Exercise 17.** Yes, given a line L and a point P not on the line, you find a line M through the point P that never intersects the original line L.

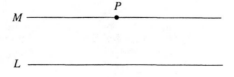

▷ **Exercise 18.** Yes, given a line L and a point P not on the line, you can find, for example, lines M and N through the point that never intersects the original line L. In the picture below, the lines look curved, but on the floppy hyperbolic surface they will be straight.

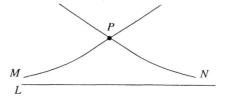

▷ **Exercise 19.** Given a line L and a point P not on the line, infinitely many parallel lines (for example, any line through P falling between M and N above) can be drawn through the point P parallel to the line L.

In Exercises 20–27, we discuss noneuclidean polygons. Their angle sums and areas are contrasted with those of euclidean polygons. We ask the students to extend the definition of regularity to noneuclidean polygons. Note that the area of a sphere of radius r is $4\pi r^2$.

▷ **Exercise 20.** One example is the triangle with one vertex at the North Pole and the other two on the equator, chosen so that the angle formed at the North Pole is 90°. Each angle will thus measure 90° for an angle sum of 270°.

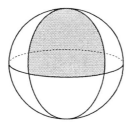

▷ **Exercise 21.** One example is the triangle with one vertex at the North Pole and the other two south of the equator, chosen so that each angle is 120°. Similarly, a triangle can be formed with angle sum more than 360°, but all triangles will have angle sum greater than 180° but less than 540° = 3 · 180°.

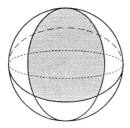

▷ **Exercise 22.** The area is greater than one-half of the base times the height. For example, in the triangle of Exercise 20, the base and the height are each one-quarter of the circumference of a great circle. If the sphere has radius r, then $b = h = \frac{\pi r}{2}$, so $\frac{1}{2}bh = \frac{\pi^2 r^2}{8}$. The true area of this spherical triangle is one-eighth of the surface area of the sphere, so $A = \frac{1}{8}(4\pi r^2) = \frac{\pi r^2}{2}$. Then $4 > \pi$ implies that $\frac{\pi r^2}{2} > \frac{\pi^2 r^2}{8}$, so we see that $A > \frac{1}{2}bh$. Another way of explaining this is that an elliptic surface is formed as in Exercise 2 by increasing the area while leaving the perimeter unchanged, so that the area is greater than that given by the formula $\frac{1}{2}bh$.

169

▷ **Exercise 23.** You cannot find a square (a four-sided figure with four equal sides and four right angles) on the surface of the sphere, though you can construct a regular quadrilateral in the sense of having four equal angles and four equal sides. Similarly, any other regular n-sided polygon can be constructed, and its angle sum will be strictly greater than $180°(n-2)$.

▷ **Exercise 24.** The angle sum of a hyperbolic triangle will be less than $180°$.

▷ **Exercise 25.** No triangle in hyperbolic space can have angles that add up to more than $360°$, but all will have angle sum less than $180°$.

▷ **Exercise 26.** The area is less than the base times the height. One way of explaining this is forming a hyperbolic surface as in Exercise 1, where the perimeter is increased (thus increasing the base and height) while the area is unchanged.

▷ **Exercise 27.** Again, while squares (with four equal sides and four right angles) do not exist, regular n-sided polygons of all degrees do with angle sum less than $180°(n-2)$.

11.2. Map Projections

Exercises 1–4 investigate the nonmathematical aspects of mapping. For these exercises to be most effective, the students would draw the maps before they knew what the follow-up exercises ask. We wish to show how a person's individual experiences and culture affects what is drawn on a map. For this, it is essential that one be able to compare maps drawn by different people, ideally from different cultures. You will find that most of the world maps, especially for American students, approximate Mercator's projection. The accuracy and number of countries (or even continents) pictured varies greatly from person to person, quite aside from their artistic abilities. The convention that up indicates north is almost universally respected (except for a very few aberrant Australians). One's native country always tends to be more detailed and larger than it ought to be. In the United States, Florida always makes a remarkable showing. As for the campus maps, if you have time, encourage the students to compare their findings or even have a class discussion. Students can often tell where someone lives, what their major is, whether they have a car, or play a sport, based on what dorms, classroom buildings, roads, parking lots, and playing fields are shown on the map and which are not. A general class discussion almost always yields a pair of students in each of the categories above.

▷ **Exercise 1.** Sketch a map of campus.

▷ **Exercise 2.** Consider another person's map and write a short paragraph about what is important to him or her. Note especially things that you left off your map.

▷ **Exercise 3.** Sketch a map of the world.

▷ **Exercise 4.** Discuss the questions in the text about your world map.

Since the degree measure of the circumference of the earth is $360°$, and the earth completes one revolution in 24 hours, each degree of longitude represents $\frac{24}{360} = \frac{1}{15}$ hours. Therefore, $15°$ of longitude corresponds to one hour.

▷ **Exercise 5.** At the instant when the sun is directly over the point where the prime meridian and the equator intersect, it is 1 o'clock in the afternoon at longitude 15 E. It is midnight at the date line. It is 7 o'clock in the morning in Washington, D. C. The latitude doesn't matter.

In Exercises 6 and 7, we indicate certain keys points and lines on a ball. This ball will be used in some of the later exercises, so make sure your students make the markings carefully and keep the ball. If one measures the distance on the surface of the ball from North Pole to South Pole, the equator is halfway between. The equator and the circles of latitude at $30°N$, $60°N$, $30°S$, and $60°S$ will divide the length of the spherical distance between the poles into sixths. The indicated lines of longitude will go through the poles and divide the equator into fourths.

171

▷ **Exercise 6.** Mark and label the poles and the longitudinal lines at 0°, 90° E, 180°, and 90° W.

▷ **Exercise 7.** Mark and label the equator and circles of latitude at 30°N, 60°N, 30°S, and 60°S. Draw a triangle on your ball and label its vertices A, B, and C. Make sure the triangle has sides that are straight lines relative to the ball (that is, sections of great circles), rather than relative to the edge.

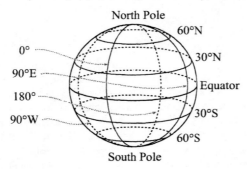

Exercises 8–10 are meant to convince the student that there is no perfect map of the earth: no flat material can conform to the contours of a ball, and the surface of a ball cannot be laid out flat without tearing.

▷ **Exercise 8.** A piece of paper cannot lie smoothly on the surface of a ball without wrinkling.

▷ **Exercise 9.** The peel of an orange cannot lie flat without tearing.

▷ **Exercise 10.** All maps must have some distortion.

In Exercise 11, we ask the student to try to invent a map projection (it need not be a very good one). They will need to figure out a systematic way of transferring their markings made in Exercises 6 and 7 from the ball to a piece of paper. Let them take their time to figure out a method for doing this. They are most likely going to come up with some variation on one of the known projections.

▷ **Exercise 11.** The answers will vary with the individual. Map the ball onto a sheet of paper and transfer the key markings to your map. Answer the questions in the text about your map.

In Exercises 12–19, we investigate the simplest common map projections and the distortions inherent in each. In Exercises 12 and 13, we study three different cylindrical projections. For the equal-area cylindrical projection (A), wrap a sheet of transparency film around the ball so that the film touches the ball along the equator and tape up the seam. One can use pins through the film and into the ball to both secure the ball in position and to mark where the lines of longitude cross the equator. Mark lightly the circles of latitude and the position of the poles by sighting horizontally at the markings on the ball. Then unwrap the sheet of transparency film. Trim it so that its width is equal to the length of the equator (the tape will show where to start and stop). Redraw the horizontal line representing the equator using a ruler. The lines of longitude will be drawn vertically at the holes made by the pins. The circles of latitude will be drawn as horizontal straight lines at the indicated marks. The poles will also be represented by horizontal lines on the map. One can also trim the map at the poles.

For the equirectangular cylindrical projection (B), repeat the process of fitting a new sheet of transparency film around the equator and using pins to mark the location of the lines of latitude. Unwrap the ball and redraw the horizontal line representing the equator and the vertical lines representing the lines of latitude. Transfer the circles of latitude by setting the ball on the flat transparency film at the equator. Slowly roll the ball along a longitudinal line until the 30° N circle of latitude on the ball comes into contact with the film. Mark this point on the film. Continue to roll the ball until the 60° N circle of latitude on the ball comes into contact with the film and mark this point. Repeat until the North Pole comes into contact with the film and mark that point. Draw horizontal lines at these marks on the film. Repeat for the southern hemisphere, or take advantage of the symmetry to find where to place the southern circles of latitude and the South Pole. Alternatively, fit string from the equator to the North Pole on your ball and mark the positions of the latitude lines on the string. Then use the string to measure up (north) on the map to figure out the position of the horizontal latitude lines.

For the central cylindrical projection (C), again fit a sheet of transparency film around the equator of the ball and use pins to mark the positions of the lines of longitude. Mark lightly the positions of the circles of latitude by trying to visualize the line running from the center of the ball through the circle of latitude to a point on the transparency film. This projection assumes an infinite cylinder of transparency film, so the poles will not appear on your map. Unwrap the ball and redraw the horizontal line representing the equator, the vertical lines representing the lines of latitude, and the horizontal lines representing the circles of latitude.

▷ **Exercise 12.   Cylindrical Projections**

A. Equal-area cylindrical projection: The illustration below shows a cross-section of the globe and the map. The map will have height equal to the diameter of the globe and width equal to the circumference, so it is $2r$ tall and $2\pi r$ wide.

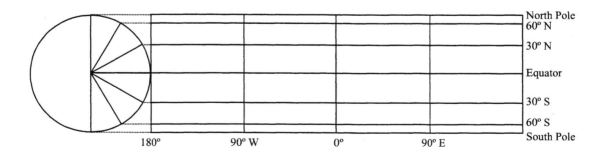

B. Equirectangular cylindrical projection: The illustration on the next page shows a cross-section of the globe and the map. The map will have height equal to the distance from the North Pole to the South Pole on the sphere, that is, half of the circumference of the ball, or πr, divided into equal sections by the equator and the latitudinal circles on the globe. The width of the map will be equal to the circumference of the ball, so it is $2\pi r$ wide.

173

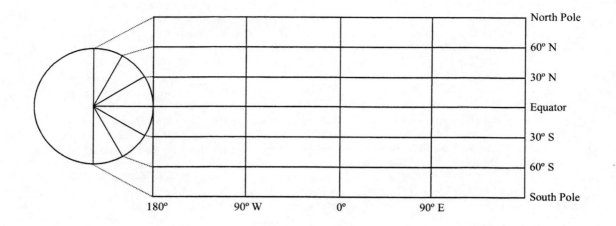

C. Central cylindrical projection: The illustration below shows a cross-section of the globe and the map. The map will have infinite height (in practice, the upper and lower portion, above the Arctic Circle and below the Antarctic Circle, are abbreviated) and width equal to the circumference of the ball $(2\pi r)$.

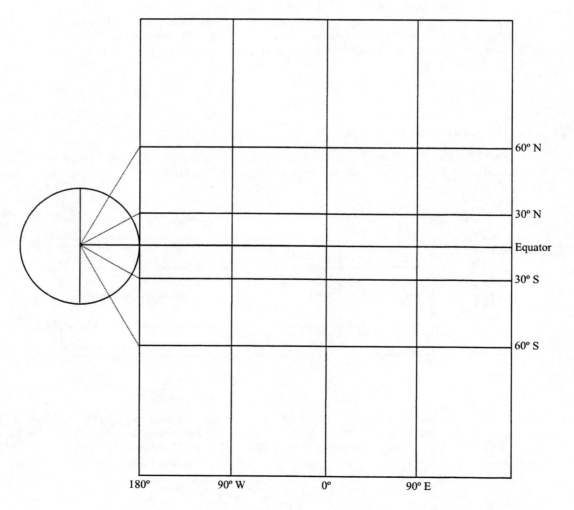

You will need to be prepared to suggest features for the students to consider for the projections analyzed in Exercises 13, 15, 17, and 19. When asking if lines are preserved, emphasize that great circles are considered to be lines on the sphere. Therefore, we are asking if all great circles are mapped to straight lines. Students should consider the longitudinal lines and the equator, as well as skew great circles, such as the one passing through the points $0°N$-$90°W$, $30°S$-$0°E$, $0°N$-$90°E$, and $30°N$-$180°E$. To see if circles are preserved, consider the latitudinal circles marked on the ball, as well as small circles centered on the equator. One such circle will pass through the points $0°N$-$30°W$, $30°N$-$0°E$, $0°N$-$30°E$, and $30°S$-$0°E$. Be careful—even if a map preserves distances in the vertical and horizontal directions, it may not preserve oblique distances. In considering area, one can first consider one hemisphere (with area $2\pi r^2$) and its image on the map. Then consider triangles for which it is easy to compute the area, such as the one with one vertex at the North Pole forming an angle of $90°$ and two vertices on the equator. This triangle forms one-eighth of the sphere and so has area $\frac{\pi r^2}{2}$. Compare this with the area of the region on the map that the triangle is sent to by the projection. The lengths of the longitudinal lines and the equator are usually easy to compare with the lengths of their counterparts on the map. To see if angles are preserved, first consider the angles formed by the longitudinal lines and the equator and the latitudinal circles. All of these angles measure $90°$ on the ball, and it is usually easy to find the measures of their images on the map. However, one should also consider other angles, such as the the $45°$ angle that bisects the angle between the $90°W$ line of longitude and the equator. This will cross the $0°$ line of longitude at $45°N$. Since lines may not be preserved, one must consider the angles formed by whatever shape the spherical angle is mapped to. Whether shape is preserved is generally easy to determine by considering various triangles and circles on the ball and their images. We consider that shape is preserved if, for example, a four-sided region on the sphere is mapped to a four-sided region (whose sides may not be straight lines) with the same angles and proportions. If a map distorts points, it is most commonly the poles that are affected.

The equal-area cylindrical projection (A) sends the longitudinal lines to vertical lines, but does not preserve other lines: consider the great circle passing through the equator at $90°W$ and $90°E$ and dipping down to $30°S$ at longitude $0°$ and rising up to $30°N$ at longitude $180°$. Mark these points on the map and it is clear that the image will not be a straight line. It also does not send circles to circles (for example, a small circle centered at the equator will be distorted into an ellipse), since horizontal distances along the equator are preserved but vertical distances are not. This can also be seen by drawing the circle on the ball and wrapping the map on the transparency film around the ball. It is area preserving, as one might guess from its name, though proving this is beyond this course. One example you can suggest the students consider is a triangle with base along the equator and the third vertex at the North Pole or South Pole. If the upper angle is something nice (like $90°$), it is easy to compute the area of the spherical triangle if one knows that the area of a sphere is $4\pi r^2$. For example, the triangle with an angle of $90°$ at the North Pole and the other two vertices on the equator is one-eighth of the sphere and so has area $\pi r^2/2$. Its projection is a rectangle with height equal to the radius of the sphere and base one-quarter of the circumference of the ball and so also has area $\pi r^2/2$. Another way to explain why area is preserved without getting into a proof is to show that as you move away from the equator, the projection of vertical distance is too small but the horizontal distance is too big and balances it out. Length clearly is distorted (for example, along the circles of latitude). To see that angle measure is distorted, consider the $45°$ angle that bisects the angle between the $90°W$ line of longitude and the equator. This will cross the $0°$ line of longitude at $45°N$. Mark these lines on your map and wrap the map around the ball and trace the image of this angle. It is clear that this angle is distorted on the map. Considering the triangle formed by two lines of longitude and the equator shows that shape is not preserved. Since the North Pole and South Pole are represented as lines, points are not preserved.

The equirectangular cylindrical projection (B) also sends the longitudinal lines to vertical lines, but does not preserve other lines: again consider the great circle passing through the equator at 90°W and 90°E and dipping down to 30°S. It sends the latitudinal circles to straight horizontal lines on the map. To see that other circles are not preserved, note that while vertical distances from the equator are preserved, horizontal distances are stretched. It is not area preserving, as one can see by considering the four-sided region formed by two lines of longitude, the equator, and a circle of latitude. This is sent to a rectangle of clearly larger area. Length also is clearly distorted (for example, along the circles of latitude). To see that angle measure is distorted, again consider the 45° angle that bisects the angle between the 90°W line of longitude and the equator. Considering the triangle formed by two lines of longitude and the equator shows that shape is not preserved. Since the North Pole and South Pole are represented as lines, points are not preserved.

The central cylindrical projection (C) also sends the longitudinal lines to vertical lines and does not preserve other lines. Have the students experiment with their ball and the transparency film. It will not send circles to circles since horizontal distance is preserved along the equator but vertical distance is distorted. It is not area preserving, as one can see by considering the triangular region formed by two lines of longitude and the equator. This is sent to a rectangle of infinite area. Length also is clearly distorted (for example, along the lines of longitude). To see that angle measure is distorted, again consider the 45° angle that bisects the angle between the 90°W line of longitude and the equator. Considering the triangle formed by two lines of longitude and the equator shows that shape is not preserved. Since the North Pole and South Pole are represented as lines at infinity, points are not preserved.

▷ **Exercise 13.**

Comparison of Map Projections

Map preserves	Lines	Circles	Area	Length	Angle	Shape	Points
Cylinder A	no	no	yes	no	no	no	no
Cylinder B	no	no	no	no	no	no	no
Cylinder C	no	no	no	no	no	no	no
Orthographic	no	no	no	no	no	no	yes
Stereographic	no	yes	no	no	yes	yes	no
Gnomonic	no	yes	no	no	yes	yes	no

To transfer the markings on the ball to the transparency film using the orthographic projection for Exercise 14, note that the equator will be mapped to a circle with the same radius. The North Pole will be mapped to the center of this circle. The Southern Hemisphere will not appear at all. The lines of longitude will be represented by diameters of the circle. The circles of latitude will be concentric circles.

176

▷ **Exercise 14.** Orthographic Projection:

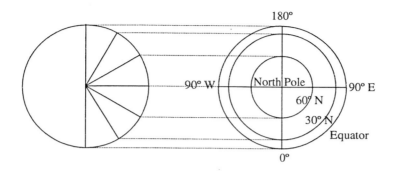

For Exercise 15, consider the great circle passing through the equator at 90° W and 90° E and passing through the point at longitude 0° and latitude 30° S. Marking these three points on your map makes it clear that lines are not preserved. It is easy to see that circles centered on one of the circles of latitude will be distorted. The area of the entire Northern Hemisphere on the map is πr^2, so this map is not area preserving. Length, for example, along a line of longitude, is distorted. To see that angle measure is distorted, again consider the 45° angle that bisects the angle between the 90° W line of longitude and the equator. Since latitudinal distance is correct but longitudinal distance is not, shape is not preserved. However, points are preserved.

▷ **Exercise 15.** See the table of Exercise 13.

To transfer the markings on the ball to the transparency film using the stereographic projection for Exercise 16, note that the equator will be mapped to a circle of twice the radius. The North Pole will be mapped to the center of this circle. The South Pole will not appear at all. The lines of longitude will be represented by diameters of the disc. The circles of latitude will be concentric circles. In the picture on the next page, I ran out of room to represent the 60° S and 60° N circles of latitude.

For Exercise 17, consider the great circle passing through the equator at 90° W and 90° E and passing through the point at longitude 0° and latitude 30° S. Marking these three points on your map makes it clear that lines are not preserved. It is more difficult to see that in fact this projection preserves circles. The latitudinal circles are clearly mapped to circles. For a small circle centered, for example, on the equator, the portion in the Northern Hemisphere will shrink, but the portion in the Southern Hemisphere will grow proportionally. Area is not preserved, since the Southern Hemisphere stretches out to infinity. The area of the Northern Hemisphere on the map will be $4\pi r^2$. Length, for example, along a line of longitude is distorted. Angle measure is preserved, though this is somewhat harder to see. For regions that do not include the South Pole, shape will be roughly preserved. Points are distorted, since the South Pole goes to infinity.

177

▷ **Exercise 16.** *Stereographic projection:*

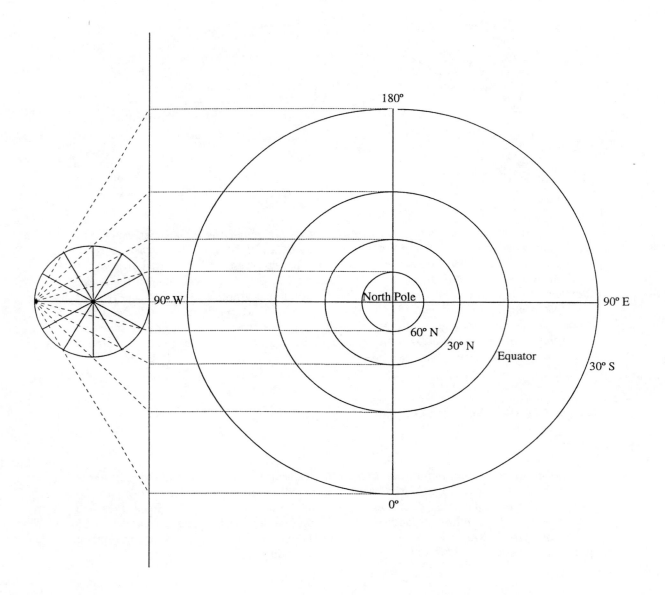

▷ **Exercise 17.** See the table of Exercise 13.

Note that there is another mapping projection, which is also commonly called the gnomonic projection, in which one hemisphere is mapped to the plane by imagining placing the North Pole tangent to the mapping plane and projecting the image of each point by using the line from the center of the ball through the point to the mapping plane. This projection does preserve lines, since any great circle is the intersection of a plane through the center of the ball with the surface of the ball. This plane will intersect the mapping plane in a straight line. The projection in the text, which we call the gnomonic projection, is sometimes also called the central stereographic projection.

To transfer the markings on the ball to the transparency film using the gnomonic projection of this text for Exercise 18, note that the equator will be mapped to a circle of the same radius. The North Pole will be mapped to the center of this circle. The South Pole will not appear at all. The lines of longitude will be represented by diameters of the disc. The circles of latitude will be concentric circles. In the picture below, I ran out of room to represent the 60° S circle of latitude.

▷ **Exercise 18. Gnomonic Projection:**

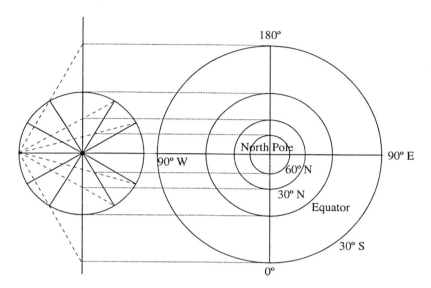

For Exercise 19, consider the great circle passing through the equator at 90° W and 90° E and passing through the point at longitude 0° and latitude 30° S. Marking these three points on your map makes it clear that lines are not preserved. The latitudinal circles are clearly mapped to circles. For a small circle centered, for example, on the equator, the portion in the Northern Hemisphere will shrink, but the portion in the Southern Hemisphere will grow correspondingly. Area is not preserved, since the Southern Hemisphere stretches out to infinity. The area of the Northern Hemisphere on the map is πr^2. Length, for example, along a line of longitude is distorted. Angle measure is preserved, though this is somewhat harder to see. For regions that do not include the South Pole, shape will be roughly preserved. Points are distorted, since the South Pole goes to infinity.

▷ **Exercise 19.** See the table of Exercise 13.

11.3. Curvature of Curves

In order to measure curvature, we need to introduce the idea of tangent lines and tangent circles. Some students will have already been exposed to at least the idea of a tangent line, but this will be new to others. Our approach is entirely geometric, and we only ask that they be able to roughly sketch the tangent line and identify the approximate slope as large positive (slope somewhat greater than 1), moderate positive (slope around 1), small positive (slope less than 1), zero (horizontal tangent), small negative (slope between 0 and -1), moderate negative (around -1), and large negative (somewhat less than -1).

▷ **Exercise 1.**

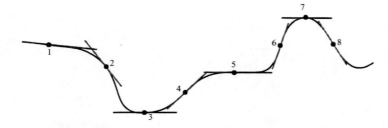

(1) slope is small negative

(2) slope is moderate negative

(3) slope is zero

(4) slope is moderate positive

(5) slope is zero

(6) slope is large positive

(7) slope is zero

(8) slope is moderate negative

In Exercises 2–7, we ask the student to approximate the curvature to a variety of curves at the given points. They should do this with circle templates, choosing the circle that best fits the curve and then applying the formula $\kappa = \frac{1}{r}$ where r is the radius of the chosen circle. Note that answers will depend on whether the student is using a metric or English unit template. What is important is that the answers be consistent: very flat curves will have κ close to 0, while tight curves will have large curvature. One can instead direct the students only to give answers such as large positive, moderate positive (curvature close to 1), small positive, zero, small negative, moderate negative, and large negative. Note that most circle templates have the sizes of the circles marked by the diameter rather than the radius.

The sign of the curvature indicates on which side of the curve the osculating circle lies. For curves that represent the graphs of functions, this translates into positive if the circle lies above the curve and negative if it lies below the curve (or vice versa—it does not actually matter as long as one is consistent). For closed curves, things get a bit more complicated. Probably the best way to explain this to your students is to have them imagine walking around the curve with one arm stuck out at right angles to the curve. If you reach one of the indicated points with your arm pointing toward the center of the osculating circle, then let the curvature be positive. If the center of the circle is on the opposite side of the curve from your arm, then let the curvature be negative. This obviously depends on which direction you choose to walk and which arm you stick out, but other choices will only reverse all of the signs. Again, consistency matters most of all.

You can first introduce this explanation for the ellipse of Exercise 2 where the above-or-below convention does not make sense for the points at the far right and left. Otherwise, you can let the students figure out for themselves how to interpret the signs for this simple case. Exercises 3 and 4 involve curves that are graphs of functions, so the above-or-below rule works fine for these.

▷ **Exercise 2.** The smaller ends of the ellipse can be approximated by circles of diameter .7 and so the radius of curvature is $r = .35$ and the curvature at these points is $\kappa \approx 2.9$. The flatter top and bottom points can best be approximated by circles of diameter 2.8, so at these points the radius is $r = 1.4$ and $\kappa \approx .7$.

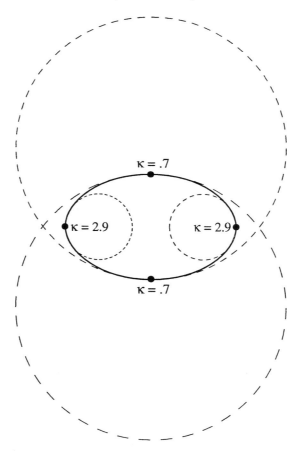

▷ **Exercise 3.** The middle point on the catenary is approximated by a circle of diameter 1.8 and so has radius .9 and curvature $\kappa \approx 1.1$. The next two points on either side can be approximated by circles of diameter 2, and so $\kappa = 1$. These two circles have their centers so very close that they may appear to form a single circle. The two points farthest out can be approximated by circles of diameter 2.2 and so have radius 1.1 and $\kappa \approx .9$.

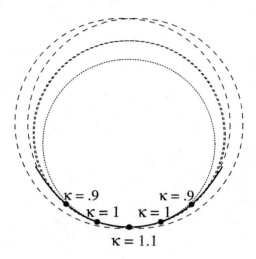

▷ **Exercise 4.** Working from the left to the right on the sine curve, the first point can be approximated by a circle of diameter 1/3 and radius $\approx .17$. However, this circle lies below the curve, so we say that the curvature is negative and $\kappa \approx -5.8$. The second point has the same curvature but the osculating circle lies above the curve so $\kappa \approx 5.8$. The next point is best approximated by a line instead of a circle, so $\kappa = 0$. The fourth point has the same radius of curvature as the first two points, and the circle lies below the curve so $\kappa \approx -5.8$. The last point can be approximated by a circle of diameter .9 lying above the curve, so $\kappa = \frac{1}{.45} \approx 2.1$.

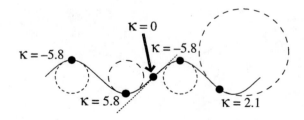

For Exercises 5–7, one must start paying attention to the sign of the curvature. Carrying out the thought experiment of walking around the curve with one arm stuck out should convince the students that the signs of the curvatures at each of the indicated points on the logarithmic spiral should be the same. The lemniscate and the limaçon are more complicated.

▷ **Exercise 5.** Working from the outermost point in, the first point marked on the logarithmic spiral is approximated by a circle of diameter $\frac{23}{16}$ so $\kappa \approx 1.4$. The next point has diameter of curvature $\frac{7}{8}$ and $\kappa \approx 2.3$, the next has diameter slightly more than $\frac{1}{2}$ and $\kappa \approx 3.8$, and so on. All of the osculating circles lie on the same side of the curve, so they all have the same sign, which we will choose to be positive.

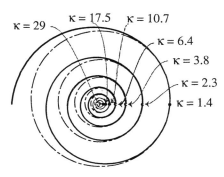

▷ **Exercise 6.** Imagine walking around the lemniscate with one arm sticking out and the other folded close to your body. A bird's eye view of this is shown on the left and illustrates that the osculating circles of the next picture change from one side of the curve to the other. We have chosen the signs as shown, but the opposite interpretation is equally valid. In any case the central point is best approximated by a straight line and so has curvature $\kappa = 0$. The two points at the ends are approximated by circles of diameter .7 and so have curvature $\kappa \approx 2.8$ but with opposite signs. The four middle points can each be approximated by circles of diameter 1.3 and so have curvature $\kappa \approx 1.5$ with signs as indicated.

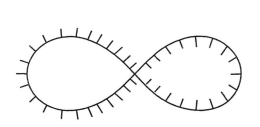
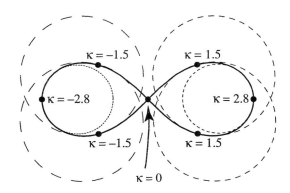

▷ **Exercise 7.** Repeat the thought experiment of walking around the limaçon with one arm stuck out and you can see that the signs of the curvature at each of the points will be the same. We have chosen to make them all positive. The point on the far right can be approximated by a circle of diameter 2.4, so the curvature there is $\kappa \approx \frac{1}{1.2} \approx .8$. The highest and lowest points are approximated by circles of diameter 2.1, so $\kappa \approx 1$. The leftmost-indicated points are approximated by circles of diameter $1\frac{2}{3}$, so $\kappa \approx \frac{6}{5} = 1.2$. The inner point is approximated by a circle with diameter .44, so $\kappa \approx 4.5$.

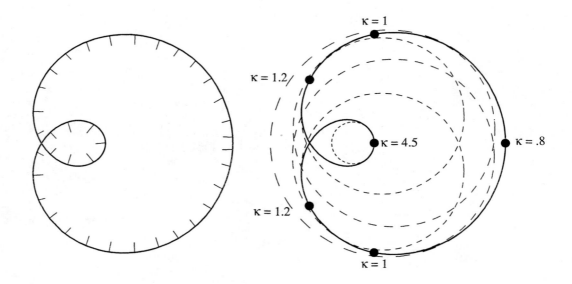

▷ **Exercise 8.** A Slinky^{TM} has curvature $\frac{1}{r}$ where r is the radius. This does not vary whether the Slinky is at rest or stretched (as long as it is not warped completely out of shape).

In Exercises 9–15, we calculate mean curvatures for various vegetables. The answers will, of course, depend not only on the type of vegetable but on the individual variations present in the species. To find the mean curvature at a point on a potato, slice the potato perpendicularly to the tangent plane and along the curve of greatest curvature. Use a circle template to estimate the curvature. Reassemble your potato and reslice it again along the curve of least curvature. These curves may not meet at right angles at the point. Then measure that curvature. The mean curvature is the average of these two: $H = \frac{1}{2}(\kappa_1 + \kappa_2)$. A rough idea of the curvature for potatoes can be estimated by remembering that the mean curvature for a ball of radius r is $H = \frac{1}{r}$. Thus large (spherical) potatoes will have smaller curvature than small ones. A mean curvature of 0 indicates either a flat surface in all directions or a hyperbolic surface with one positive and one negative principal curvature.

▷ **Exercise 9.** Calculate the mean curvature at a point on the potato. Note that the mean curvature of a perfect sphere of radius r is $H = \frac{1}{r}$.

▷ **Exercise 10.** Find the point on your potato with the smallest mean curvature and the point with the largest mean curvature. The potato will be most curved at the point with the largest mean curvature, and flattest at the point with smallest mean curvature.

▷ **Exercise 11.** Repeat Exercises 9 and 10 for a much smaller potato.

▷ **Exercise 12.** Repeat Exercises 9 and 10 for a cucumber. Generally, the point with largest mean curvature will occur at one of the ends, while the cylindrical sides will have smaller mean curvature, with one of the principal curvatures (in the flat direction) very close to zero.

▷ **Exercise 13.** Repeat Exercises 9 and 10 for a cabbage leaf taken from the outer leaves. The outer leaves of a cabbage will tend to be shaped like a largish sphere.

▷ **Exercise 14.** Repeat Exercises 9 and 10 for a cabbage leaf taken from the inner leaves. The inner leaves of a cabbage will tend to be shaped like a smallish sphere.

▷ **Exercise 15.** Repeat Exercises 9 and 10 for a kale leaf. The ripply outer edges of a kale leaf should exhibit curvature close to zero, since the principal curvatures will have opposite signs.

> *In Exercises 16–21, we compute the Gaussian curvature for the same vegetables. Having found the principal curvatures, this goes quickly, since $K = \kappa_1 \cdot \kappa_2$. Again, a rough approximation can be made by remembering that the Gaussian curvature of a sphere of radius r is $K = \frac{1}{r^2}$. A Gaussian curvature of 0 indicates that the surface is flat in at least one direction. A negative curvature indicates that the surface bends in two different directions, like a hyperbolic surface such as kale.*

▷ **Exercise 16.** Find the Gaussian curvature for the point on the potato from Exercise 9. Note that the mean curvature of a perfect sphere of radius r is $K = \frac{1}{r^2}$.

▷ **Exercise 17.** Find the Gaussian curvature for the point on the potato from Exercise 11.

▷ **Exercise 18.** Find the Gaussian curvature for the point on the cucumber from Exercise 12.

▷ **Exercise 19.** Find the Gaussian curvature for the point on the cabbage leaf from Exercise 13.

▷ **Exercise 20.** Find the Gaussian curvature for the point on the cabbage leaf from Exercise 14.

▷ **Exercise 21.** Find the Gaussian curvature for the point on the kale leaf from Exercise 15.

▷ **Exercise 22.** A sphere of radius r will have Gaussian curvature $K = \frac{1}{r^2}$ and mean curvature $H = \frac{1}{r}$.

11.4. Curvature of Surfaces

In this section, we extend our study of the curvature of surfaces initiated in Section 11.3. We start by investigating the seemingly unrelated concept of angular deficit. The angular deficit at a vertex of a polyhedron is simply the difference between 360° and the sum of the angles meeting at that vertex. The total angular deficit for a polyhedron is the sum of all the vertex angular deficits. Students find these quite easy to compute and this reinforces the angle formulae of Section 1.2 (recall that a vertex angle for a regular n-sided polygon will measure $\frac{(n-2)180°}{n}$). In Exercises 1–4, we compute the total angular deficits for regular polyhedra, a pyramid, a prism, and an antiprism. From this data, the student is asked in Exercise 5 to formulate a hypothesis about the total angular deficit for any convex polyhedron.

▷ **Exercise 1.** Fill in this table:

Angular Deficits

Polyhedron	δ	# of vertices	Δ
Tetrahedron	$360° - 3 \cdot 60° = 180°$	4	720°
Cube	$360° - 3 \cdot 90° = 90°$	8	720°
Octahedron	$360° - 4 \cdot 60° = 120°$	5	720°
Dodecahedron	$360° - 3 \cdot 108° = 36°$	20	720°
Icosahedron	$360° - 5 \cdot 60° = 60°$	12	720°

▷ **Exercise 2.** At the apex of the pyramid, four equilateral triangles meet, and at each of the four bottom vertices, two triangles and one square meet. Therefore, the apex of this pyramid has angular deficit $\delta = 360° - 4 \cdot 60° = 120°$ and the four bottom vertices have $\delta = 360° - 2 \cdot 60° - 90° = 150°$, so the total angular deficit is $\Delta = 120° + 4 \cdot 150° = 720°$.

▷ **Exercise 3.** At each of the ten vertices, two rectangles and one regular pentagon meet, so each vertex has $\delta = 360° - 2 \cdot 90° - 108° = 72°$. The total angular deficit is $\Delta = 10 \cdot 72° = 720°$.

▷ **Exercise 4.** At each of the ten vertices, three equilateral triangles and one regular pentagon meet, so each vertex has $\delta = 360° - 3 \cdot 60° - 108° = 72°$. The total angular deficit is $\Delta = 10 \cdot 72° = 720°$.

▷ **Exercise 5.** The total angular deficit of any convex polyhedron is 720°.

In Exercises 6–8, the students are asked to compute angle sums and areas for triangles on the sphere. Then in Exercise 9 we ask them to form a hypothesis on the relationship between the angle sum and the area. Students may need a hint to first subtract π or $180°$ from the angle measure, and then to try to find a relationship between this difference and the area. This relationship will be quite obvious if both angles and areas are expressed in the same terms, but this requires that the angles be written in radians rather than degrees.

If your students insist on measuring the angles in degrees, then one needs to rewrite the area of a sphere as $A = 4\pi r^2 = 720°(\frac{\pi}{180°}r^2)$. If all of the areas of the spherical triangles are rewritten to contain the factor $(\frac{\pi}{180°}r^2)$, then the relationship between the angle sum (in degrees) and the areas will be obvious.

▷ **Exercise 6.** The sum of the angles is $270° = \frac{3\pi}{2}$ and the area of this spherical triangle is one-eighth of the sphere, or $\frac{\pi}{2}r^2$ (or $90°(\frac{\pi}{180°}r^2)$ if angles are measured in degrees).

▷ **Exercise 7.** The sum of the angles is $210° = \frac{7\pi}{6}$ and the area of this spherical triangle is one twenty-fourth of the sphere, or $\frac{\pi}{6}r^2$ (or $30°(\frac{\pi}{180°}r^2)$ if angles are measured in degrees).

▷ **Exercise 8.** The sum of the angles is $300° = \frac{5\pi}{3}$ and the area of this spherical triangle is one-sixth of the sphere, or $\frac{2\pi}{3}r^2$ (or $120°(\frac{\pi}{180°}r^2)$ if angles are measured in degrees).

▷ **Exercise 9.** A formula for the area of a spherical triangle is $A = [(\text{sum of the angles}) - \pi]r^2$, where the angles are measured in radians. If the angles are measured in degrees, then the formula is $A = [(\text{sum of the angles}) - 180°](\frac{\pi}{180°}r^2)$.

In Exercises 10 and 11 we apply the formula found in Exercise 9.

▷ **Exercise 10.** Rewrite the angles as $45° = \frac{\pi}{4}$, $60° = \frac{\pi}{3}$, and $90° = \frac{\pi}{2}$. The area of this triangle is $A = [\frac{\pi}{4} + \frac{\pi}{3} + \frac{\pi}{2} - \pi]r^2 = \frac{\pi}{12}r^2$.

▷ **Exercise 11.** Rewrite the angles as $61° = \frac{61\pi}{180}$, $62° = \frac{62\pi}{180}$, and $63° = \frac{63\pi}{180}$. The area of this triangle is $A = [\frac{61\pi}{180} + \frac{62\pi}{180} + \frac{63\pi}{180} - \pi]r^2 = \frac{\pi}{30}r^2$.

The illustration that the students are asked to draw in Exercise 12 is essential to understanding the proof in the text of the area formula that the students proposed in Exercise 9. The formula is generalized to angle sums and areas of other spherical polygons in Exercise 13. Remind your students that for the formula for the area of the triangle, the number π, which is the sum of the angles in a euclidean triangle, played an important role. In fact, the key quantity in that formula was what is called the excess of the triangle: the difference between the angle sum for the spherical triangle and what it would be if it were a euclidean triangle. The quantity $\pi(n-2)$, which is the sum of the angles of an n-sided polygon in euclidean geometry, will play a similar role in the formula for the area of a spherical polygon. The triangle formula is then applied to find the radius of a certain sphere in Exercise 14.

▷ **Exercise 12.** Draw and shade the triangle and the lunes. Note that the triangle (and its shadow on the back of the ball) is part of all three lunes.

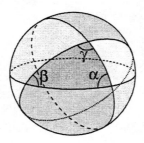

▷ **Exercise 13.** A formula for the area of a spherical n-gon is $A = [(\text{sum of the angles}) - \pi(n - 2)]r^2$.

▷ **Exercise 14.** $r = \sqrt{\frac{720}{\pi}}$

▷ **Exercise 15.** Since the angle sum or a hyperbolic triangle must be between 0 and $180° = \pi$, the formula $A(\text{triangle}) = (180° - \text{sum of the angles in the triangle})k$ implies that the area of the triangle must be between 0 and πk.

In Exercises 16–22 and the accompanying text, we relate our findings on angular deficit to approximating curvature and use this to find the curvature of various vegetables. This technique is much easier (though it does not give a precise answer) than the techniques of the previous section. Be sure to cut the strips of peel as the boundary of a disclike region of radius 1.

▷ **Exercise 16.** Build three different cones and measure their angular deficits at the vertex.

▷ **Exercise 17.** At an elliptic point, the signs of the angular deficit and the Gaussian curvature will both be positive, at a flat point both will be zero, and at a hyperbolic point both will be negative.

▷ **Exercise 18.** Measure the curvature for one region for each of your vegetables.

▷ **Exercise 19.** The curvature gets bigger at inner layers.

▷ **Exercise 20.** Find regions of one of your vegetables with approximate curvature: (a) 0°: choose a region that is very flat.
(b) 90°: choose a region that approximates a largish ball.
(c) 180°: choose a region that approximates a medium-sized ball.
(d) 360°: choose a region that approximates a small ball.
(e) −90°: choose a region of a kale leaf that is somewhat hyperbolic.

▷ **Exercise 21.** Of course, there are other possible answers: (a) Potatoes generally have positive curvature.
(b) Cucumbers and bananas have approximately zero curvature on their sides.
(c) Kale will have negative curvature.

Another way to think of these computations of curvature is to imagine a disc of radius one with a bit of string threaded through the outer circumference. The quantity $K = 2\pi - L$ measures how much string one pulls out, like a drawstring purse. The more string one pulls, the tighter the purse closes and the smaller a sphere it approximates. Exercise 22 refers back to the initial exercises of Section 11.1 and the relationship between circumference and curvature.

▷ **Exercise 22.** Use a map measure to measure the Gaussian curvature of several regions on a potato.

11.5. Soap Bubbles

In Exercises 1–7, we ask the students to experiment with soap films on three wire frames: one that has two parallel circles, one with a twisted circle, and one with a knot. You can have the students construct the frames, but it is much more efficient to make enough ahead of time so that each group of students has a copy of each frame. While experimenting, they will find that there are sometimes several forms that a soap film can make on a given frame. However, they should observe that these forms are remarkably consistent: repeated experimentation will only result in the same few forms. For example, the soap film on the parallel circle frame can take one of three forms, one of which is somewhat unstable and forms a bridge between the other two. These exercises should give the students experience with the natural area-minimizing tendency of soap films and provide some preliminary evidence about the angles formed by soap films.

In working with these frames, use the solution suggested in the text: 12 cups of water, 1 cup of dishwashing soap (legend has it that blue Dawn works better than green), and a quarter cup of glycerin (available at most drug stores). Mix these gently, trying to avoid creating foam or froth, as that will disturb the shapes we are trying to make. It is best to mix the solution at least an hour before the class is held to let the foam settle. To get all three desired shapes for these frames, try dipping the frame at different angles, blowing very gently on the soap film from different angles, dipping it once and then redipping it while it has the initial film still on the frame, or dipping it once and then submerging the frame halfway. You should be able to get three forms for each of these frames. However, for each frame, one of the forms will be an unstable transitional form between the other two, and so might only appear briefly. Tell students that dipping the frames and removing them slowly will not only minimize the foam (resulting in better surfaces) but can also help create some of the more difficult surfaces.

▷ **Exercise 1.** Try to get all three forms.

▷ **Exercise 2.** The angle between the sheets of soap film should be about 120°.

▷ **Exercise 3.** This depends somewhat on the radius of the rings and the distance between them. Let r be the radius of the rings and h the distance between parallel rings. Then the first form has area $2\pi r^2$ and the second can be approximated by the area of a cylinder, which is $2\pi rh$. The third form is approximately the area of the cylinder plus the area of a disc (though actually the sides of the cylinder will bow in even more than in the second form), which is $2\pi rh + \pi r^2 = \pi r(2h + r)$. If $r < h$, then the first form has smaller area than the second. If $r < 2h$, then the first form has smaller area than the third. The third form always has greater area than the second.

▷ **Exercise 4.** The first form looks like a disc twisted to form a figure 8: there are two sheets of film. The third form pictured has a sheet of soap forming a twisted cylindrical wall (or Möbius band) between the rings. The second transitional form has this twisted wall with a central disc spanning the inner circle of the figure 8.

▷ **Exercise 5.** In general, the third form has the least area, if the distance between the rings is less than the radius.

▷ **Exercise 6.** Again, you will get self-intersecting sheets and twisted bands and a transitional form between the two.

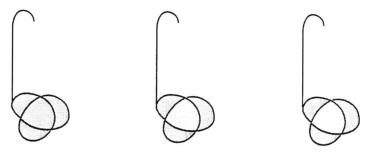

▷ **Exercise 7.** In general, the third form has the least area, if the distance between the outer portions of the knot is less than the radius of the inner circular area.

In Exercises 8 and 9, we try to get the students to observe that the soap film effortlessly forms 120° angles whenever three sheets of film meet.

▷ **Exercise 8.** The angle made by the intersection of the soap film with itself should be approximately 120°.

▷ **Exercise 9.** Pour a small amount of bubble solution onto a plate and blow through a straw to build bubble clusters. Sketch a cluster of bubbles, paying particular attention to the way they intersect. The angle formed between two sheets of soap film should always be 120°.

For Exercise 10, students need to know that the angle formed between a radial line and a tangent line is always 90°. Thus, we know that $DE \perp AD$, $DF \perp BD$, and $DG \perp CD$. Also by the hypotheses about the tensions exerted by the soap film, we know that $\angle EDF = \angle FDG = \angle GDE = 120°$. In Exercises 11 and 12, we ask the student to construct the wall between two bubbles, knowing that the angles formed between the centers of the circles and the point where the bubbles meet will be 60°.

191

▷ **Exercise 10.** Since $\angle EDF = 120°$ and $\angle EDA = 90°$, then $\angle ADF = 360° - 120° - 90° = 150°$. Since $\angle BDF = 90°$, $\angle ADB = \angle ADF - \angle BDF = 60°$. Similarly, since $\angle CDG = 90°$ and $\angle GDF = \angle EDF = 120°$, we know that $\angle FDC = 30°$ and thus $\angle BDC = 60°$.

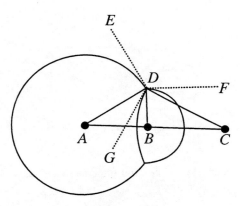

▷ **Exercise 11.** Draw a circle of radius 2 centered at point A. Choose a point D on the edge of the circle (this will be one of the points where the bubbles meet). Construct a 60° angle with one side AD. Use your compass to find the point B on the other side of the angle so that $DB = 1$. Draw a circle centered at B with radius $BD = 1$. Construct another 60° angle with one side BD. Draw the line AB and extend it until it meets the other side of this second 60° angle at point C. Draw a circle centered at C with radius CD. This will form the inner wall between the two bubbles. Highlight the portions of the three circles that form the double bubble.

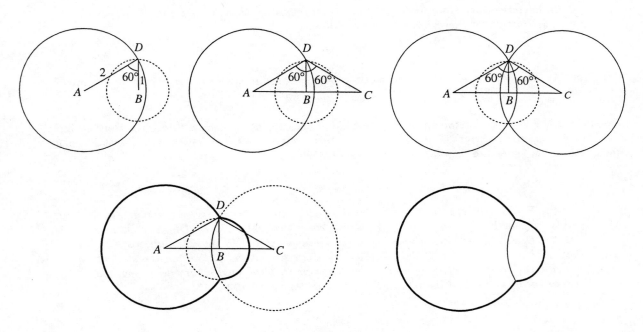

192

▷ **Exercise 12.** Repeat the process of Exercise 11, using circles of radius 1.5 and 1.

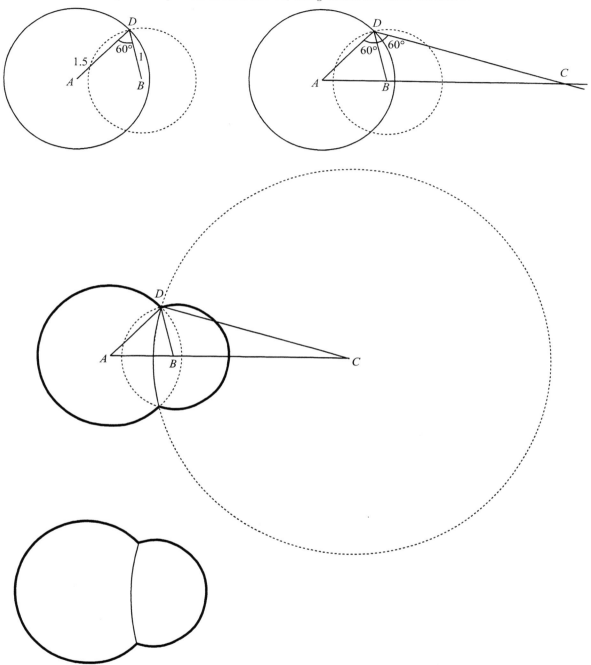

In Exercises 13 and 14, we experiment with polyhedral frames and note that the soap films form angles of 120° whenever three sheets meet, but 109° 28′ 16″ when four sheets meet. Of course, we hardly expect students to notice the precise value of this angle, but they should see that an angle other than 120° is made and that again the angle is surprisingly consistent.

▷ **Exercise 13.**   Dip the cubic frame into the bubble solution and sketch the results. You should be able to get both forms shown below. If you have trouble obtaining the second, dip to get the first form and then slowly lower this into the soap solution about halfway and remove.

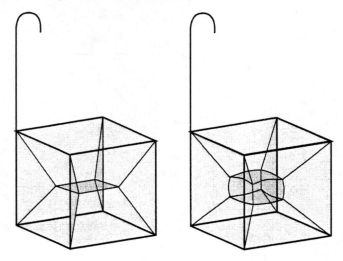

▷ **Exercise 14.**   Dip the octahedral frame into the bubble solution and sketch the result. You should be able to get the form shown below on the left as well as the form with an octahedral bubble in the center.

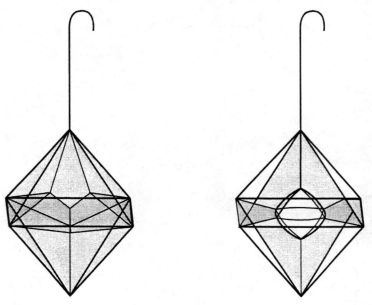

Students uncomfortable with variables will need Exercise 15 explained so that they know to find conditions regarding r and h that are necessary and sufficient for the question.

▷ **Exercise 15.**   (a) $r < h$.
(b) $2h < r$.

In Exercises 16–19, the student experiences minimal surfaces, as much as one can without delving into far more complex mathematics.

▷ **Exercise 16.** The catenoid has one negative curvature and one positive, which cancel out to give the mean curvature $H = 0$.

▷ **Exercise 17.** The helicoid is approximately flat everywhere, so both principle curvatures are zero and the mean curvature $H = 0$.

▷ **Exercise 18.** Dip the tetrahedral frame and pop sections of the soap film as shown. The remaining soap film should form a single sheet.

▷ **Exercise 19.** Dip the cubic frame and pop sections of the soap film as shown. The remaining soap film should form a single sheet.

Chapter 12. Graph Theory

★ **12.1. Graphs**
  Dependencies: None

- Classic problems: the Königsberg bridge problem, the handshake problem, and the utility company problem
- Graphs
- Euler circuits and paths
- Complete graphs and complete bipartite graphs
- Digraphs

★ ★ **12.2. Trees**
  Dependencies: Chapter 12.1
  References: Chapter 11.5 (regarding the area-minimizing property of soap film)

- Trees
- Euler characteristic
- Steiner trees

★ ★ **12.3. Mazes**
  Dependencies: Chapter 12.1, 12.2

- Unicursal mazes or labyrinths
- Maze solution algorithms
- Tremaux's algorithm

This chapter discusses graph theory and some of its applications. The first section covers some of the basic ideas, uses, and terminology of graphs. Three major problems, the Königsberg bridge problem, the handshake problem, and the utility company problem, motivate the discussion. Solving the Königsberg bridge problem gives rise to drawing graphs indicating relationships, the concept of degree, and the definition of Euler circuits and paths. Students are asked to figure out necessary and sufficient conditions for an Euler circuit or path to exist. The handshake problem requires a more detailed look at degrees. The utility problem brings in the ideas of bipartite graphs and complete graphs. The section ends with an optional subsection (after Exercise 22) on digraphs and their application to the house swap problem.

The second section is devoted to trees: graphs without cycles. The Euler characteristic, met in the chapter on polyhedra, is reintroduced and shown to be effective in distinguishing trees from other graphs. If one's main interest in this section is preparation for the next section on mazes or if the class has not covered Section 11.5, one could stop at this point (after Exercise 3). Otherwise, the text next goes on to discuss Steiner trees and the problem of finding the shortest network. This is somewhat dependent on Section 11.5, but the instructor could instead briefly discuss the property of soap films to form an energy-minimizing $120°$ angle whenever three sheets of film meet.

The last section is on mazes and solution algorithms for them. In our experience, students have been consistently entranced with mazes. The text discusses various ways of drawing mazes and labyrinths. Three maze solution algorithms are presented: the maze-centered dead-end rule, the person-centered right-hand rule, and the person-centered Tremaux's algorithm. The occasional failure of the right-hand rule for nonsimply connected mazes (whose graph of paths does not form a tree) is shown as justification for the introduction of the far more cumbersome Tremaux's algorithm.

12.1. Graphs

This section begins with the statement of three of the major problems of graph theory. Each of these could be solved with common sense and the invention of appropriate diagrams, but students are more likely to need further assistance, which they will gain by working through the rest of the section. However, we encourage you to copy the statements of these problems and have your students try to work on them in groups before turning to the text. Even if they don't solve the problems, in this way they will familiarize themselves with some of the ideas and difficulties and often come up with very good ideas to pursue after they do gain some vocabulary and notation after returning to the text.

For Exercise 1, it is not clear whether Euler's route should be a circuit (starting and ending at home) or merely a path (so the endpoint may not be the same as the starting point). Neither is possible, so choose whichever option you prefer if your students ask, or ask them to address both problems.

▷ **Exercise 1.** It is not possible to cross each bridge only once, as will be explained later.

▷ **Exercise 2.** Ben shook two people's hands.

▷ **Exercise 3.** It is not possible to connect the utility companies to the three houses as directed, as will be explained later.

In Exercises 4–6 the students are asked to draw graphs representing various simple situations. Note that almost every student I have had forgot the loops even though they are explicitly mentioned in the text. My students don't bother reading, but just find the exercises and ask questions later.

▷ **Exercise 4.**

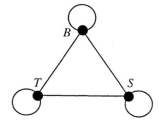
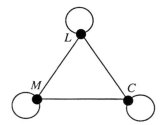

197

▷ **Exercise 5.**

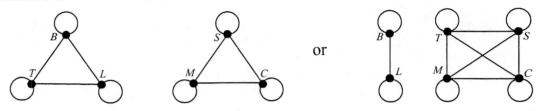

Remind your students to express the relationship represented by an edge in Exercise 6 in complete, grammatically correct sentences.

▷ **Exercise 6.** Create a graph using the students of this class as the vertices and make up your own relationship for the edges.

In Exercise 7, we ask the students to figure out (at this point by trial and error) whether an Euler circuit exists for the given examples. You may need to remind them that a circuit must return to the starting vertex. In Exercise 8, we ask them to use these findings to hypothesize when an Euler circuit will not exist (the question is initially easier to answer in the negative). Their answer to Exercise 8 will not at this time involve the word "degree," but should be phrased more or less as an Euler circuit will not exist if any of the vertices have an odd number of edges meeting there. They are unlikely to think of trying disconnected graphs, so you may need to suggest that they try one or two. Otherwise, Exercise 13(c) will introduce the idea and they can fix their conjectures themselves. Some students think about the degree right away. Others have tried rules such as "if the graph has a curved edge, it will have an Euler circuit." Plan to suggest graphs to lead your students away from misconceptions. Remind them that there is not automatically a vertex where edges seem to cross in Exercise 7(b).

▷ **Exercise 7.** a) Yes
 b) No
 c) No
 d) Yes

▷ **Exercise 8.** There is no Euler circuit if any of the vertices have an odd number of edges meeting there or if the graph is not connected.

In Exercise 9, we ask the students to figure out (at this point by trial and error) whether an Euler path exists for the given examples. A path need not return to the starting vertex. In Exercise 10, we ask them to use these findings to hypothesize when an Euler path will not exist. Their answer to Exercise 10 will not at this time involve the word "degree," but should be phrased more or less as an Euler path will not exist if more than two of the vertices have an odd number of edges meeting there. If you gave the hint from Exercise 8, they should think of trying disconnected graphs. Many students really struggle here. I go back to the idea of bridges. If you start on an island with an odd number of bridges to the mainland and cross each bridge once, can you end up in the same place? If you start on the mainland, where will you end up? One odd vertex to start on and one to end one gives the desired result.

▷ **Exercise 9.** a) Yes
  b) Yes
  c) No
  d) Yes
  e) No
  f) No

▷ **Exercise 10.** There cannot be an Euler path if more than two vertices have an odd number of edges or if the graph is not connected.

> *The Handshake problem is solved in Exercise 11, with the advantage of the experience and vocabulary gained in the previous exercises. Have the students draw a graph representing the situation and have them discuss the possible numbers of hands that can be shaken.*

▷ **Exercise 11.** Since everyone Alice asked shook a different number of hands, and no one shakes his or her own or their partner's hand, the possible number of handshakes is four, three, two, one, and zero. Thus each person is represented by a vertex with one of those degrees, except for Alice. Let the couples be denoted X-x, Y-y, and Z-z. One person, X, shook four hands. Therefore, x must be the person who shook no hands, since everyone else has had their hand shaken at least once, as shown below on the left. Another person, Z, shook three hands which will not include z or x but will include X. Therefore, Z must shake hands with X, Y, and y, and so only z can shake exactly one hand, as shown below on the right. Therefore Y and y shook two hands each. Since only Alice can shake the same number of hands as someone else, y and Y must be Ben and Alice, so Ben must shake two hands.

> *In Exercise 12, we ask the students to restate their results of Exercises 8 and 10 using the terminology of degrees. They should at this point be able to state these rules correctly and concisely. In Exercise 13, we ask them to go on and state rules for when Euler circuits and paths will exist, negating their answers for Exercise 12. If you did not encourage the idea of disconnected graphs in Exercise 8, many students will insist that Exercise 13(c) is, in fact, two graphs, even though they have seen disconnected graphs in Exercises 4 and 5. Reinforce the idea here and they will get the correct answers.*

▷ **Exercise 12.** There cannot be an Euler circuit if any of the vertices have odd degree or if the graph is not connected. There cannot be an Euler path if more than two vertices have odd degree or if the graph is not connected.

▷ **Exercise 13.** An Euler circuit exists if a graph is connected and all vertices have even degree. An Euler path exists if the graph is connected and exactly two vertices or no vertices have odd degree.

*If students have trouble with Exercises 14 and 15, have them consider several examples
of graphs and the degrees of all the vertices. It should soon occur to them that each edge
gets counted twice, so that the sum of all the degrees must be even. From this it is easy
to answer both exercises.*

▷ **Exercise 14.** In adding up the degree for all of the vertices, each edge is counted twice: once at each
endpoint.

▷ **Exercise 15.** The sum of the degrees must equal twice the number of edges, and so must be an even
integer. Therefore, there must be an even number of vertices with odd degree.

*In Exercise 16, we ask the students to draw complete graphs. In doing this, they should
notice that each vertex is joined to every other vertex.*

▷ **Exercise 16.**

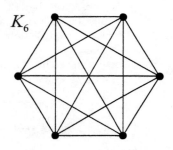 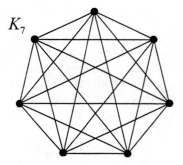

*In Exercises 17 and 18, we ask the student to draw and figure out the number of edges in
complete bipartite graphs.*

▷ **Exercise 17.**

 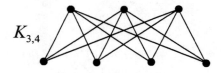

▷ **Exercise 18.** Since each of the n upper vertices will have m edges connecting it to the lower vertices,
$K_{n,m}$ has nm edges.

*In Exercise 19, we ask that the students try to redraw $K_{3,3}$ as a planar graph. This will
require considerable experimentation and some discussion before the students can verbalize
why this is not possible. But herein lies the solution to the utility company problem, so
they are already familiar with the situation and its constraints. In Exercise 20, we ask
them to show that $K_{2,4}$ and $K_{2,5}$ are planar. If the students have difficulty with these,
you may want to show them how to redraw $K_{2,2}$ and $K_{2,3}$ as planar graphs. In Exercise
21, we ask them to experiment with K_5 to see if it is planar and to explain why it is not
in Exercise 22.*

▷ **Exercise 19.** $K_{3,3}$ is not planar, so this is not possible.

▷ **Exercise 20.**

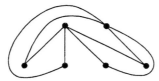 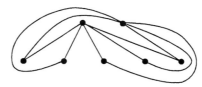

▷ **Exercise 21.** K_5 cannot be drawn so that the edges do not intersect.

▷ **Exercise 22.** See the illustration below. First draw the outer pentagon and then connect A to C and D. This blocks the center of the pentagon, so the edge from B to D must go around the outside. But then C is hemmed in and one cannot draw an edge from C to E without intersecting another edge. Thus K_5 is not planar.

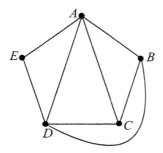

In Exercises 23–25, we apply the idea of a digraph to the house swap problem. In Exercise 23, we ask the student to draw the digraph representing the problem given in the text, and to find the appropriate circuit and solve the problem in Exercise 24. Exercise 25 is another, more complex situation of the same type.

▷ **Exercise 23.**

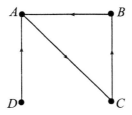

▷ **Exercise 24.** The circuit is $A \to C \to B \to A$, so A moves to C's house, C moves to B's house, and B moves to A's house. D stays put (his third choice).

Students often want A to get his first choice just because A is first in the alphabet. Reiterate the warning that person A is no better than anyone else in the problem. Selfishness is also inherent in the method. Originally, I phrased the goal as maximizing happiness or satisfaction. Students observed that in some graphs if one person could be talked into his second choice, everyone else could get their first choice.

▷ **Exercise 25.** Note that $C \to E \to C$ is a circuit, shown in the digraph on the left. Thus, first C and E swap houses. Removing C and E from the graph gives the digraph at the center. Since F can no longer choose E or C (his first two choices), he will choose F (his third choice). This second digraph has circuit $F \to F$, so F keeps his house. Removing F gives the digraph of the right. A can no longer choose F, so must go to his second choice, D. D can no longer choose F, E, or C, so chooses B (his fourth choice). The only circuit is $B \to D \to B$, so B and D swap houses. Removing B and D leaves A no choice but to stay put (his fifth choice).

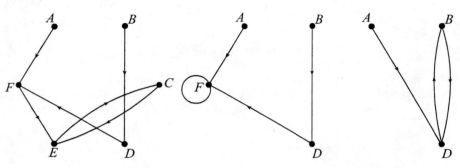

12.2. Trees

The first part of this section (through Exercise 3, with Exercise 4 optional) is all that is required for Section 12.3, and also can serve as an introduction to the Euler characteristic and the idea of connectivity, as studied in Section 13.3. The second part of the section extends the principles of soap films from Section 11.5 to the design of shortest networks.

In Exercises 1 and 2, we study the Euler characteristic of graphs and trees. The Euler characteristic of any tree is 1, while the Euler characteristic for a graph is $1 - n$ where n is the number of circuits in the graph. Students may have trouble deciding what constitutes a circuit. Consider these pictures:

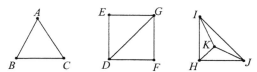

In the first picture, everyone will agree that there is one circuit, which could be labeled $ABCA$. A little more thought makes it clear that the circuit $ABCA$ is the same as the circuits $BCAB$ and $CABC$. We also do not distinguish between these and the clockwise circuits $ACBA$, $CBAC$, and $BACB$. In the second picture things get more interesting. One could make a good case that this graph contains three circuits: $DEGD$, $DGFD$, and $DEGFD$. However, in a sense the circuit $DEGFD$ is a combination of $DEGD$ and $DGFD$: the edge DG is repeated twice if one travels around $DEGD$ and then $DGFD$, but once forward and once backward and one could claim that these cancel. Similarly, one could claim that the last picture has seven circuits: $HIKH$, $HJKH$, $IJKI$, $HIJKH$, $HIKJH$, $HJIKH$, and $HIJH$. Again, some of these can be thought of as combinations of others. The most efficient way to count circuits is to remove edges from the graph (but leave the endpoint vertices of these edges behind). If one does this carefully for a graph with n circuits, one can remove n edges from the graph and still have a connected tree, but removing the $(n+1)$st edge will disconnect the graph. For example, in the second picture if one removes the edges DF and DE, what is left forms a connected tree. Therefore the second graph should be considered to have two circuits. One could instead remove the two edges DE and DG. One needs to remove one edge from each circuit. Be careful though: if one removed the edges DE and EG, one would not have a tree, but a graph with a circuit and with one isolated vertex at E, so this graph is not connected. Thus, there are several correct choices of which two edges one could remove to obtain a tree, but there are also incorrect choices, which do not destroy the circuits but which break the graph into more than one component.

▷ **Exercise 1.** (a) $\chi = 0$ (b) $\chi = -1$ (c) $\chi = -2$

Remind your students that a loop is a circuit and can be removed from any graph without disconnecting it. You may need to suggest they draw some other graphs if your students are having trouble coming up with the correct rule. Though often very helpful, my students always resist looking at any situation other than the ones in the text.

▷ **Exercise 2.**   (a) 1 circuit   (b) 2 circuits   (c) 3 circuits   Thus, $\chi = 1-$ the number of circuits.

▷ **Exercise 3.**

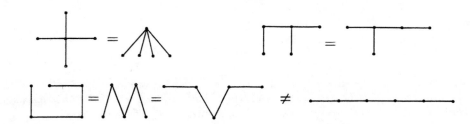

Make sure that your students understand the ideas that equivalent graphs must have the same number of vertices and that changing an angle does not significantly change a graph before they attempt Exercise 4.

▷ **Exercise 4.**

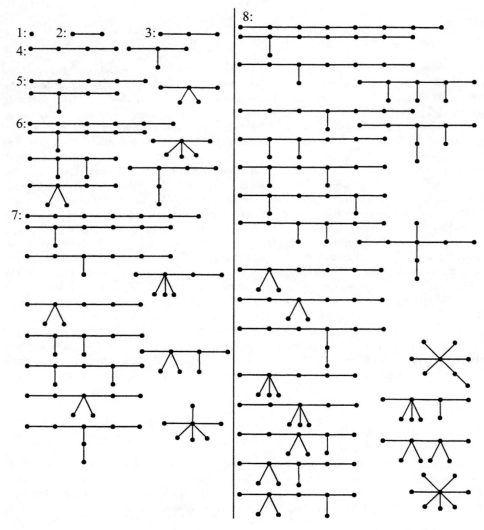

204

In Exercises 5–9, we experiment with finding the shortest network of roads between three cities. Exercise 5 sets the framework for these networks, by pointing out that what may be the most obvious network is inefficient. The experiments in Exercises 6–9 should be done either with a software package such as The Geometer's Sketchpad® or with the soap film contraption described in the text. Exercise 6 could be done without either of these, since students could try various positions for the central point and measure the length of the network with a ruler, but The Geometer's Sketchpad can be programmed to measure this length automatically as one varies the position of the point. The soap film will naturally conform to the shortest network. If you use the soap, be sure to make the mixture well ahead of time to minimize foam and also use a wide bowl or pan so you can dip the Plexiglas^{TM} assembly flat. If you dip an edge into a deep but narrow bucket, sometimes the weight of the solution will pull the film down and pop it. Lifting the structure at a slight angle from the horizontal will let most of the excess solution run off without affecting the bubble structure.

▷ **Exercise 5.** There are redundant roads: for example, there are two ways to get from A to B. In other words, circuits are wasteful.

▷ **Exercise 6.** The total length is minimized when the fourth point is at the center of the triangle. Note that the interior angles then measure 120°.

▷ **Exercise 7.** The "road structure" around the central point should always form 120° angles.

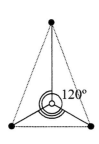 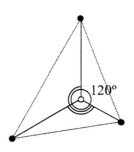 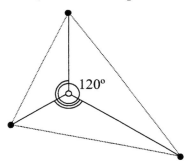

▷ **Exercise 8.** Using two sheets of glass, three thumb tacks, and the soap solution, make an equilateral triangle and dip into the soap solution. The resulting soap film forms the figure that minimized total length in Exercise 6.

In Exercise 9, first consider a right triangle. The shortest network is shown on the next page, satisfying the condition that an interior point is added forming 120° angles with the vertices. A triangle with one angle of 100° would have a similar interior Steiner vertex. However, for a triangle with one angle of 120°, the Steiner vertex coincides with this vertex, and the shortest network will be formed by the two shortest legs of the triangle. For a triangle with one angle greater than 120°, the shortest network will also be formed by the two shorter legs of the triangle. Note that the soap films form the angles quickly but are a bit of a mess. Software takes longer to move the interior point around to minimize total length, but students can compare the lengths of different schemes more easily.

▷ **Exercise 9.** Below are shown four triangles: the first has its largest angle equal to 90°, the second 100°, the third 120°, and the last 150°. For triangles all of whose angles are less than 120°, the shortest network is found by adding an interior vertex forming 120° angles. For triangles with one angle greater than or equal to 120°, the shortest network is found by taking the two shortest legs of the triangle.

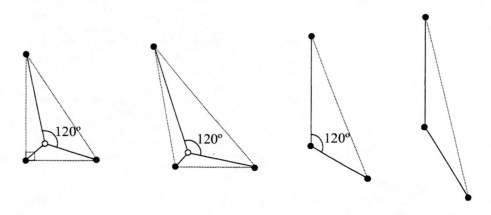

In Exercises 10–12, we experiment with the shortest network for four cities arranged in a square. Students should find, using rulers, The Geometer's Sketchpad, or soap films, that the shortest network involves adding two new vertices with the roads meeting at these vertices to form 120° angles. This works best with soap. Using rulers or software, one wonders if more points are needed, and moving two points to minimize distance takes a bit of practice. In Exercise 13, we ask the students to draw the Steiner tree (shortest network) for some other placements of four cities. Exercise 14 contrasts two different Steiner trees, both satisfying the 120° condition. One of these is shorter than the other, but the soap film may form either.

▷ **Exercise 10.** If the sides of the square each have length 1, then the first road plan has total length 3 and the second has length $2\sqrt{2} \approx 2.828427$. The road plan that minimizes length is shown below on the right, with total length $1 + \sqrt{3} \approx 2.732051$:

▷ **Exercise 11.** Build a model using the glass sheets and four tacks. In order to form the surface area minimizing 120° angles, two interior vertices are needed. See the solution for Exercise 10.

▷ **Exercise 12.** Three planes meet at each interior vertex, forming 120° angles.

▷ **Exercise 13.** Model the situation created by having four towns at random points in the plane. The shortest networks are shown below:

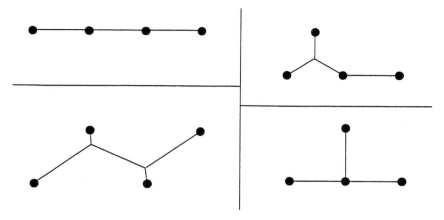

▷ **Exercise 14.** See if you can form the longer tree (the second illustration) using the soap solution.

12.3. Mazes

For this section, only basic information about the definition of a tree and whether a graph contains a circuit is needed. To make it easier to redraw the tree of paths in Exercise 1, we have labeled the nodes and end vertices. Use graph paper or the grid of Template 1 of the Appendix for Exercises 2 and 3. In drawing the graph of a maze in Exercise 1 and some of the later exercises, remind your students that it is the branching that matters, not the length or shape of the edges. In simplifying a graph, it is easiest to redraw it in stages: first simplify the dead ends, keeping the main structure pretty much as it is drawn on the maze, then keep straightening out the paths. Labeling makes it easier to explain to the students and makes it clear where each node or endpoint goes, but is not necessary. Of course, these maze trees and graphs can be drawn in a number of ways, all equivalent.

▷ **Exercise 1.** Below on the left is the maze and the tree formed by all the paths. Note that the paths do not form any circuits, so this is indeed a tree. This tree is abstracted in the second picture and all of the nodes or points where two or more paths join are labeled with capital letters, while dead ends are labeled with lower case. The third picture shows this tree, with the labeling, simplified. In the last picture, the simplified tree alone is shown.

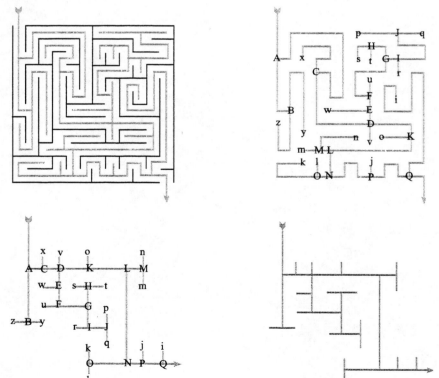

▷ **Exercise 2.** Draw a different maze using a 10 by 10 grid of squares.

208

▷ **Exercise 3.** Draw a different labyrinth.

Next we ask the students to draw two Cretan mazes. Such mazes have been found on Cretan coins and are used in children's games. Students should be able to abstract the process in the text to the more complex situations of Exercises 4 and 5.

▷ **Exercise 4.**

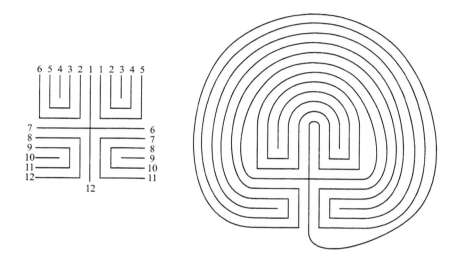

▷ **Exercise 5.**

In Exercises 6 and 7, we solve two mazes using the method of shading the dead ends. This method is easy to apply, but only works well for an outside viewer. Students should shade the dead ends in stages: first the most obvious dead ends, then pathways leading only to already shaded dead ends, and so on.

▷ **Exercise 6.**

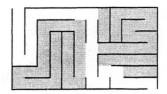

▷ **Exercise 7.**

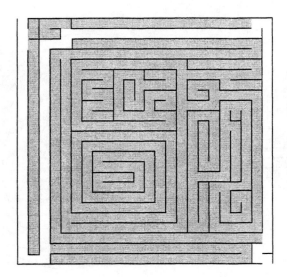

In Exercises 8 and 9, we solve two (simply connected) mazes using the right-hand rule. This method is easy to apply and works well for a person inside the maze, although it does not lead to the shortest path through the maze. Many of our students want to simply solve the maze visually. Insist that they actually use the right-hand rule, pointing out that if they were actually walking through a hedge maze, they couldn't use the techniques they are used to.

▷ **Exercise 8.**

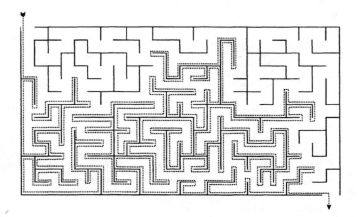

▷ **Exercise 9.** Note that many students who are using the right-hand rule correctly want to skip out from the point marked with a ∗, saying that they can see the exit from there. Insist that they imagine that either it is nighttime or they are blindfolded.

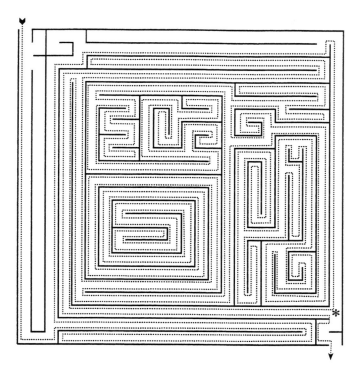

In Exercise 10 and 11, we ask the student to draw the graph or tree of paths for a maze and to simplify this as much as possible. If the students have trouble with this, have them label the nodes and end vertices as we did in Exercise 1. It is important that students be able to distinguish between simply connected mazes (whose graphs form trees) and nonsimply connected ones. The right-hand rule may not work for nonsimply connected mazes.

▷ **Exercise 10.**

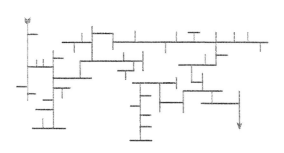

▷ **Exercise 11.**

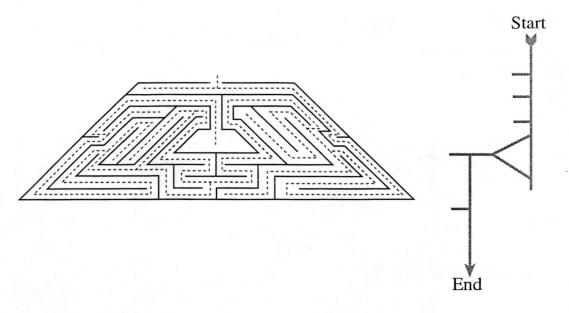

Start

End

Exercises 12 and 13 involve nonsimply connected mazes and what happens when one tries to apply the right-hand rule to such mazes.

▷ **Exercise 12.** The right-hand rule is shown as dotted, while the left-hand rule is dashed. Note that every path is covered twice, except for the circuit shown in the graph of Exercise 10.

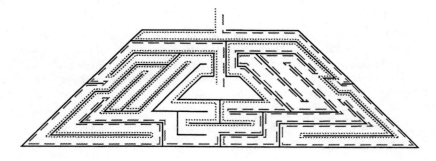

▷ **Exercise 13.**

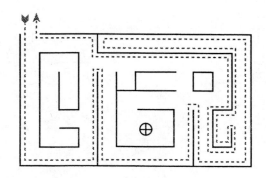

Students find Tremaux's algorithm difficult to follow, mostly because they tend to skip steps. Exercises 14-16 are designed to familiarize them with the algorithm and to justify why it works by investigating the outcome of certain cases.

▷ **Exercise 14.**

Case 1: After entering the node, by Rule 3 you should choose any path you haven't been on before. You happen (by accident) to choose the path that goes straight on, thus bypassing the loop. Note that rocks are left where you entered the node and where you left.

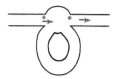

Case 2: (a) After entering the node, you choose the first path on the right. Leave a rock at the path where you entered the node and where you left.

(b) You are now on a path you have not been on before and you follow it back to the node.

(c) The rocks at the node indicate that you've been here before, so by Rule 5 you double back along the path, leaving two rocks behind (one for emerging from the path and one for leaving on the path).

(d) You come out at the node again on the path that you have traveled before, leaving another rock to show that you've come out of that path.

(e) Since you've been on the loop path before, by Rule 6 you should take a new path if possible. The only path that has not been traveled (as indicated by the rocks) is the one that leads straight on.

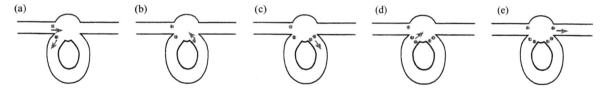

Case 3: (a) After entering the node, you choose the second path on the right. Leave a rock at the path where you entered the node and where you left.

(b) You are now on a path you have not been on before and you follow it back to the node.

(c) The rocks at the node indicate that you've been here before, so by Rule 5 you double back along the path, leaving two rocks behind (one for emerging from the path and one for leaving on the path).

(d) You come out at the node again on the path that you have traveled before, leaving another rock to show that you've come out of that path.

(e) Since you've been on the loop path before, by Rule 6 you should take a new path if possible. The only path that has not been traveled (as indicated by the rocks) is the one that leads straight on.

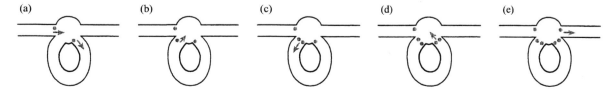

▷ **Exercise 15.**

Case 1: (a) After emerging at the first node (and leaving a rock), by Rule 3 you should choose any path you haven't been on before. You happen to choose the first path to the right, leaving a rock at the entrance to this path.

(b) Emerging from this path at the second node, by Rule 3 again, you should choose any path you haven't been on before. You choose the first path to your left, leaving another rock.

(c) This path takes you back to the first node, so by Rule 5 you double back to the second node, leaving behind two rocks to mark the entrance to this path.

(d) Rule 6 now applies, so you should choose a new path if possible. The rocks show that the only path that hasn't been traveled is the one straight ahead.

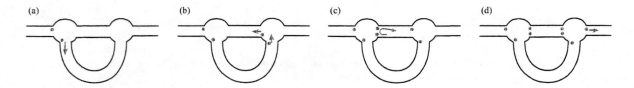

Case 2: (a) After emerging at the first node (and leaving a rock), by Rule 3 you should choose any path you haven't been on before. You happen to choose the first path to the right, leaving a rock at the entrance to this path.

(b) Emerging from this path at the second node, by Rule 3 again, you should choose any path you haven't been on before. You choose the first path to your right, leaving another rock. This path takes you on away from the circuit.

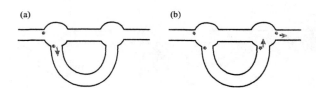

Case 3: (a) After emerging at the first node (and leaving a rock), by Rule 3 you should choose any path you haven't been on before. You happen to choose the second path to the right, leaving a rock at the entrance to this path.

(b) Emerging from this path at the second node, by Rule 3 again, you should choose any path you haven't been on before. You choose the first path to your right, leaving another rock.

(c) This path takes you back to the first node, so by Rule 5 you double back to the second node, leaving behind two rocks to mark the entrance to this path.

(d) Rule 6 now applies, so you should choose a new path if possible. The rocks show that the only path that hasn't been traveled is the one straight ahead.

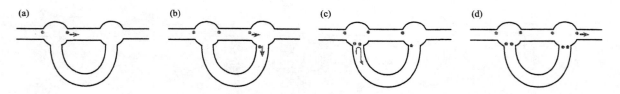

Case 4: (a) After emerging at the first node (and leaving a rock), by Rule 3 you should choose any path you haven't been on before. You happen to choose the second path to the right, leaving a rock at the entrance to this path.

(b) Emerging from this path at the second node, by Rule 3 again, you should choose any path you haven't been on before. You choose the path straight ahead, leaving another rock. This path takes you on away from the circuit.

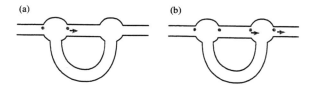

▷ **Exercise 16.**

(a) Note that if you entered the node by the path on the left, then Rule 6 applies and you should take the path with no rocks. If you entered the node from the right, then Rule 5 applies and you should double back to the right.

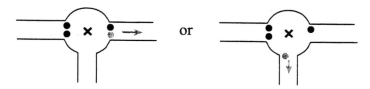

(b) In this case you must have entered the node from the left, so Rule 5 applies and you can take either unmarked path.

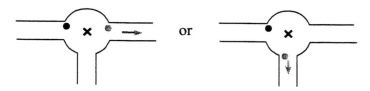

(c) No matter how you got to the node, either Rule 5 or Rule 6 applies and both say you should take the path that has only one rock, leaving a rock behind.

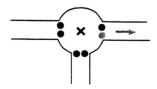

Exercises 17 and 19 are nicely complicated mazes for the student to solve. The maze at Chevening is a nonsimply connected maze (one of the first such hedge mazes ever planted). Dudeney's Philadelphia maze of Exercise 19 is repeated in Template 47 of the Appendix, as students are likely to need several copies before they succeed in solving this maze.

215

▷ **Exercise 17.** Here is one solution, found using Tremaux's algorithm, though there are many others.

▷ **Exercise 18.** Draw the graph for the Chevening maze.

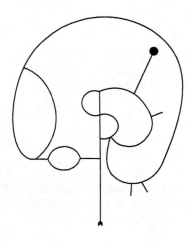

▷ **Exercise 19.** Here is one solution of many. Also see Template 47 in the Appendix.

Chapter 13. Topology

This chapter introduces some of the concepts and objects of topology. The first section gives a more formal introduction to the idea of dimension. This concept was first met in Chapter 6, and the familiarity with the idea and its difficulties may help the students to appreciate its subtleties. However, the current section is not dependent on the previous discussion and takes a more rigorous approach.

The second section of this chapter introduces the definition and standard examples of topological surfaces or two-dimensional manifolds, both with and without boundary. Examples include the sphere, n-holed torus, Möbius band, Klein bottle, and projective plane. The connected sum construction for joining two surfaces is explained. The property of orientability is defined.

Section 13.3 is devoted to studying topological properties of the objects introduced in the previous section. Orientability and boundary were previously introduced. The Euler characteristic is applied to surfaces. This has been previously used, especially in Chapter 7 for polyhedra and Section 12.2 for graphs and trees. Familiarity with those sections (especially Section 12.2) may help the student understand the significance of the Euler characteristic, but is not essential. The main new topological property is connectivity, not to be confused with connectedness. The classification theorem for surfaces is stated and the higher dimensional analogue, the Poincaré conjecture, is briefly discussed.

The last section of the text is on map coloring problems and the Four-Color Conjecture. This provides an application of the Euler characteristic for surfaces and gives a proof of the number of colors that are necessary and sufficient for coloring maps on the torus and projective plane. The six-color theorem is proved for maps on the sphere or plane, and the Four-Color Theorem is stated but not proved.

13.1. Dimension

This section begins with a nontechnical introduction to the main ideas of the mathematical field of topology. After discussing what a topological invariant is and why one would like to find some, the idea of dimension, implicit in much of the preceding chapters, is introduced. Two different definitions of dimension are given: covering dimension and embedding dimension. Examples are given for each, and the student should see that one need not get a unique dimension for an object, but that this depends on which of the two definitions one uses. Exercises 1–3 will be redundant if your students have gone through Chapter 6. However, they may serve to refresh the students' memories. For these exercises, we expect the students to use their pre-existing idea of dimension gained in earlier courses or from previous chapters of the text.

▷ **Exercise 1.** You get a line segment, which is one-dimensional.

▷ **Exercise 2.** You get a square, which is two-dimensional.

▷ **Exercise 3.** You get a cube, which is three-dimensional.

In Exercises 4–9, we work with the concept of covering dimension. You will need to supply (or ask the students to bring) an ample number of discs, such as pennies. The objects you will find the dimensions of should be suitably scaled. For example, if all of the objects (points, line segments, and surfaces) are so small that each could be hidden under a single penny, then your findings won't mean much. Remind your students that ideally the discs could be arbitrarily small.

▷ **Exercise 4.** If your collection of points are spaced far enough apart (or if your "pennies" are small enough), the pennies will not overlap, so the thickest intersection is one penny.

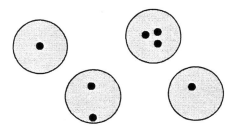

▷ **Exercise 5.** The thickest intersection of pennies should be two pennies thick. In the first illustration, note that the enlargement shows two pennies that are tangent (just touching but not overlapping) leave a tiny section of the string uncovered. Therefore, the pennies must overlap. In the second picture, the pennies are arranged so that three overlap at the shaded region. The correct arrangement is shown in the third picture: the pennies are at most two deep.

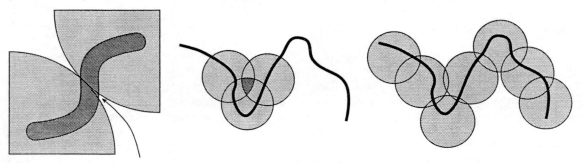

▷ **Exercise 6.** The thickest intersection of pennies should be three pennies thick.

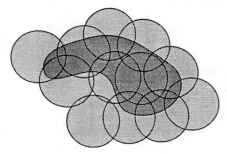

▷ **Exercise 7.** The thickest intersection of balls should be four balls thick.

Students should already have the idea that a line segment is one-dimensional and that a square is two-dimensional. From this, they should be able to generalize to realize that the string of Exercise 5 ought also be one-dimensional and that the shape of Exercise 6 is two-dimensional. From this and their answers for Exercises 4–6, they ought to be able to find the formula for Exercise 8. They will be less comfortable with the idea of a point (or collection of points) being zero-dimensional, but its dimension clearly must be less than one, so there are not a lot of choices here.

▷ **Exercise 8.** A definition of covering dimension would be the number of pennies in the thickest overlap minus one.

▷ **Exercise 9.** As in Exercise 5, pennies can be rearranged if necessary to cover the bent line so that only two overlap at a time.

▷ **Exercise 10.** As in Exercise 5, the balls will have to overlap so that they don't leave bits of the line uncovered. By choosing very small balls, these could be run along the knotted line (like beads on a string) and always overlap two at a time. No two-dimensional picture can adequately convey the situation.

In Exercises 11–15, we discuss the related concept of embedding dimension: the smallest dimensional space that an object can fit into. Note that some of the examples already studied will have the same covering and embedding dimensions, while others will differ. Note that the embedding dimension of a knotted bit of string is 1 if the ends are loose, since one can untie it to make a straight line. If one forms a nontrivial knot and then glues the ends together, as in the trefoil knot illustrated in Exercise 11, then this will have an embedding dimension of three.

▷ **Exercise 11.** A knotted bit of string with the ends glued together (such as the trefoil knot below) cannot be fit back into one- or two-dimensional space without cutting it, so it will have an embedding dimension of three.

▷ **Exercise 12.** A collection of several points requires one-dimensional space to exist, since the points cannot overlap.

▷ **Exercise 13.** Convince yourself that the (infinitely thin) bent plane is actually a two-dimensional object, using the definition found in Exercise 8 and visualized balls in three-dimensional space.

▷ **Exercise 14.** A sphere (picture this as the infinitely thin skin of a ball and visualize covering it with three-dimensional balls) or a cylinder has covering dimension two but cannot fit into two-dimensional space.

If students have trouble with Exercise 15, have them collect their data from the examples and exercises, as shown in the table below:

Dimensions

Object	Covering Dimension	Embedding Dimension
Point	0	0
Several points	0	1
Straight line	1	1
Bent line	1	1
Trefoil knot	1	3
Fox-Artin curve	1	3
Circle	1	2
Plane	2	2
Bent plane	2	2
Twisted cylinder	2	3
Sphere	2	3

▷ **Exercise 15.** An object with covering dimension n will fit in $(2n + 1)$-dimensional space, and so will have embedding dimension no more than $(2n + 1)$.

13.2. Surfaces

This section introduces some of the more popular topological surfaces and explores their properties, introducing appropriate vocabulary and notation. Exercises 2–7 concern the connected sum operation and encourage students to use their visual imagination to classify objects as one of the standard surfaces.

▷ **Exercise 1.** Trick question: the traditional doughnut hole is spherical.

▷ **Exercise 2.** The connected sum of two spheres is a sphere (or a sphere with a wart on it, which can then be reabsorbed): $\mathbb{S}\#\mathbb{S} = \mathbb{S}$.

▷ **Exercise 3.** The connected sum of a torus and a sphere is a torus (or a torus with a wart on it, which can then be reabsorbed): $\mathbb{S}\#\mathbb{T} = \mathbb{T}$.

▷ **Exercise 4.** The first picture is a five-holed torus (note the central hole), $\mathbb{T}\#\mathbb{T}\#\mathbb{T}\#\mathbb{T}\#\mathbb{T}$, while the second picture is a four-holed torus, $\mathbb{T}\#\mathbb{T}\#\mathbb{T}\#\mathbb{T}$.

▷ **Exercise 5.** This is a five-holed torus, $\mathbb{T}\#\mathbb{T}\#\mathbb{T}\#\mathbb{T}\#\mathbb{T}$. The framework of a cube can be laid flat as shown below. This is the Schlegel diagram for the cube, as studied in Section 7.2.

 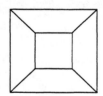

▷ **Exercise 6.** A sphere with two punctures forms a cylinder (imagine straightening the walls).

▷ **Exercise 7.** A pair of pants is a sphere with three punctures (imagine inflating the pants).

In Exercises 8–14, we explore the Möbius band and what properties make it different from the quite similar cylinder. These exercises are designed to involve the use of a physical model.

▷ **Exercise 8.** Build a cylinder and a Möbius band from strips of paper.

▷ **Exercise 9.** The boundary of the Möbius band is one circle, wrapped around twice to form a sort of figure 8.

▷ **Exercise 10.** Both sides of the Möbius band will get colored the same.

▷ **Exercise 11.** You get two identical short cylinders.

▷ **Exercise 12.** Cut along the dotted line shown in the top illustration below. You should get a twisted band (half the thickness of the original Möbius band and twice as long around), with two twists and thus orientable. Below the picture of the Möbius band is a series of illustrations diagraming the process: first, the flat model (planar diagram) of the Möbius band before taping it together and showing the dotted line where we will cut; second, the planar diagram after cutting along the dotted line; and third, how the pieces will have to be taped together to satisfy the instructions for making a Möbius band. Note that the lower rectangle in the second picture must be turned over to fit correctly in the third picture.

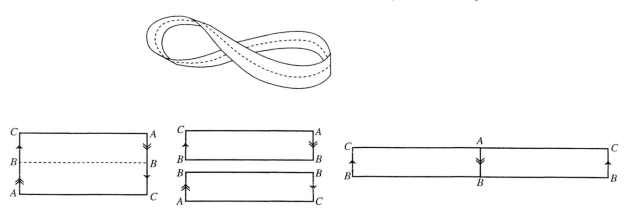

▷ **Exercise 13.** You get a thin Möbius band (the same length around as the original but one-third as thick), and a band that is one-third as thick as the original and twice as long. This band has two twists, and so is orientable. The process is illustrated here for the planar diagram.

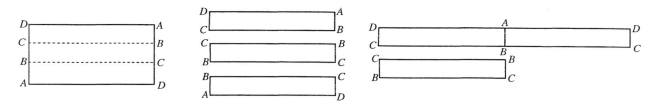

▷ **Exercise 14.** You get two bands that are one-fourth as thick as the original and twice as long. These bands have two twists, and so are orientable.

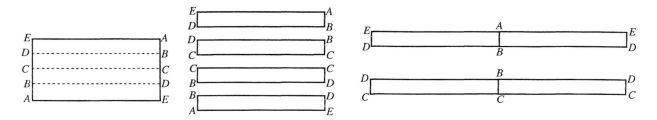

In Exercises 15–19, we explore the nonorientable surfaces: the Klein bottle and the projective plane. While students can usually visualize a Klein bottle with a bit of practice, the projective plane is far more difficult. But that is, perhaps, its importance: that mathematics can deduce the existence of something quite unimaginable and that one can figure out a surprising amount about this object without visualizing it.

▷ **Exercise 15.** The Klein bottle is nonorientable. A Möbius band is shaded in the planar diagram below:

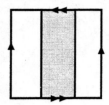

▷ **Exercise 16.** The connected sum of a Klein bottle and a sphere is a Klein bottle (or a Klein bottle with a wart on it, which can then be reabsorbed): $\mathbb{S} \# \mathbb{K} = \mathbb{K}$.

▷ **Exercise 17.** This forms a sphere $\mathbb{S}$. Actually, you get a sort of pointy envelope, which could then be inflated to form a sphere.

▷ **Exercise 18.** The projective plane contains a Möbius band shown below and so is nonorientable.

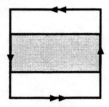

▷ **Exercise 19.** It is worth trying to follow the directions, but at one point you will need to sew an inside point to an outside point and will then have to give up.

13.3. More About Surfaces

In this section we discuss topological properties and classification of surfaces. Exercise 1 introduces the one-dimensional analog of connectivity: using the removal of single points to decide if two spaces are topologically equivalent.

▷ **Exercise 1.** After removal of the two indicated points, the first figure falls into three disconnected components, while the second figure, no matter which two points are removed, will always fall into two pieces. Note that it is possible to remove two points from the first figure so that either it remains in one piece or falls into two pieces. Thus it matters very much which points are removed.

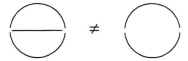

Exercise 2 applies the idea developed in the previous exercise: removing points to justify one's intuitive sense that two figures are the same or different in topology. This will test whether students understand the admittedly nonrigorous definition of topologically equal. Note that different fonts may yield different classifications. We have chosen a simple sanserif font.

▷ **Exercise 2.** A=R, B=8, C=G=I=J=L=M=N=S=U=V=W=Z=2=5=7, D=O=0, H=K, P=6=9, Q=4, X, E=F=T=Y=1=3

Exercises 3 and 4 are easy, merely asking students if certain surfaces contain a cavity or not.

▷ **Exercise 3.** The torus contains a cavity, since air cannot escape an inner tube unless it is punctured, which is why one uses them at all.

▷ **Exercise 4.** The Klein bottle does not contain a cavity: everything inside could flow back out. Klein bottle inner tubes would be worthless.

Exercises 5 and 6 set the groundwork for the idea of connectivity: removing circles until a surface disconnects. Again it matters very much which circles one removes. This is something that we have had to repeatedly remind our students of. Exercises 7–10 follow up on the idea, asking the students to compute the connectivity number for various surfaces without boundary.

▷ **Exercise 5.** When you remove a circle from a sphere, the result is disconnected, no matter which circle is removed.

▷ **Exercise 6.** Removing a circle from a torus may give a connected or disconnected result, depending on which circle is removed. Below on the left, a circle disconnects the torus, but the picture on the right shows that it is possible to remove a circle from the torus without disconnecting it.

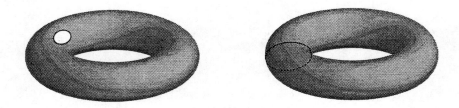

▷ **Exercise 7.** $C(\mathbb{T}) = 3$. The two circles shown below on the left can be removed without disconnecting the torus, but removing one more must disconnect it. Note that removing these two circles would leave a shape that could be stretched and laid flat to form a square, and that the edges of this square, when glued together as indicated, form the two circles.

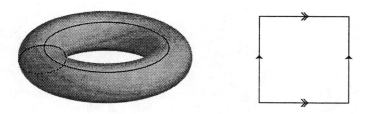

▷ **Exercise 8.** Four circles can be removed from the 2-holed torus without disconnecting it, as shown in the top illustration, so $C(\mathbb{T}\#\mathbb{T}) = 5$. Six circles can be removed from the 3-holed torus, as shown at the bottom, so $C(\mathbb{T}\#\mathbb{T}\#\mathbb{T}) = 7$.

▷ **Exercise 9.** Generalizing from Exercises 7 and 8, $C(n\mathbb{T}) = 2n + 1$.

▷ **Exercise 10.** The results of Exercise 7 can be modified to show that $C(\mathbb{K}) = 3$.

Emphasize to the students that for a surface with boundary, the first cut must be a boundary cut: a line with both endpoints on the boundary. After that, one can use either boundary cuts or circle cuts. One can point out that for the torus and other previous examples, removing the first circle creates a surface with boundary and some of the remaining cuts were then boundary cuts such as these. Also emphasize that the cuts must reduce the surface into a space without holes or punctures (ideally, a disc or rectangle).

▷ **Exercise 11.** Cutting the Möbius band along the dotted line gives the rectangle of the planar diagram shown on the right. Any additional cut would disconnect it, so $C = 2$.

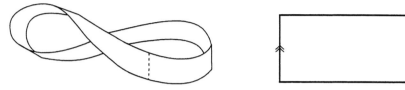

For Exercises 12 and 13, ask the students to show that their cuts do not disconnect the figure and that the result after making their cuts does not have any punctures. Also show them some cuts that do not work and ask them to explain why these fail. One possibility might be to make the three boundary cuts that go from puncture to puncture in the disc with three punctures: this results in two pieces, one of which has a hole in it.

▷ **Exercise 12.** Three boundary cuts can be made without disconnecting the figure, so $C = 4$. Below are several choices for how to make these cuts.

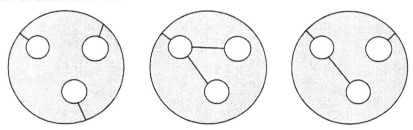

▷ **Exercise 13.** Four boundary cuts can be made without disconnecting the figure, so $C = 5$. Below are several choices for how to make these cuts.

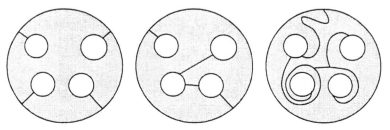

In Exercise 14, we ask the students to generalize to find a formula for the connectivity of a disc with n punctures. We then apply this formula to other objects.

▷ **Exercise 14.** Note that the cylinder could be flattened out and considered as a disc with one puncture and connectivity $C = 2$. From this and the examples of Exercises 12 and 13, we generalize to find that the disc with n punctures has $C = n + 1$.

▷ **Exercise 15.** A pullover sweater could be deformed into a disc with three punctures (the neckhole and two holes at the end of the sleeves, with the waist forming the outer boundary circle), so $C = 4$.

▷ **Exercise 16.** We use the same cuts as for Exercise 7, but the first cut is now a boundary cut, with both endpoints on the puncture, so $C = 3$.

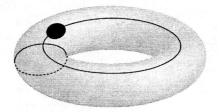

In Exercises 17–21, we shift focus to the Euler characteristic. If students have seen this before, either in Chapter 7 or in Section 12.2, this will go faster, but previous knowledge is not required. Emphasize that each face must form a disclike region with no punctures.

▷ **Exercise 17.** The Möbius band as pictured below has two vertices, A and B, three edges (top, bottom, and the two sides, which are considered as a single edge after gluing them together), and one face, so $\chi = 2 - 3 + 1 = 0$.

▷ **Exercise 18.** As shown the the planar diagram below, the Klein bottle has one vertex (all four corners will be glued together in building the Klein bottle), two edges (the single arrow and the double arrow edges), and one face, so $\chi(\mathbb{K}) = 1 - 2 + 1 = 0$.

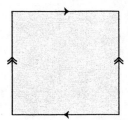

▷ **Exercise 19.** The sphere can be thought of as either a single disc with its boundary gathered together at a point (think of a drawstring bag gathered tight), so $v = 1$, $e = 0$ and $f = 1$ and $\chi(\mathbb{S}) = 1 - 0 + 1 = 2$, or as the diagram of Exercise 13.2.17, which has $v = 3$, $e = 2$, and $f = 1$ and the same Euler characteristic.

▷ **Exercise 20.** Modify the connectivity cuts of Exercise 8(a) so that they intersect (otherwise the 2-holed torus would be cut open to form a disc with a puncture) as shown below. This gives the planar diagram on the right, which has $v = 1$, $e = 4$, and $f = 1$, so $\chi(\mathbb{T}\#\mathbb{T}) = 1 - 4 + 1 = -2$.

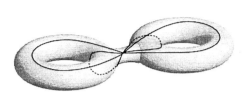
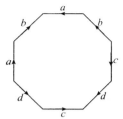

▷ **Exercise 21.** Modify the connectivity cuts of Exercise 8(b) to get the planar diagram shown below with $v = 1$, $e = 6$, and $f = 1$, so $\chi(\mathbb{T}\#\mathbb{T}\#\mathbb{T}) = 1 - 6 + 1 = -4$.

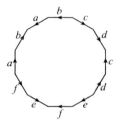

Exercise 22 summarizes all of the data we have collected. Note that no one of the topological properties we have studied is sufficient to completely identify a surface, but rather some combination of them is needed. For example, "the surface without boundary which contains a cavity and has Euler characteristic 0" completely describes the torus, as does "the orientable surface without boundary with connectivity 3."

▷ **Exercise 22.** Fill in the table below:

Properties of Surfaces

Surface	Orientable	Cavity	Boundary	Connectivity	χ
$\mathbb{S}$	yes	yes	none	1	2
$\mathbb{T}$	yes	yes	none	3	0
$\mathbb{T}\#\mathbb{T}$	yes	yes	none	5	-2
$\mathbb{T}\#\mathbb{T}\#\mathbb{T}$	yes	yes	none	7	-4
$\mathbb{P}$	no	no	none	2	1
$\mathbb{K}$	no	no	none	3	0
Cylinder	yes	no	two circles	2	0
Möbius band	no	no	circle	2	0

▷ **Exercise 23.** Let S be the surface with punctures, S^* the same surface with its punctures patched, and h the number of punctures, then $\chi(S) = \chi(S^*) - h$.

229

13.4. Map Coloring Problems

This section is on map coloring problems, an application of our knowledge of surfaces and the Euler characteristic. Exercises 1–7 help set the framework. Emphasize to the students that all countries must be connected and disclike. Of course, one could color all of the countries different colors if one had 40 million crayons, but we are trying to find out how many colors are necessary and sufficient as a minimal number of colors needed so two countries that share a border edge (not just a vertex) are different colors. In this group of exercises, students will become familiar with this basic idea and the types of situations that require one to get a new crayon out of the box. For Exercises 3, 4, and 6, we remind the students to use complete, grammatically correct sentences.

▷ **Exercise 1.**

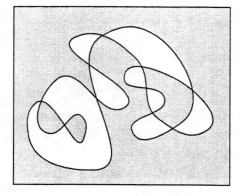

▷ **Exercise 2.** Draw another map (with at least six countries) that requires only two colors.

▷ **Exercise 3.** Note that this map was modified from the one in Exercise 1 by moving two vertices into positions marked with a ∗ where two countries meet at the middle of an edge for a third country, sort of like a "T" intersection. Thus, three countries meet at these two vertices, so one is forced to use three colors.

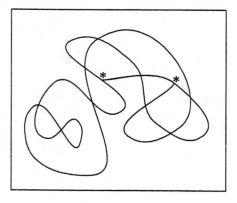

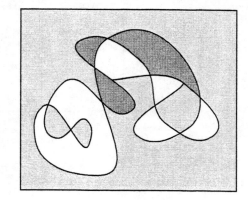

230

▷ **Exercise 4.** This map has a number of "T" intersections, marked with a ∗, where one is forced to use three colors.

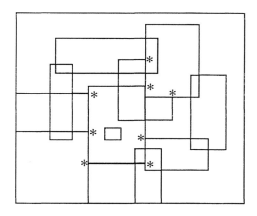 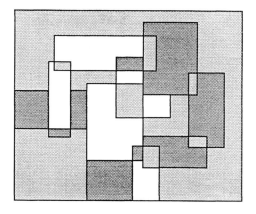

▷ **Exercise 5.** Draw another map (with at least six countries) that requires three colors.

▷ **Exercise 6.** This map has one country, marked with a ∗, which has three neighbors, each of which shares a border with each of the others. Therefore, these four countries must be different colors.

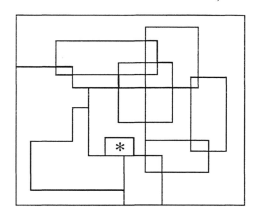 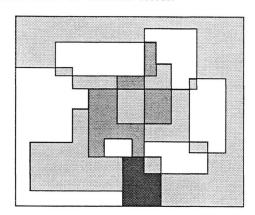

▷ **Exercise 7.** Draw another map (with at least six countries) that requires four colors.

Exercise 8 helps to justify the counting argument that follows. Do not count the outer edges or vertices, only the bold interior ones.

▷ **Exercise 8.** The disassembled puzzle has ten faces, 34 interior edges, and 27 interior vertices. In the assembled map, $f = 10$, $e = 17$, and $v = 8$. Thus, the number of faces is the same, the number of edges in the disassembled puzzle is $2e$, and the number of vertices in the disassembled puzzle is greater than $3v$.

Exercises 9 and 10 apply the key step of the proof to two particular surfaces. This helps force the students to understand the formula and its application. Remind students that the quantity $\frac{2e}{f}$ is the average number of edges per country, and therefore one country must have no more than $\frac{2e}{f}$ edges and thus neighbors.

▷ **Exercise 9.** Since $\frac{2e}{f} \leq 6 \left(1 - \frac{\chi(S)}{f}\right)$ and $\chi(\mathbb{S}) = 2$, we have $\frac{2e}{f} \leq 6 \left(1 - \frac{2}{f}\right) < 6$. This means that the map M must have at least one country with no more than $\frac{2e}{f} < 6$ edges. Since the number of neighbors for this country must be an integer and must be less than 6, it is clear that any map drawn on the sphere must have at least one country with no more than five neighbors.

▷ **Exercise 10.** Since $\frac{2e}{f} \leq 6 \left(1 - \frac{\chi(S)}{f}\right)$ and $\chi(\mathbb{T}) = 0$, we have $\frac{2e}{f} \leq 6 \left(1 - \frac{0}{f}\right) \leq 6$. This means that the map M must have at least one country with no more than $\frac{2e}{f} \leq 6$ edges, so any map drawn on the torus must have at least one country with no more than six neighbors.

Considerable experimentation went into our recommendation to use a bagel in Exercise 11. Try to find a bagel with a nice open hole in the center. In Exercise 12, care must be paid to how the edges fit together in showing that each country borders all of the others. Students may want to transfer this map to another bagel. Otherwise, copy the map on paper and roll it to see how the edge colors match.

▷ **Exercise 11.** Draw and color the given map on the surface of a bagel.

▷ **Exercise 12.** Note that each country borders each of the other countries, so all seven colors are necessary.

There are many maps on the Klein bottle requiring six colors for Exercise 13. The ideal will have just six countries, each of which shares a border with all of the others.

▷ **Exercise 13.** Note that after gluing the edges together as directed, each country is connected and borders each of the others.

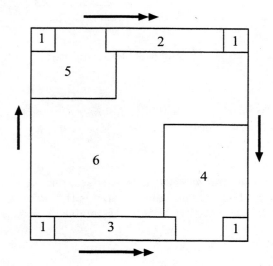

▷ **Exercise 14.** Draw the map on a strip of paper. Note that you should color both sides of the paper. After taping along the seam, each country is connected and borders all of the other countries.

232

▷ **Exercise 15.** Five colors are necessary, but this does not contradict the Four-Color Theorem, which requires that countries be connected.

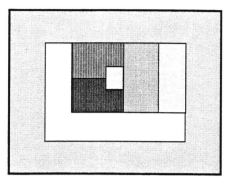

Students will need several copies of Gardner's map, since they will almost certainly do it wrong at least once. Additional copies can be made using Template 48 of the Appendix. Note that numbers or labels can be used for the regions at first (they are easier to erase) and the colors put in only after one has found a scheme that works.

▷ **Exercise 16.**

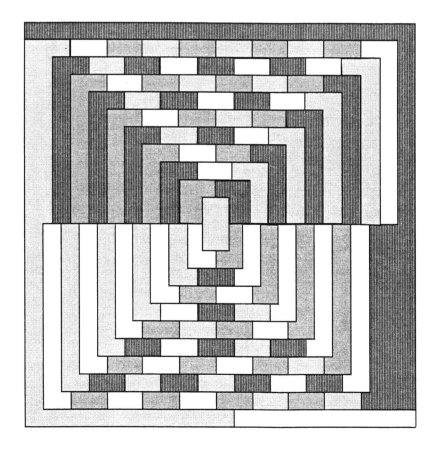

233

Appendix: Templates

Chapter 2.1: Billiards
- **Template 1:** Grid paper

Chapter 2.2: Celtic Knots
- **Template 2:** Grid of dots paper

Chapter 3.4: Knots and Stars
- **Template 3:** 8-dot paper
- **Template 4:** 9-dot paper
- **Template 5:** 12-dot paper
- **Template 6:** 15-dot paper
- **Template 7:** 21-dot paper
- **Template 8:** 24-dot paper

Chapter 4.1: Tilings
- **Template 9:** Regular polygons: triangles (3 sides)
- **Template 10:** Regular polygons: squares (4 sides)
- **Template 11:** Regular polygons: pentagons (5 sides)
- **Template 12:** Regular polygons: hexagons (6 sides)
- **Template 13:** Regular polygons: heptagons (7 sides)
- **Template 14:** Regular polygons: octagons (8 sides)
- **Template 15:** Regular polygons: nonagons (9 sides)
- **Template 16:** Regular polygons: decagons (10 sides)
- **Template 17:** Regular polygons: dodecagons (12 sides)
- **Template 18:** Regular polygons: pentakaidecagons (15 sides)
- **Template 19:** Regular polygons: octakaidecagons (18 sides)
- **Template 20:** Regular polygons: icosagons (20 sides)
- **Template 21:** Regular polygons: tetrakaicosagons (24 sides)

Chapter 4.1: Irregular Tilings
- **Template 22:** Basic tiles

Chapter 4.3: Penrose Tilings
- **Template 23:** Penrose tiles

Chapter 5.4: Wallpaper Patterns
- **Template 24:** Exercises 1 and 9
- **Template 25:** Exercises 10, 11, 13
- **Template 26:** Exercises 15, 16, 17
- **Template 27:** Exercises 18, 19, 20
- **Template 28:** Exercises 22, 23, 24

Chapter 5.5: Islamic Lattice Patterns
- **Template 29:** Exercise 4
- **Template 30:** Exercise 6
- **Template 31:** Exercise 10
- **Template 32:** Exercise 13

Chapter 7.1: Pyramids, Prisms, and Antiprisms: Use Templates 9 and 10.

Chapter 7.2: Platonic Solids: Also use Templates 9, 10, and 11.
- **Template 33:**   Nets for the Platonic solids: cube, tetrahedron, octahedron, icosahedron, dodecahedron

Chapter 7.3: Archimedean Solids: Also use Templates 9, 10, 11, 12, 14, and 16.
- **Template 34:**   Nets for the Archimedean solids: truncated cube, truncated tetrahedron, truncated octahedron, truncated icosahedron
- **Template 35:**   Nets for the Archimedean solids: truncated dodecahedron, cuboctahedron, icosidodecahedron, rhombicuboctahedron
- **Template 36:**   Nets for the Archimedean solids: great rhombicuboctahedron, snub cube, rhombicosidodecahedron
- **Template 37:**   Nets for the Archimedean solids: snub dodecahedron
- **Template 38:**   Nets for the Archimedean solids: great rhombicosidodecahedron

Chapter 7.5: Models of Polyhedra
- **Template 39:**   Plaited polyhedra 1: cube, octahedron, diagonal cube
- **Template 40:**   Plaited polyhedra 2: tetrahedron, icosahedron

Chapter 8.1: Symmetries of Polyhedra
- **Template 41:**   Exercises 17 and 18: Tetrahelices

Chapter 8.2: Three-Dimensional Kaleidoscopes
- **Template 42:**   Nets for the cubic orthoscheme
- **Template 43:**   Nets for the octahedral orthoscheme
- **Template 44:**   Nets for the tetrahedral orthoscheme

Chapter 9.1: Spirals and Helices
- **Template 45:**   Polar graph paper

Chapter 9.2: Fibonacci Numbers and Phyllotaxis: Use Template 43.

Chapter 10.2: Optical Illusions
- **Template 46:**   Blueprint for Ames room

Chapter 12.3: Mazes
- **Template 47:**   Dudeney's Philadelphia maze

Chapter 13.4: Map Coloring Problems
- **Template 48:**   Martin Gardner's hoax map

• **Template 1:** Grid paper

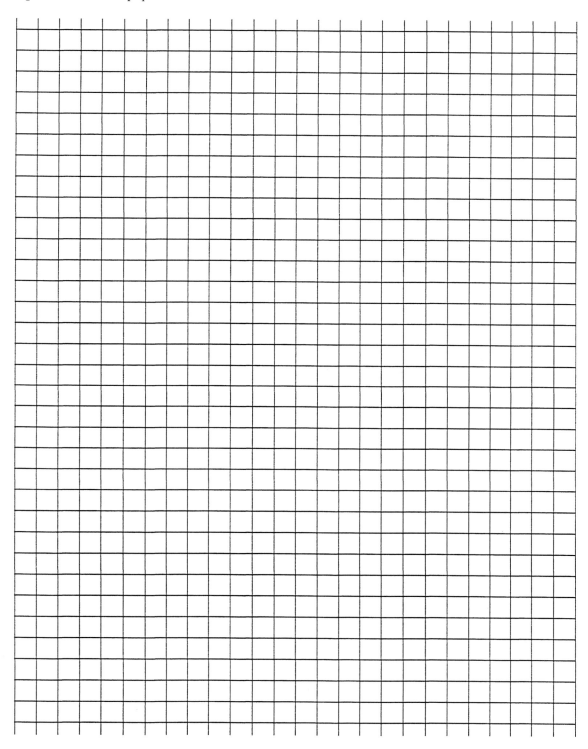

• **Template 2:**   Grid of dots paper

• **Template 3:**   8-dot paper

• Template 6:   15-dot paper

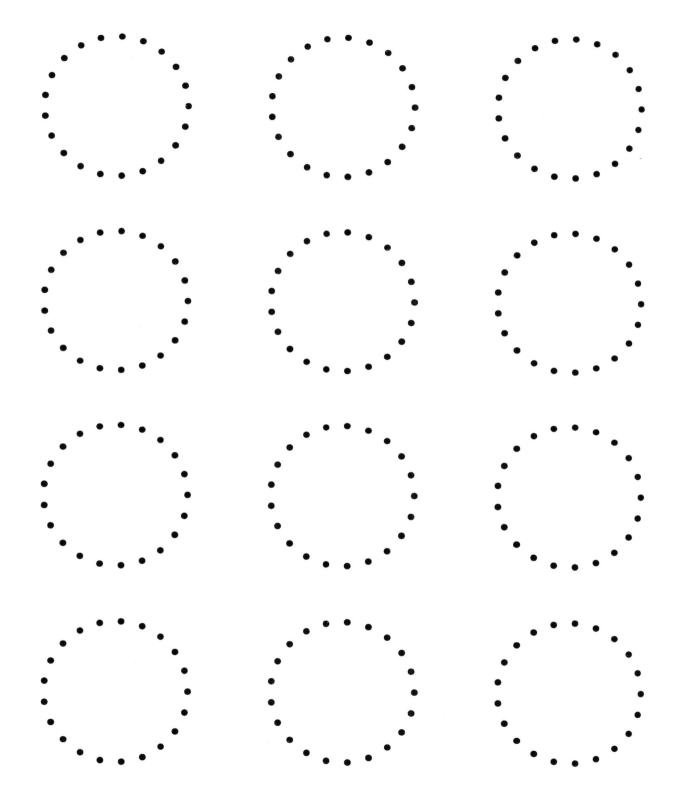

• **Template 8:**   24-dot paper

• **Template 11:** Regular polygons: pentagons (5 sides)

● **Template 12:**   Regular polygons: hexagons (6 sides)

- **Template 15:** Regular polygons: nonagons (9 sides)

• **Template 16:**   Regular polygons: decagons (10 sides)

• **Template 17:**   Regular polygons: dodecagons (12 sides)

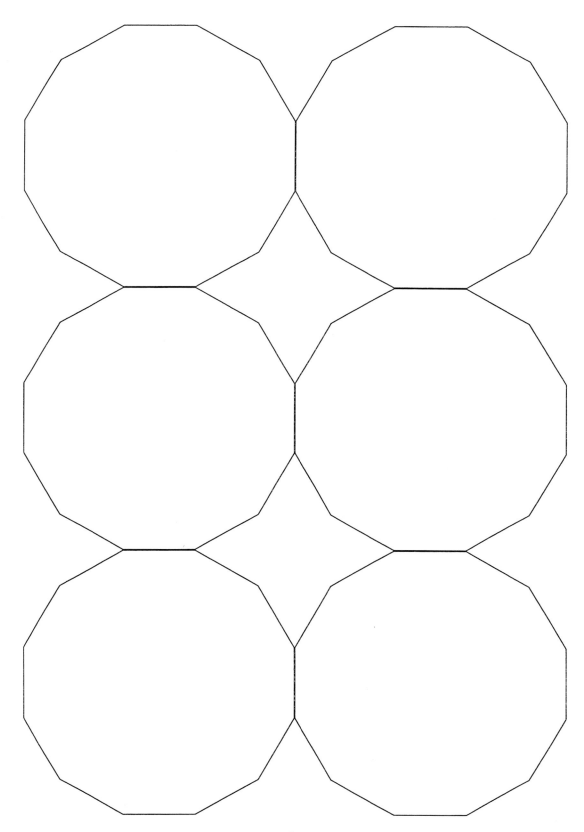

- **Template 18:** Regular polygons: pentakaidecagons (15 sides)

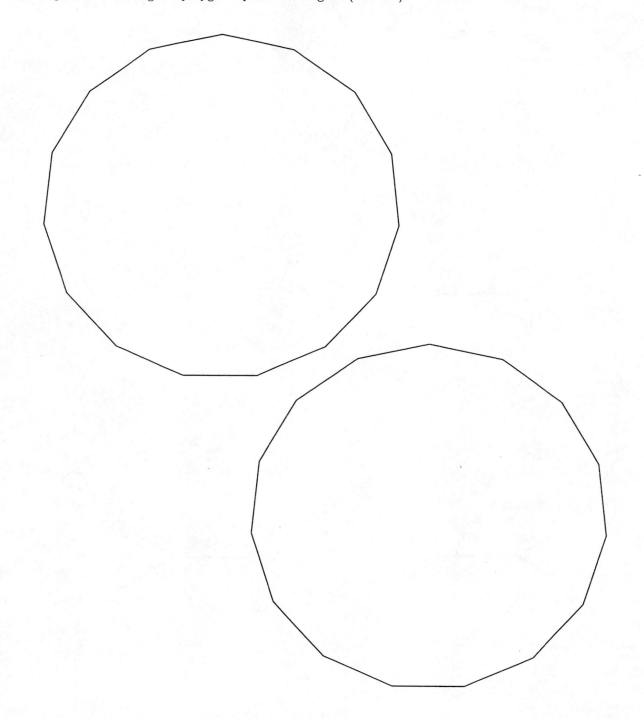

- **Template 19:**   Regular polygons: octakaidecagons (18 sides)

- **Template 20:** Regular polygons: icosagons (20 sides)

- **Template 21:**   Regular polygons: tetrakaicosagons (24 sides)

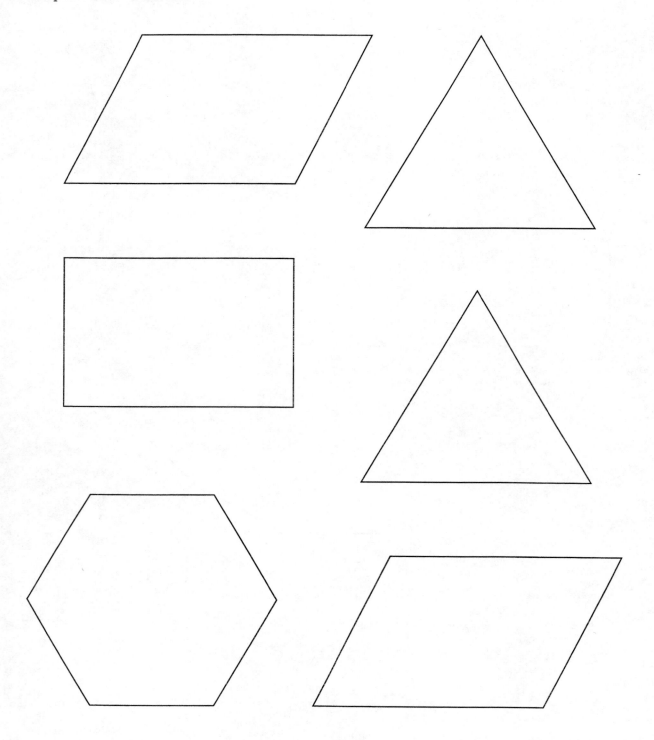

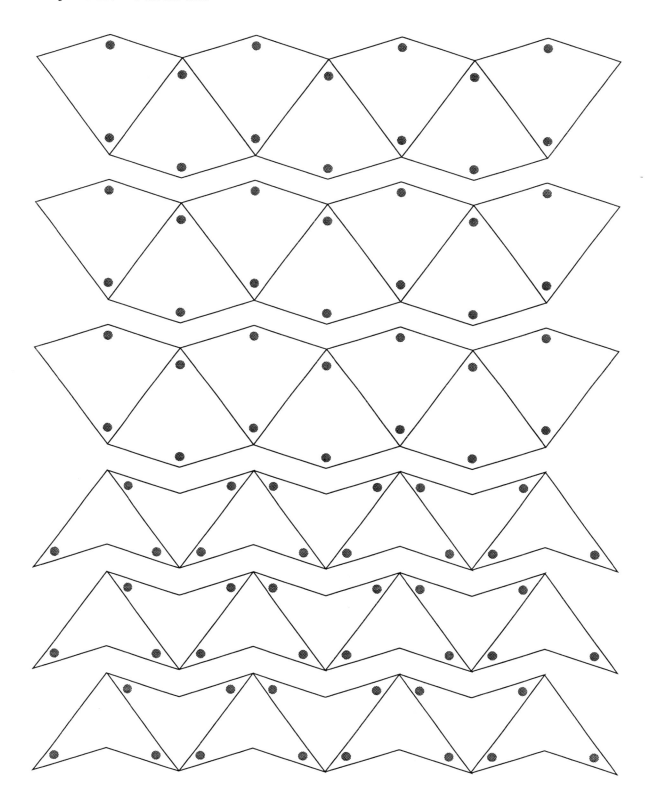

• **Template 24:**   Wallpaper Exercises 1 and 9

▷ **Exercise 5.4.1.** Find the images of the original motif below after a reflection across the dashed line, and after a glide reflection along the dotted line. How are the images of the reflection and the glide reflection related?

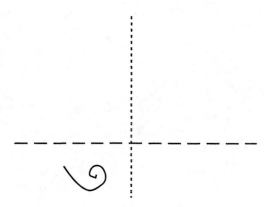

▷ **Exercise 5.4.9.** Here is a partial basic cell for a **p2** or **p211** wallpaper pattern, with the rotation centers marked. Fill in the rest of the basic cell (you will need one more copy of the motif within the cell) and then draw a section of the wallpaper, four cells wide and three cells tall.

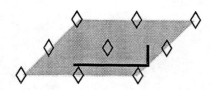

• **Template 25:** Wallpaper Exercises 10, 11, 13

▷ **Exercise 5.4.10.** Here is a basic cell for a **p1g1** wallpaper pattern, with the lines of glide reflection marked. Because the motifs do not line up, note that one copy of the motif is split in two, but when you draw the wallpaper, these pieces should fit together. Draw a section of the wallpaper, four cells wide and three cells tall.

▷ **Exercise 5.4.11.** Here is a section of **p1m1** wallpaper. Draw two arrows indicating the directions of translation. Draw lines of reflection in red. Outline and shade the basic cell (it will contain two repetitions of the motif, one each of the two orientations).

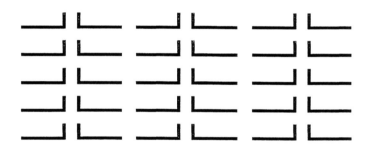

▷ **Exercise 5.4.13.** Here is a section of **p2gg** wallpaper. Draw two arrows indicating the directions of translation. Draw lines of glide reflection in blue. Put ◊ marks at the 2-fold rotation points. Outline and shade the basic cell, remembering that the corners should be centers of rotation and that the cell should contain copies of the motif in each of its configurations.

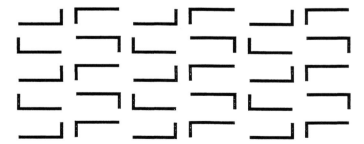

▷ **Exercise 5.4.15.** Here is the original motif, a shaded partial basic cell, and the lines of reflection and 2-fold rotation centers for the pattern **p2mm**. Note that ◆ is used, since the rotation centers are on the lines of reflection. Fill in the pattern, first in the basic cell, and then in the rest of the grid shown.

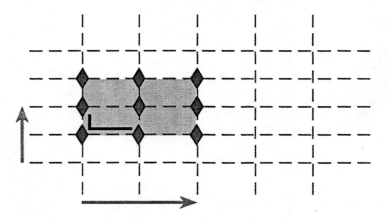

▷ **Exercise 5.4.16.** Below is a piece of a **c2mm** pattern, with the centered cell shaded. Draw reflection lines in red and glide reflection lines in blue. Indicate the 2-fold centers of rotation with a ◆ if on a mirror line, ◇ if not (this pattern has both).

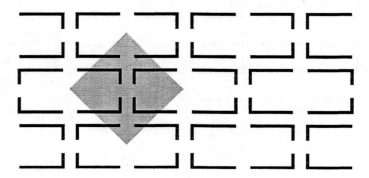

▷ **Exercise 5.4.17.** Here are two copies of the motif, a shaded partial basic cell, and the dashed lines of reflection and dotted lines of glide reflection for the pattern **c1m1**. As in the previous patterns **c2mm** and **p1g1**, the basic cell contains fragments instead of complete motifs, but these fragments fit together to make the pattern. Fill in the pattern, first in the basic cell, and then to cover the area shown.

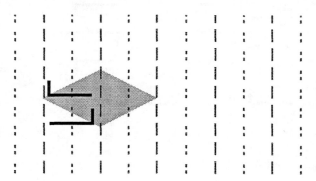

▷ **Exercise 5.4.18.** Here is the original motif and a shaded partial basic cell with the central 4-fold center of rotation marked with a □ for the pattern **p4**. Fill in the pattern first in the basic cell, then for a piece of wallpaper four cells wide and three cells tall. There are other rotation centers on the border of the cell. Mark them with the appropriate symbols.

▷ **Exercise 5.4.19.** Here is a **p4gm** pattern. Draw the reflection lines in red and the glide reflection lines in blue. You should find families of glide reflection lines in four directions. Indicate the centers of rotation appropriately. Shade a square basic cell.

▷ **Exercise 5.4.20.** Show what happens when you reflect the motif across the dashed lines, which meet at a 45° angle. Be sure to get all the repetitions of the figure.

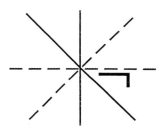

• **Template 28:**   Wallpaper Exercises 22, 23, 24

▷ **Exercise 5.4.22.** Below is a motif and a cell for **p3** showing the rotation centers. Fill in the pattern first in the basic cell, then for a piece of wallpaper four cells wide and three cells tall.

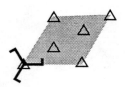

▷ **Exercise 5.4.23.** The patterns **p3m1** and **p31m** are often confused, even in some textbooks. Below are examples of each. Draw the reflection lines in red and the glide reflection lines in blue. Indicate the centers of rotation appropriately. One key difference between the two is that **p3m1** has all rotation centers on the red lines, while **p31m** has some on the red lines and some not. Figure out which is which and shade the basic cells.

▷ **Exercise 5.4.24.** Show what happens when you reflect the motif across the dashed lines, which meet at a 30° angle. Be sure to get all the repetitions of the figure.

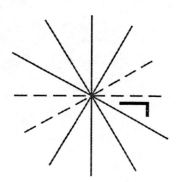

• **Template 29:**   Islamic Lattice Patterns: Exercise 4

▷ **Exercise 5.5.4.** Draw the interlace pattern started below, in which each strand forms a hexagon:

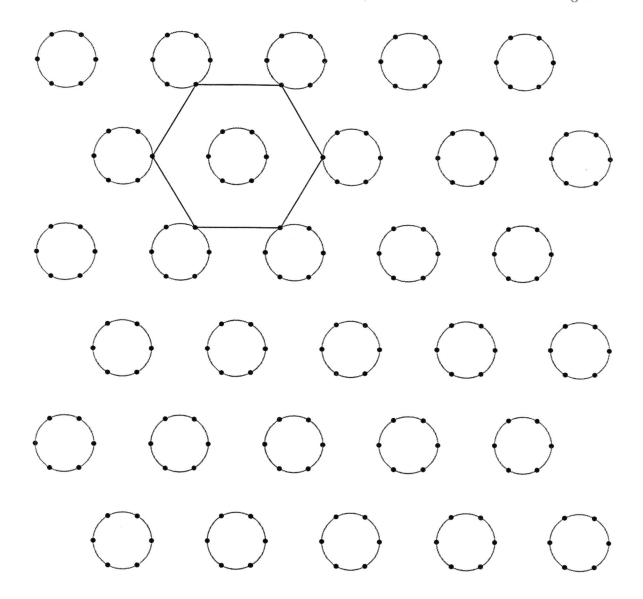

▷ **Exercise 5.5.6.** Draw the interlace pattern for the design started below, in which each strand forms a hexagon:

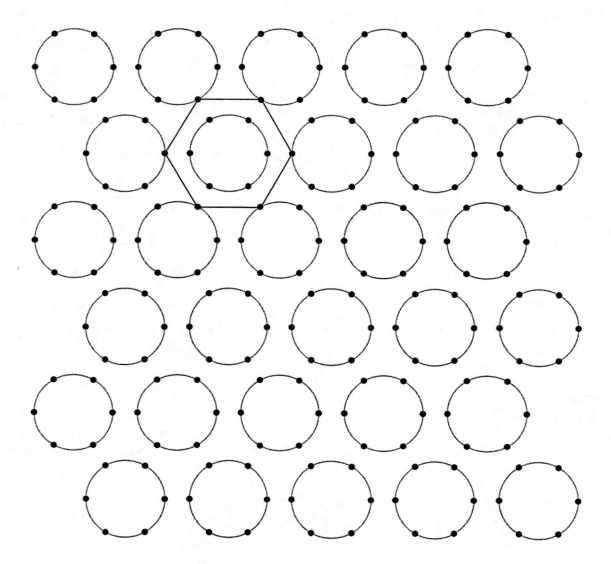

- **Template 31:**   Islamic Lattice Patterns: Exercise 10

▷ **Exercise 5.5.10.** Draw the interlace pattern associated with the design started below:

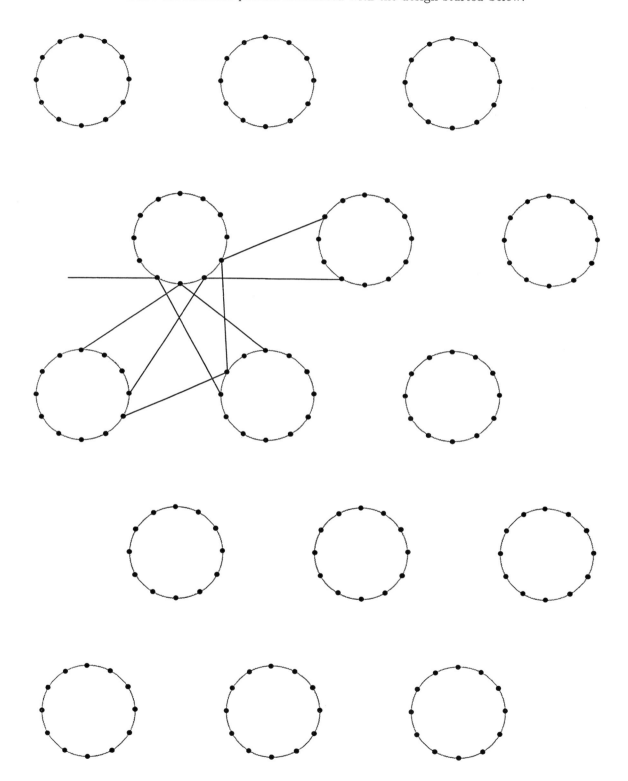

• **Template 32:**   Islamic Lattice Patterns: Exercise 13

▷ **Exercise 5.5.13.** Below is a grid of two sizes of circles, with 2, 3, and 12 dots each. I have drawn the two different types of strands. Finish the interlace pattern.

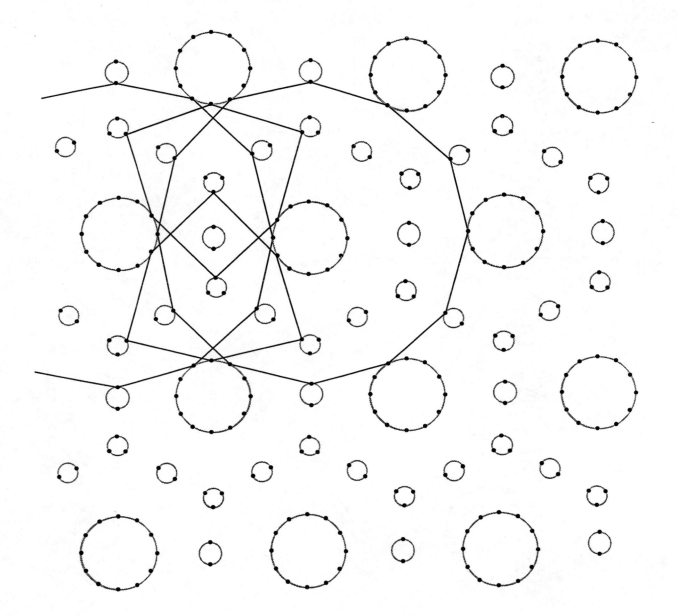

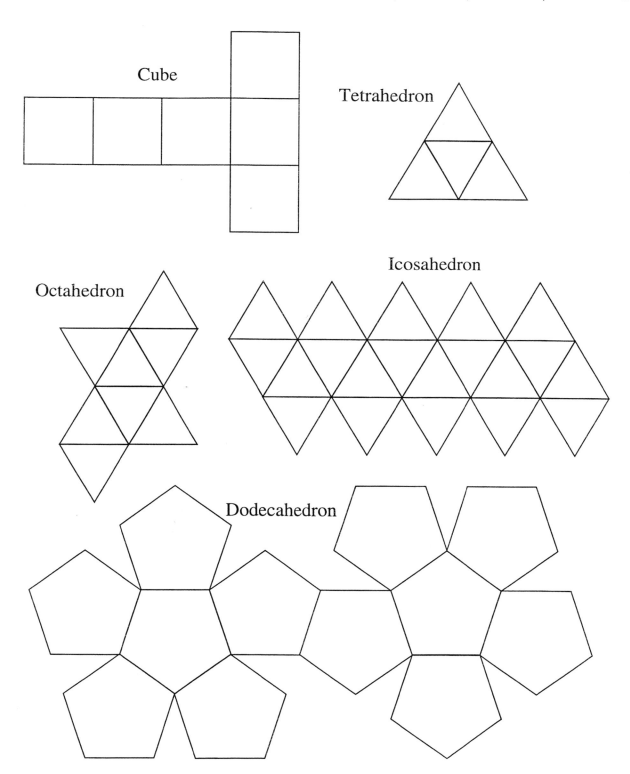

Cube

Tetrahedron

Octahedron

Icosahedron

Dodecahedron

Truncated Cube

Truncated Tetrahedron

Truncated Octahedron

Truncated Icosahedron

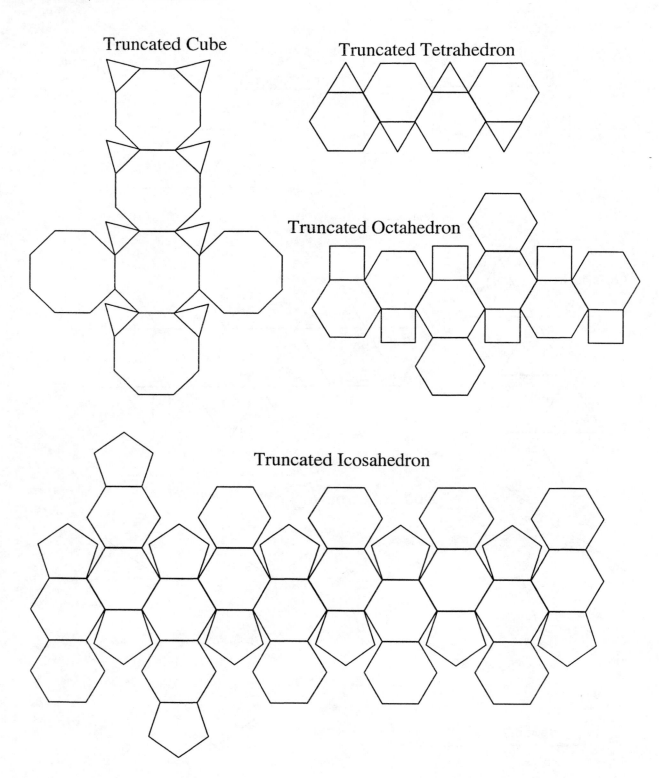

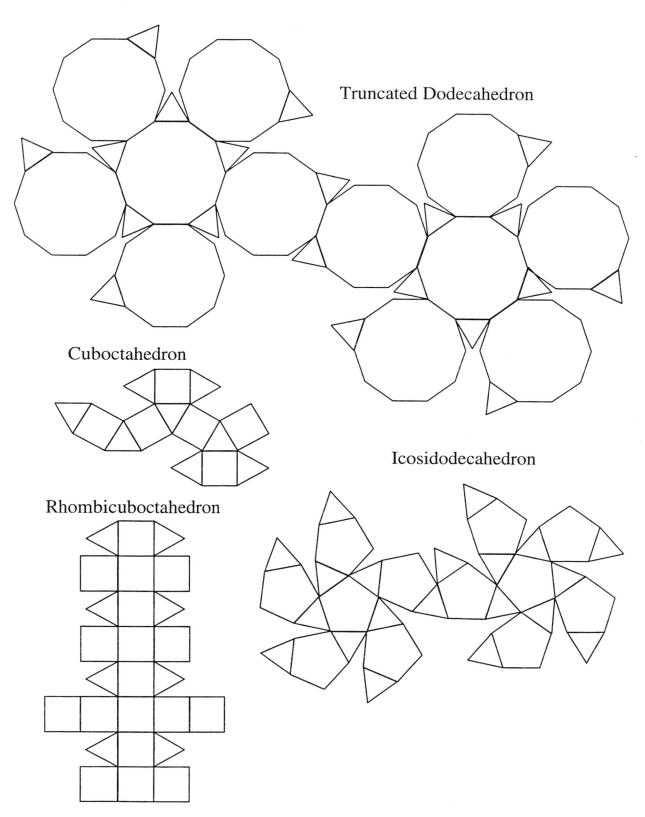

Truncated Dodecahedron

Cuboctahedron

Icosidodecahedron

Rhombicuboctahedron

Great rhombicuboctahedron

Snub cube

Rhombicosidodecahedron

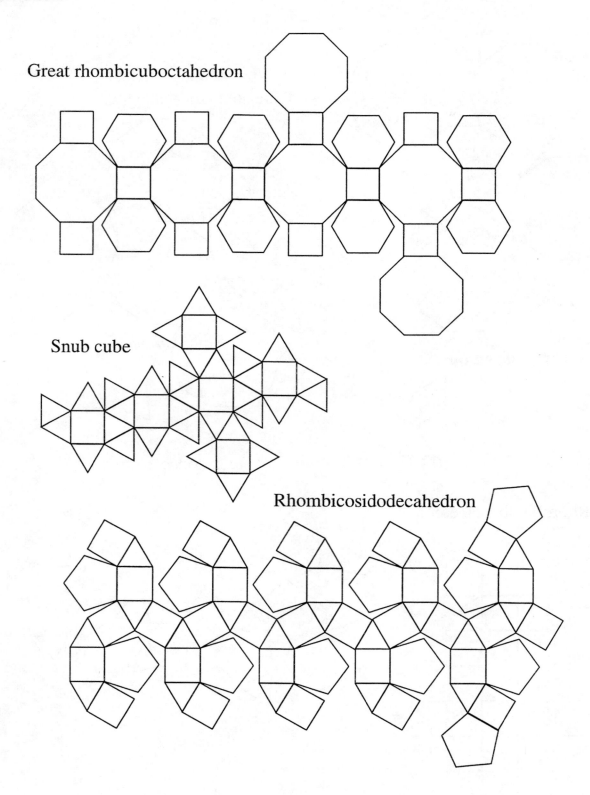

Snub dodecahedron

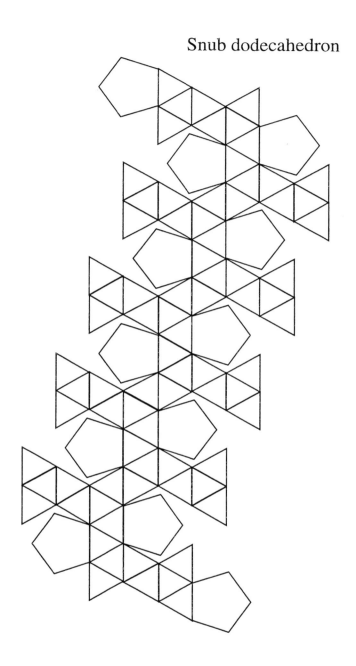

Great rhombicosidodecahedron

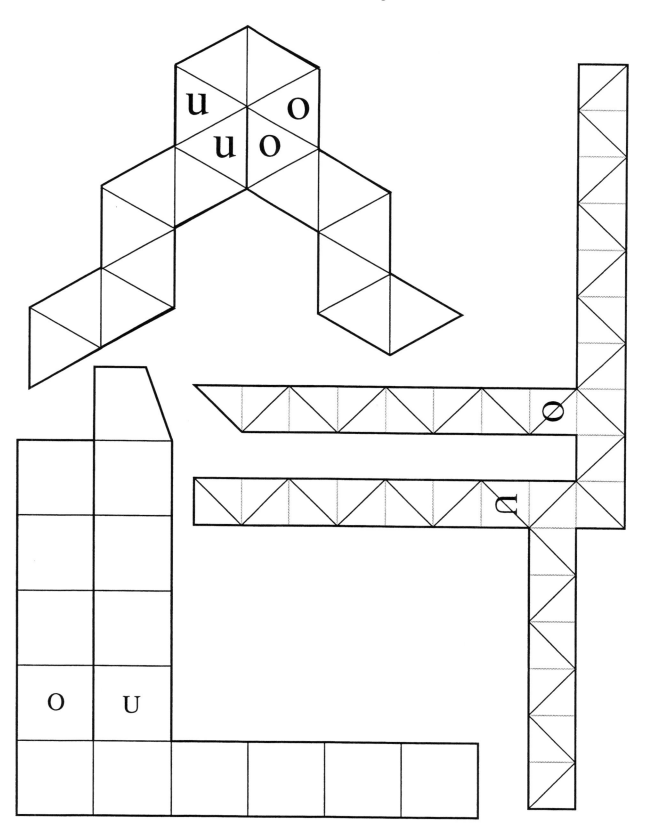

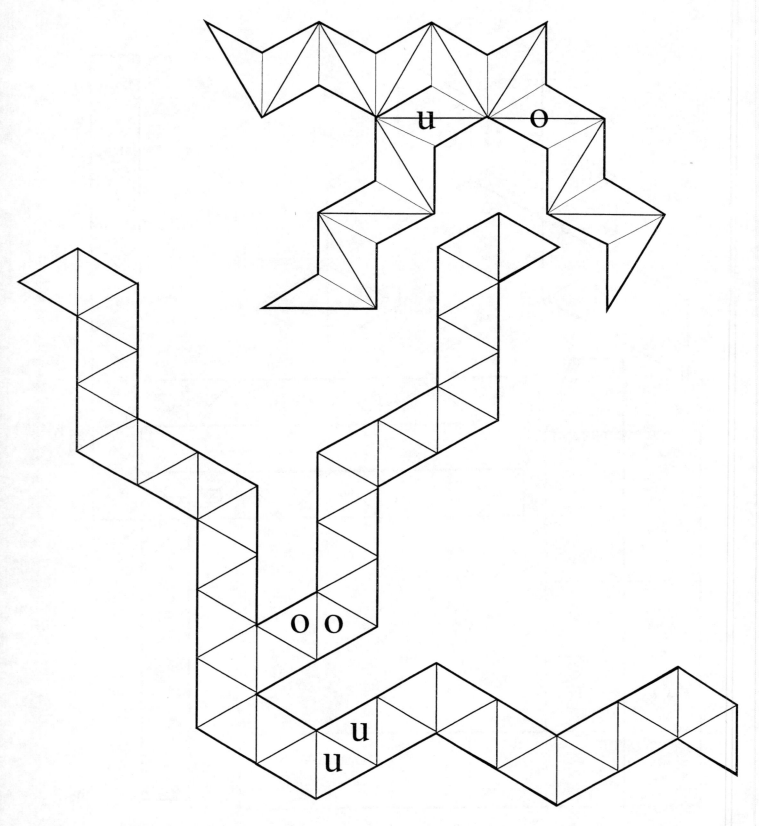

• **Template 41:** Tetrahelices

▷ **Exercise 8.1.17.** Here is another way to build a section of the tetrahelix. Cut a strip of equilateral triangles and crease along the lines as shown below. Tape the edges together according to the numbering, so that the two edges marked by a '1' get taped together, the edges marked '2' get taped together, etc.

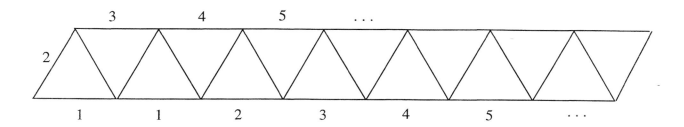

▷ **Exercise 8.1.18.** Here is yet another way to build a tetrahelix, due to Buckminster Fuller, as shown to Anthony Pugh. Make a copy of the picture below. Crease with a mountain fold along the lines marked —··—··—··—··—, and with a valley fold along the lines marked ----------------. Roll up into a cylinder, so that the shaded cells lie under the top row of triangles and then slide and twist so that the triangle marked *A* lies underneath triangle *B*.

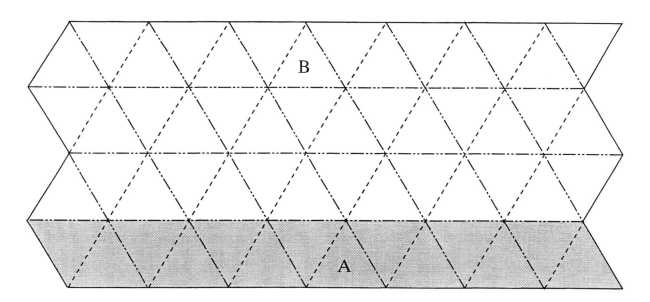

• **Template 42:** Nets for the cubic orthoscheme

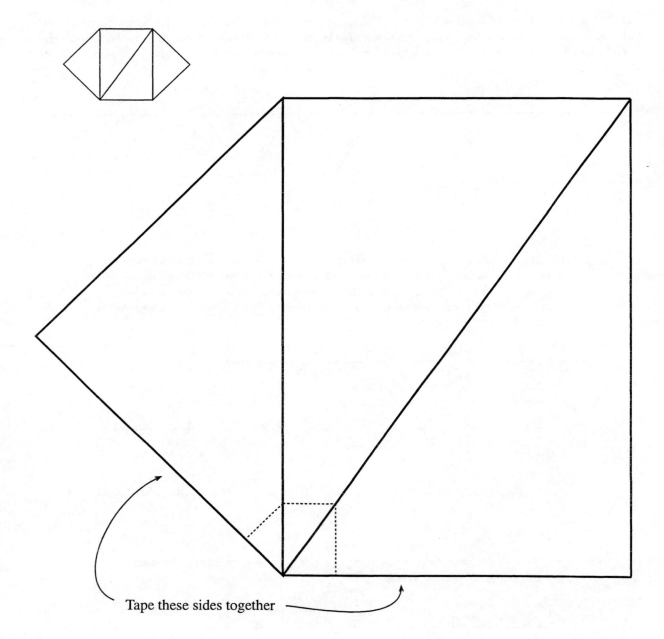

Tape these sides together

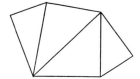

Tape these sides together

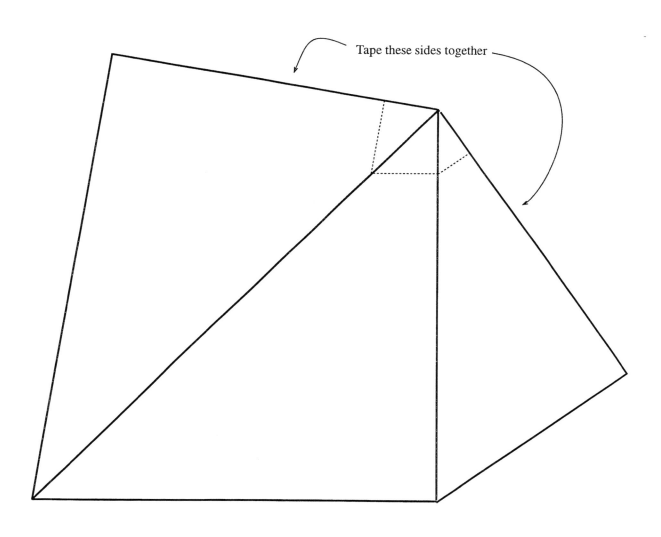

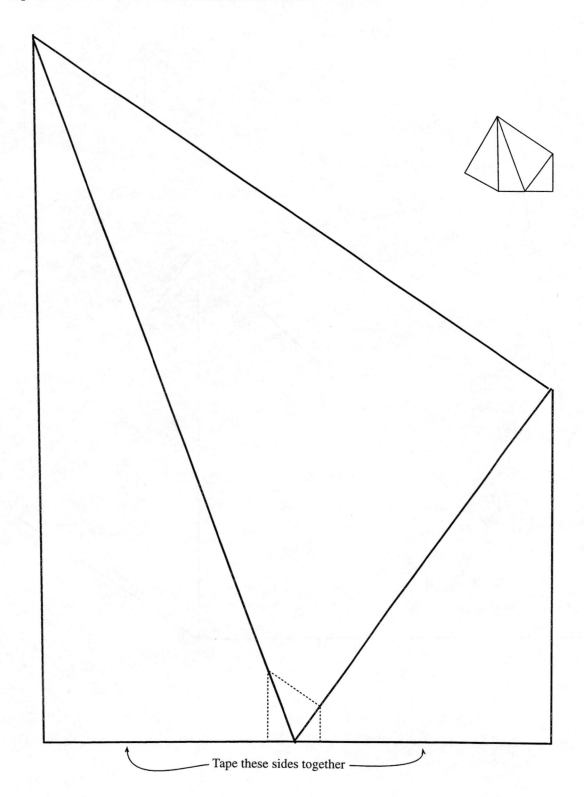

Tape these sides together

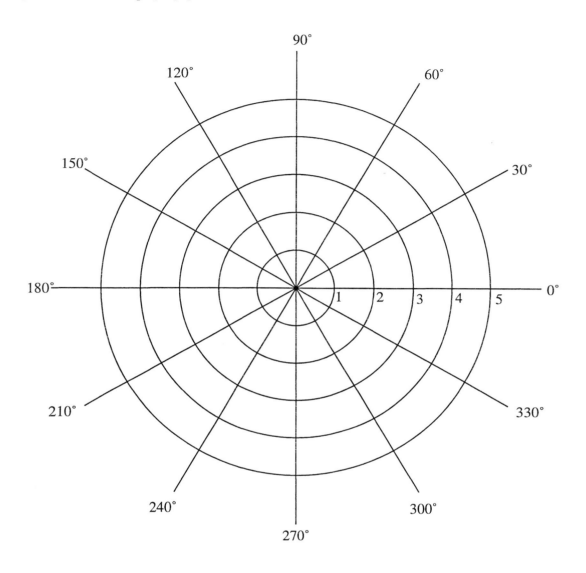

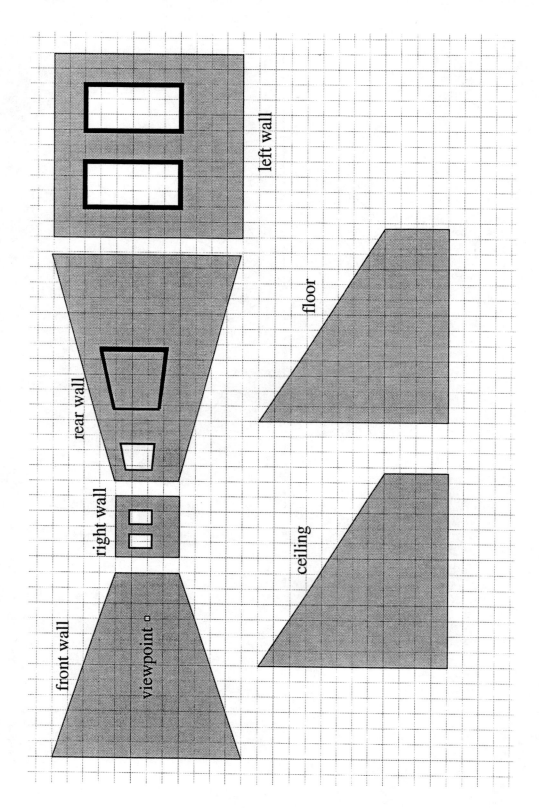

left wall

floor

rear wall

ceiling

right wall

front wall

viewpoint □